Exploring the Science, Technology and Applications of U.V. and E.B. Curing

Exploring the Science, Technology and Applications of U.V. and E.B. Curing

By

R. Stephen Davidson

Ph. D.(Leeds) D. Sc.(Leeds), C. Chem., M. R. S. C.
Emeritus Professor of Organic Chemistry, City University, London, UK
Emeritus Professor of Applied Chemistry at The University of Kent at Canterbury, UK

Published by
SITA TECHNOLOGY LIMITED
LONDON UK

Printed and bound in the UK by Short Run Press Ltd.
Bittern Road, Sowton Industrial Estate, Exeter

ISBN 0 947798412 1999

EXPLORING THE SCIENCE, TECHNOLOGY AND APPLICATIONS OF U.V. AND E.B. CURING

iv

Preface

The ideas for this book were conceived when there were very few texts teaching the principles of radiation curing available. Although a number of texts have now appeared, a need still remains for a text which would take a student having some background knowledge of chemistry from first principles through to a position having a good over-all knowledge of the technology. This is so because as the application of radiation curing technology continues to expand, so will the number of people who have to be familiar with its principles and the underlying science increase. With this remit in mind detailed discussions of specialised topics such as u.v. curable inks or formulations for wood coating are not to be found in the book. However a person who has assimilated the basic teachings of the book will be well placed to usefully read more advanced and detailed texts, appreciate the work and efforts of those who have preceded them in the field of their particular interest and develop their own ideas for use in job-related applications. A reason for including discussions of materials described in the recent research literature and of emerging applications as presented at conferences, was to encourage the reader to think of newer and hopefully better ways of using radiation curing in their own job and hence the use of the word "Exploring" in the title.

This book could not have been written without the help and encouragement of many friends and colleagues. Stimulating and thought provoking discussions have been held with Professor Dr. Hank J. Hageman (formerly of Akzo Corporate Research), Dr. Richard Holman (Paint Research Association) and Dr. Shaun Herlihy (Coates Lorilleux). Over the years I have been fortunate enough to have a number of research students who have challenged my thinking and also produced material which is contained in the book. Several companies have been kind enough to support my research over the years and in the process have helped to give me an appreciation of how radiation curing is used in industry and the types of problems that they have to face.

Bringing a book to print also requires the help and expertise of others and I should like to record my special thanks to Eva Radkowska for deciphering my handwriting and producing typed text and to Ann Crane who has changed many a scruffy drawing into a piece of art-form. A final word of thanks must go to my publisher who rescued the text when, for reasons beyond my control, I had lost hope in ever seeing it published.

R. Stephen Davidson
London 1999

Biographical Details

Stephen Davidson gained Graduate Membership of the Royal Institute of Chemistry from Leeds College of Technology in 1958. He proceeded to Leeds University where he worked under the supervision of Professor B. Lythgoe F. R. S. on the synthesis of Tachysterol$_3$ and in 1961 was awarded a Ph.D. degree. He stayed at Leeds University for a further two years as Brotherton Research Fellow and completed the synthesis of Tachysterol. He took up a Research Fellowship at Harvard University (USA) working with Professor R. B. Woodward on the synthesis of Vitamin B$_{12}$ where he played a part in synthesising the "North West Corner". In 1963 he took up the post of lecturer in Organic Chemistry at the University of Leicester where he commenced research on photchemistry. Of particular note was the work on electron transfer reactions such as the photoreactions of carbonyl compounds with amines. Much of this early work found application in radiation curing and it wasn't long before he started to apply his academic findings to this technology. In 1979 he moved to City University as Professor of Organic Chemistry where he expanded his industrial contacts and work on radiation curing. Concurrently with this work he had a group working on the applications of fluorescence and chemiluminescence to immunoassays which ultimately led to the setting up the company Citifluor Ltd. When the government axe (or maybe this was the excuse) fell on Chemistry at City University he moved to the University of Kent at Canterbury as Professor of Applied Chemistry where work on radiation curing continued until his retirement in 1999. He has published over 200 papers in refereed journals on photochemistry and its applications and has given lectures on this work at international meetings, to industry and at universities around the world. Together with Dr. Richard Holman, he tutors on the Radiation Curing Course run by the Paint Research Association and runs a consultancy, DavRad Services, whose principle business is assisting the radiation curing industry.

x

CHAPTER I

AN OVERVIEW

CHAPTER I

I AN OVERVIEW

(i) Introduction

The term radiation curing is used to describe the conversion of a liquid into a solid or to change the physical properties of a polymer, by means of radiation.[1]

Radiation commonly employed in the industry is either ultraviolet or electron beam radiation. Recently there has been renewed interest shown in pulsed light systems[2] and much effort is being expended to find systems that will use continuous wave lasers and light-emitting diodes, as sources of radiation[3] and as a consequence there is a growing interest in the use of photoinitiators that respond to visible and near infra red light.

(ii) Absorption of Light[4]

How can light be used to bring about the desired reactions? Light is energy and the amount of energy is related to its frequency.

$$\text{Energy } \alpha \quad \text{Frequency } \alpha \quad \frac{1}{\text{Wavelength}}$$

Ultraviolet radiation can be classified according to its wavelength.

UVA 315 - 380nm
UVB 315 - 280nm
UVC 280 - 100nm

For a system to be sensitive to light it must be able to absorb it and then use it to generate species which will either initiate polymerisation or undergo a crosslinking reaction. The role of a photoinitiator (A) is to generate reactive species that will initiate polymerisation whereas a photosensitiser (D) is a compound, which will energise a species that will in turn lead to the production of reactive species.

$$A \rightarrow A^* \rightarrow \text{Reactive species}$$
$$D \rightarrow D^*$$
$$D^* + A \rightarrow D + A^* \qquad \text{Energy transfer}$$
$$\qquad\qquad\qquad\qquad\quad \text{Electron or atom transfer}$$
$$A^* \rightarrow \text{Reactive species}$$

In crosslinking reactions (which change the physical properties of the polymer) a photoactive group (P) is energised by absorption of light and then undergoes reactions which lead to the creation of new bonds. Such systems can also in many cases be sensitised by energy transfer (either singlet or triplet energy transfer depending on the system being used). In this process, the sensitiser D absorbs the radiation thereby populating an excited state which can hand on its energy to the species P in a process that generates the desired excited state of P.

$$P \rightarrow P^* \rightarrow \text{P-P} \quad \text{New bond formed}$$
$$D \rightarrow D^*$$
$$D^* + P \rightarrow P^* + D \quad \text{Energy transfer}$$
$$P^* + P \rightarrow \text{P-P}$$

The absorption of light by a molecule is determined by the types of bonding which link the various atoms together. When a photon is absorbed, the energy is used to promote an electron from either a bonding molecular or non-bonding molecular orbital to an antibonding orbital. As a consequence, u.v. visible absorption spectroscopy is often referred to as electronic absorption spectroscopy. For the commonly used initiators, photosensitisers and photosensitive groups encountered in radiation curing, bonding molecular orbitals are usually π-orbitals and non bonding orbitals n-orbitals. Usually, electrons from these orbitals are promoted into a π^* antibonding orbital. Consider the carbonyl group. As shown in Figure 1 it possesses both π and n-bonding orbitals. Absorption of light may lead to the promotion of an electron from the π or n-bonding orbital to the π^* orbital. For absorption of a photon to occur its energy must match exactly the energy required to bring about the electronic transition i.e. it is a quantised process.

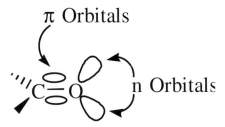

Figure 1: The n and π bonding orbitals present in a carbonyl group.

The electronic absorption spectrum of a typical ketone, e.g. benzophenone in solution reveals the presence of two types of transition (Figure 2).

How does the presence of two types of transition affect processes which are relevant to radiation curing? In orbitals which are fully occupied, ie they contain two electrons, the spins are paired and this is termed a singlet state.

The absorption of a photon is so rapid that spin is conserved and consequently an excited singlet state is produced. Due to magnetic interactions between the electrons in the half-occupied orbitals and the nucleus, spin inversion may occur and a triplet state be produced (Figure 3).

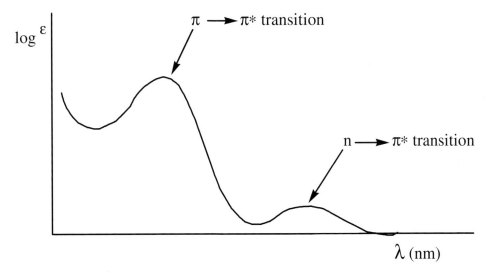

Figure 2: Absorption spectrum of benzophenone

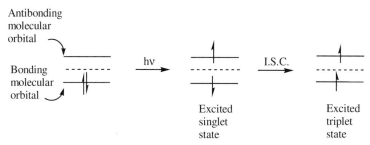

Figure 3: Diagrammatic picture showing how excited singlet and triplet states are produced

The process of spin inversion is termed intersystem crossing (ISC) and is usually relative to the process of absorption, slow ($\sim 10^{-9}$secs). For the triplet state to relax back to the ground state, spin inversion must occur and since this is slow, triplet states often have long lifetimes (10^{-8} - 10^{-3}secs). Excited singlet states relax to the ground state by a process not involving spin inversion (termed internal conversion) and as a consequence, they have relatively short lifetimes ($\sim 10^{-12}$ - 10^{-9}secs). When two transitions are present in a molecule a photon may be absorbed leading to the population of the higher energy transition. Normally, this excited state loses energy, (as heat) to the surrounding molecules thereby populating the lowest excited singlet state which may then undergo intersystem crossing etc. We can summarise all these processes by means of a Jablonski diagram (Figure 4).

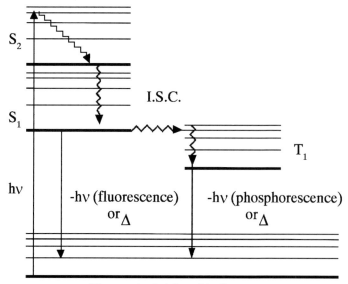

Figure 4: Jablonski diagram

In the case of benzophenone, S_2 would be populated via the $\pi\rightarrow\pi^*$ transition and S_1 via an $n\rightarrow\pi'$ transition. From Figures 3 and 4 it can be seen that absorption of radiation at 254nm will populate the S_2 state, but energy loss will occur leading to the population of S_1 and T_1 states and as a consequence, not all the absorbed radiation is available for the photochemical reaction. Nevertheless, absorption of light at these shorter wavelengths is particularly useful in improving cure at the coating-air interface.

Mention has been made that it is normal for triplet states to have a longer lifetime than excited singlet states. A consequence of triplet states having a long lifetime is that they are more likely to undergo bimolecular reactions than the shorter lived excited singlet states. The rate of a bimolecular reaction between an excited state A* and a ground state molecule M is dependent upon the lifetime of A*, the concentration of M, the rate constant for the process and the viscosity of the medium; thus high rates are favoured by A* having a longer lifetime, M being present at high concentration and the medium having a low viscosity. If the reaction of A* with M leads to initiating radicals (a Type II photoinitiator system) derived from M, the efficiency of the process will decrease as a photoinitiated polymerisation process proceeds since the viscosity of the reaction mixture increases as reaction progresses. Previously, when sensitisation was being discussed, it was noted that the energy transfer process is a bimolecular process and hence the efficiency of sensitisation is also dependent upon the viscosity of the medium and it will decrease as cure progresses. Energy transfer can also lead to energy wastage. In radiation curing many Type II initiators have relatively long lifetimes and these can be quenched by oxygen.

$$A^*_{T1} + {}^3O_2 \rightarrow A_{S0} + {}^1O_2$$

T_1 first excited triplet state

${}^3O_2$ ground state oxygen

${}^1O_2$ singlet oxygen - an excited state of oxygen

This is just one of the ways in which the presence of oxygen in a coating can reduce the efficiency of cure.

An appreciation of the information contained in an absorption spectrum such as that shown in Figure 2 is important for other reasons. If a quantitative spectrum is run, extinction coefficients can be calculated using the Beer Lambert Law.

$$OD = \log(I_0/I) = \varepsilon cl$$

Where OD = Optical density, I_0 is the intensity of the incident radiation, I = the intensity of the transmitted radiation, e = extinction coefficient, c = concentration in moles per litre and l = pathlength in cms.

When recording spectra for materials in solution it is usual to use 1 cm. cells and manufacturers of initiators often give the absorption spectra for their materials in solution run in such cells. When we are considering coatings we are talking about pathlengths of mm thickness i.e. a 10mm coating has a pathlength which is 1/1000 of a 1 cm. cell and these pathlengths are considerably shorter than those used for recording spectra. However, having calculated the extinction coefficients from solution spectra we can calculate the extent to which materials will absorb specified wavelengths in a coating. For photoinitiators it is essential that the light is efficiently absorbed throughout the coating. Poor absorption at the bottom of the coating will lead to undercure. This may occur if too little or too much initiator is used. If too much initiator is used all the light will be absorbed in the upper parts of the coating. For practical purposes it is useful to know the main emission lines of the lamp being employed and then to calculate the extinction coefficients for the initiator at these wavelengths. From a knowledge of the extinction coefficient and the thickness of the coating, the extent to which a particular wavelength is absorbed can be calculated. It is particularly important to do this when using monochromatic radiation such as that delivered by excimer lamps so as to ensure adequate absorption of light. It will be clear from a consideration of the Beer Lambert Law that high transfer process are associated with efficient absorption of light and consequently in thin films only low concentrations of the material will needed. When thick films are being used, the concentration of the material will have to be lowered if light is to reach the bottom of the film. Materials having low extinction coefficients are particularly useful if light is to reach the bottom of a thick film. If benzophenone is used as the initiator in a film of moderate thickness e.g. ~ 15mm, consideration of the absorption spectrum in Figure 2 tells us that wavelengths below 300nm. will be efficiently absorbed near the surface due to the high value of the extinction coefficient and wavelengths > 300nm will give cure through the film. It is useful to record the absorption spectra of as many of the components of a u.v. curable formulation as possible in order to determine if any components are acting as u.v. screens and preventing light being efficiently absorbed by the initiator.

(iii)   **Electron Beam Irradiation**[5, 6, 7]

When high energy electrons impinge upon organic matter ionisation occurs with subsequent loss of energy.

$$e***** + M \rightarrow *** + e + M^{+\cdot}$$

e***** - High energy electron

e   - Slow or low energy electron

$M^{+\cdot}$ - Molecular ions

The ionisation process is not selective and consequently for a particular molecule, a number of structurally different molecular ions may be produced.

e.g.

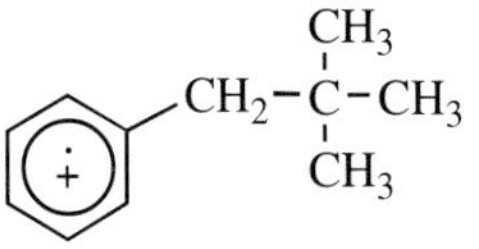

(1)

(2)

Ionisation of the aromatic residue

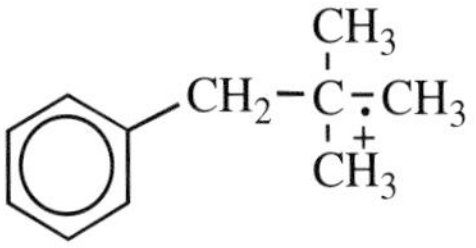

Ionisation of the side chain

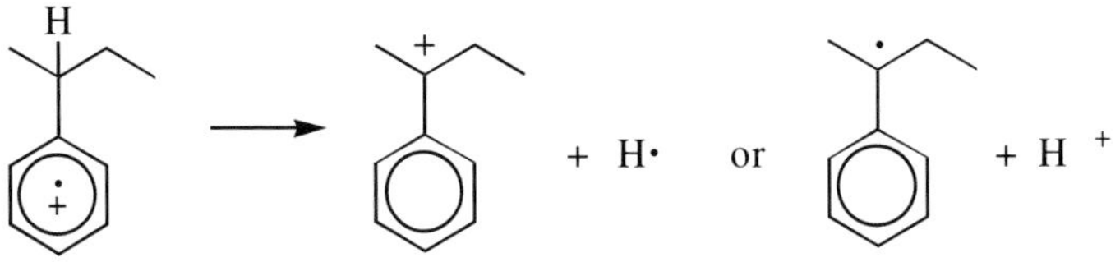

+ H·   or   + H $^+$

Despite the randomness of the initial ionisation process, hole hopping may occur to give the most stable molecular ion e.g. (2) → (1). The molecular ions may fragment to give a cation and a radical.

The chemistry of the slow, or low energy, electron is of paramount importance. Such an electron may (i) act as a reducing agent (e.g. reduce cationic photoinitiators), (ii) attach itself to a double bond (e.g. as found in an acrylate) and so generate an initiating species, (iii) attach itself to an aromatic residue giving a stable radical ion or attach itself to an aromatic residue to give a transient species which dissociates(dissociative electron capture) (Figure 5).

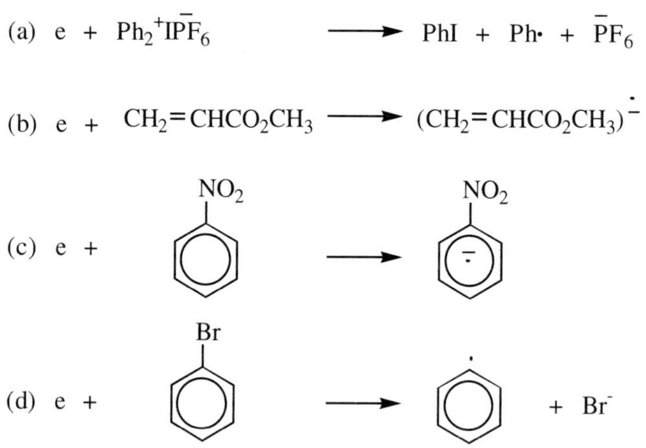

(a) $e + Ph_2^+ I\overline{P}F_6 \longrightarrow PhI + Ph\cdot + \overline{P}F_6$

(b) $e + CH_2=CHCO_2CH_3 \longrightarrow (CH_2=CHCO_2CH_3)^{\overset{\cdot}{-}}$

(c) $e +$ $\longrightarrow$

(d) $e +$ $\longrightarrow$ $+ Br^-$

Figure 5: Summary of reactions which the slow electron
may undergo

Thus electron beam radiation may lead to initiation of radical curing systems via radical cations or via the slow electron.

(iv)   Some Typical U.v. and E.b. Curing Formulations[8, 9, 10]

The simplest type of u.v curing formulation for producing a clear surface coating will contain the following ingredients:

Photoinitiator	1 - 15% w/w
Reactive diluent	~55% w/w
Prepolymer (oligomer)	~30% w/w

Such a formulation is typical for producing a clear varnish via either a free radical or cationic process. Because free radical curing proceeds suffer from oxygen inhibition a tertiary amine (~5% w/w) is added to ameliorate this effect (see Section V.(i)). A prepolymer is a relatively high molecular weight material that contains a number of functional groups responsible for the polymerisation process as well as the molecular entities which will confer the appropriate physical properties upon the cured coating. Prepolymers usually have a high viscosity and are therefore difficult to apply to a substrate via a conventional coating process. For this reason reactive diluents are added. These compounds contain polymerisable groups and serve to reduce the viscosity of the formulation and can be used to control the reactivity of the system and the crosslink density. If a coloured coating is required, the appropriate pigments are ground into the curing mixture (usually at a 15-25% w/w level). Special care has to be exercised when choosing pigments for use with cationically cured systems since they must not contain substituents or surface treatments that are basic in character.

For the production of clear surface coating, via a free radical process and e.b. radiation a similar formulation to the one shown above may be used except that the photoinitiator is omitted. Since curing is carried out under a blanket of nitrogen, ie the coating is being cured under essentially oxygen-free conditions, the presence of tertiary amine is not required. Coloured coatings may be produced by grinding in the appropriate pigments. Many pigments retard the curing process by scavenging the slow electrons. To cure a coating via a cationic process, the formulation must contain a cationic photoinitiator (see Section III.(v)). As with the u.v. cured systems, care has to be taken in selecting pigments.

(v)   U.v. Curing Equipment[11]

(a)   General

A typical u.v. curing unit may house one or more lamps as is shown in Figure 6. The material to be cured is passed underneath the lamp(s) using the moving belt. The speed of the belt determines how long the coating is exposed to the light. Another important parameter is the design of the reflector system and views vary as to which is the best type.

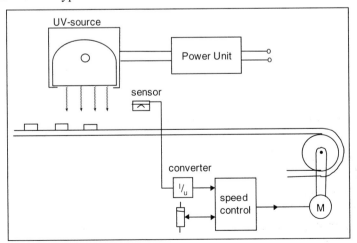

Figure 6: A laboratory u.v. curing unit.

Some take the view that it is better to use a parabolic reflector that focuses the light onto the coating whereas others prefer elliptical reflectors or a defocused parabolic reflector that enables a relatively large area of the coating to be irradiated.

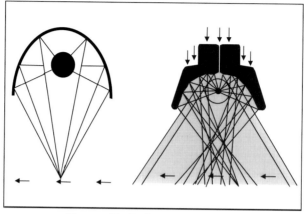

Figure 7: Reflector designs

C.Lowe in in Formulations for radiation Curable coatings in Chemistry & Technology of UV & EB Formulations for Coatings, Inks and Paints, Vol 4, p 477, ed PKT Oldring, SITA Technology Ltd 1991

Anodised aluminium is a good reflector of u.v. light and this is commonly used. Dichroic reflectors have also been made available and these are designed to transmit infra-red radiation and reflect the useful u.v. and visible radiation. Which-ever reflector system is chosen, heat management is of the utmost importance. Shutter mechanisms are fitted to most industrial units and these close if there is a power failure which causes the conveyor to stop. In this way fires caused by the radiation igniting the coating are avoided. The amount of heat in the irradiation chamber is also determined by the volume of air per unit time that is swept past the lamps by the ventilation system. If substrates are being coated that are heat sensitive chilled rollers may be used. When curing thick coatings it should be remembered that the heat of polymerisation may make a significant contribution and, with pigmented coatings, the pigment may absorb a significant amount of radiation and degrade it to heat. The type of lamp and its power rating also have a profound effect upon the efficiency of cure and on the amount of heat produced in the irradiation chamber.

All the foregoing remarks relate to a conveyor system but there are many other alternatives. Projection systems utilise a light source and an arrangement of lenses so that large areas can be irradiated/imaged and they find use in the production of posters. At the other end of the scale, spot cure systems, continuous wave lasers etc. are used to irradiate small areas as are encountered in electronics applications.

(b) Lamps

A range of lamps is available for initiating polymerisation and include the following:

- Mercury lamps (low, medium and high pressure)
- Electrodeless lamps
- Excimer lamps
- Xenon lamps (free running and pulsed)
- Spot cure lamps
- Continuous wave (c.w.) and pulsed lasers
- Light emitting diodes

For many of the lamps, their spectral output can be modified by doping and this increases the choice of materials that a formulator can use. Undoubtedly the most frequently used lamp for u.v. curing applications is the medium pressure mercury lamp. Not only does this lamp have an emission spectrum which can be used to excite the commonly used initiators but also the electrical circuitry needed to start and run the lamp is simple (usually a transformer and capacitor and additionally for smaller lamps a choke) are relatively inexpensive (given that many street lights are such lamps, this is a particularly valuable feature) and usually the lamp and its reflector can be easily retro-fitted to a production of line. Another attractive feature is that lamps of lengths up to 2.5 metres can be obtained which means that a wide range of web widths can be accommodated. Power levels in common use fall between 40 to 200 Watts/cm. and even higher levels are available for special applications.

The conventional medium pressure mercury lamp consists of a sealed cylindrical quartz tube equipped with tungsten electrodes at either end containing mercury metal and vapour and a starter gas (usually argon) (Figure 8).

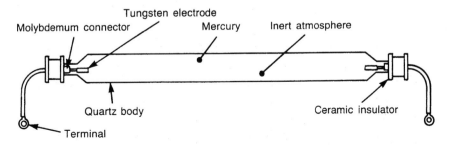

Figure 8: Medium pressure mercury arc lamp [11]

The pressure within the tube is 10^2 to 10^4 Torr (760 Torr = 1 atmosphere). When a high voltage is applied across the electrodes the starter gas is ionised.

$$Ar \rightarrow Ar^+ + e \quad \text{Ionisation}$$

$$Ar^+ + e \rightarrow Ar^* \qquad \qquad Ar^* \text{ Excited state of argon}$$

Recombination of the ionised electron with the argon cation gives an electronically excited argon atom which can energise and subsequently ionise a mercury atom.

$$Ar^* + Hg \rightarrow Ar + Hg^+ + e$$

Recombination of a mercury cation with an electron generates an electronically excited mercury atom, which loses its energy radiatively. These are just a few of the processes which take place but the combined effect is the emission of light in the u.v. and visible region (Figure 9) and the generation of heat. The heat leads to vapourisation of some of the metallic mercury. The generated mercury cations are conducting and hence the current passed between the electrodes rises until a steady state is reached.

With knowledge of the above facts it is easy to see why the following precautions should be observed when using these lamps.

(1)   Lamps should not be handled with the bare hands since this leads to proteins and other materials being deposited on the quartz envelope which subsequently carbonise when the lamp is running. These deposits act as light filters and attenuators.

(2)   Care should be exercised in disposing of lamps. Remember the lamps contain toxic material. The contents of the lamp are under pressure and therefore there is the risk of explosion. The lamps should be disposed of in accordance with local regulations since they contain mercury.

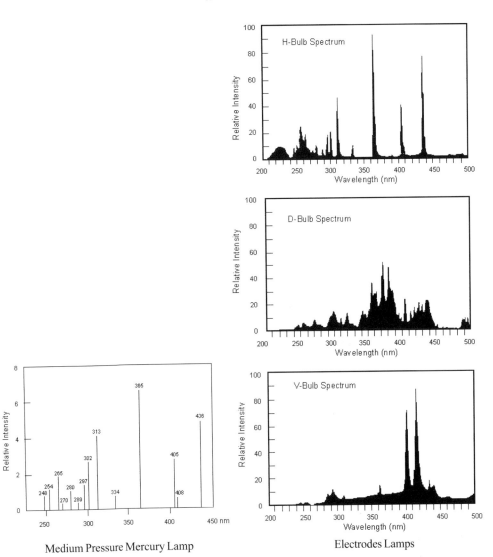

Figure 9: Spectral outputs of lamps used in u.v. curing.

Of the problems associated with using these lamps the two most serious are firstly, the lamps will not strike (ignite) whilst hot and secondly the heat released during operation has to be managed otherwise products may be spoiled e.g paper carbonised or polyester softened or melted. The first problem arises when a line has to be stopped in the middle of a run to rectify a fault and there is the wish to resume operations as soon as possible. Generation of heat when the lamps are running has benefits as previously described but precautions have to be taken when coating heat sensitive substrates, to avoid volatalisation of volatile components and to avoid fires should the conveyor system stop leaving the coated substrate under the lamp. As stated earlier, a good airflow past the lamps is used to regulate the temperature, and chilled rollers may be used to keep the heat-sensitive substrate at the desired temperature.

Whilst the lamps have good lifetimes (often in excess of 3,000 hours) the intensity of the emitted light and the relative intensity of the spectral lines change with time. The fact that a lamp strikes is no guarantee that its output is as when new and it may have decreased with time to such a level that it is unable to trigger cure. Devices are available (spectro-radiometers) which can monitor these changes and the information they provide is very useful in trouble shooting.

The spectral output of the medium pressure mercury lamp can be altered by adding a little metal halide to the gas mix. Commonly used doped lamps are iron and gallium lamps.

The spectral output of some of these lamps compared with an undoped lamp are shown in Figure 10. Doped lamps find use in the curing of heavily pigmented systems.

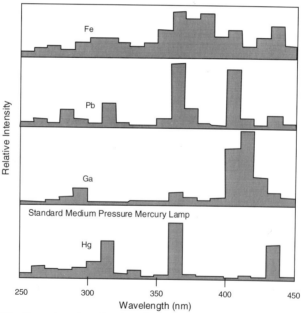

Figure 10: Spectural outputs of some typical metal halide lamps compared to that from standard mercury lamp [11]

Low pressure mercury lamps usually consist of a quartz cylinder having electrodes at either end (Figure 11) although other shapes can be fabricated. The cylinder contains a mixture of mercury and argon at a low pressure 10^{-2} to 10^{-3} Torr. The emission from these lamps is at 254 nm. but if high quality quartz is used in the construction some 189 nm. light is produced. These lamps are usually of relatively low power and are not commonly used for production of surface coatings but are of value in resist technology for the production of microchips. If the inside of the tubes is coated with a suitable phosphor, lamps having a range of different spectral emissions can be obtained e.g. lamps having an emission centred around 300nm and around 350nm. are available. The power of these lamps is low but they find use where slow curing can be tolerated or is required e.g. in the production of liquid crystal displays.

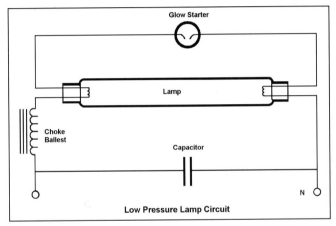

Figure 11: Low pressure lamp circuit [11]

High pressure lamps operate, as their name implies, at high pressures (10 atmospheres), and two types are available. One is a point source (Figure 12) and this facilitates focussing so that a small diameter spot of intense radiation can be produced.

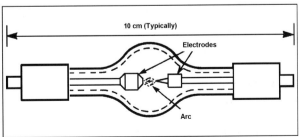

Figure 12: Compact arc lamp [11]

The other type is a capillary lamp (Figure 13) and these can be used with small webs. Advantages of the high over the medium pressure lamps include the characteristics of their spectral output. The emission lines exhibited by the medium pressure lamps are present in the high pressure lamps are but are considerably broadened and consequently the spectral-output takes on the appearance of a continuum. This richness in output means that far more wavelengths are available for initiation. The other attribute is the very high power of these lamps (150 - 2880 Watts/cm). The downside to these lamps include the limited sizes in which they are available and their short operating lives -usually hundreds rather than thousands of hours.

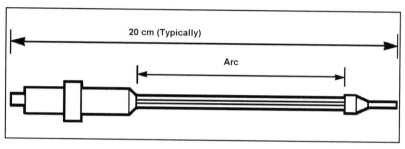

Figure 13: Capillary lamp [11]

Many electrodeless lamps have similar emission characteristics to medium pressure doped and undoped mercury lamps (Figure 9). They are in fact mercury lamps but differ from the conventional lamps in that the tubes are free of electrodes (Figure 14).

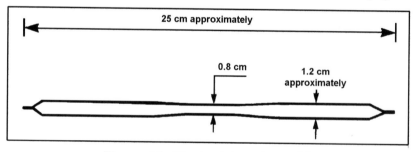

Figure 14: Electrodeless lamp [11]

Excitation of the mercury atoms is achieved by means of microwave power which is generated by magnetrons. The housing of these power modules and the reflector system is integral and consequently this unit is somewhat larger than the equivalent medium pressure lamp together with its reflector system. Such considerations need to be taken into account when retro-fitting is being considered. The available sizes of lamps is somewhat restricted (up to 25 cm) and therefore when used with large web widths several modules mounted end to end.

A variety of gas fills for the lamps is available thereby giving good coverage of the u.v. and visible spectrum. Since lamp changes can be effected relatively easily there is no particular problem in using the appropriate lamp for the job in hand.

Some of the perceived merits of the electrodeless lamp systems include:

- The modular lamp, reflector system is simple and easy to install.
- Lamp lifetimes are longer (~ 3000 hours compared with ~1000 hours for electrode containing lamps).
- Fast warm up times (2 to 3 seconds)
- Following switching off the lamps there is no requirement to allow the lamps to cool before re-igniting.

Disadvantages associated with the use of these lamps include:

- The only lamp length commonly available is 24 cm. Longer lamp lengths would require a series of 4 or more matched magnetrons which would make the system very expensive.
- The relatively expensive magnetrons require replacement approximately every 5000 hours.
- High power input due to the low efficiency microwave generation process.
- The modular arrangement to accommodate large web widths requires a lot of space.

Both electrode containing and electrodeless lamps are in common usage and each type has its own advantages.

Excimer lamps are a development of excimer lasers. The lasers are used to deliver high power pulses of essentially monochromatic light and are finding increasing use in the fabrication of semiconductor devices. Patterning by means of short wavelength (e.g. 222 nm.) u.v. light using the process of laser induced ablation is very popular. Excimer lamps, like the lasers deliver essentially monochromatic radiation with the wavelength being determined by the gas fill. Currently the wavelengths available[12] are 172 nm. (xenon), 222 nm. (krypton chloride), and 308 nm. (xenon chloride).

The construction of a commercialised system is shown in Figure 15.

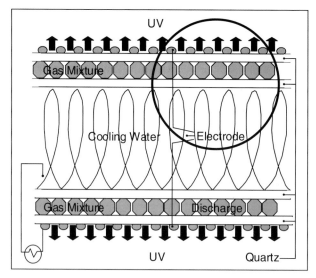

Figure 15: Structure of an excimer lamp [13]

The lamp consists of two concentric cylindrical tubes, sealed at the ends with the gas being contained between the walls of the tubes. Water passes through the inner space so as to cool the unit. A high frequency alternating voltage is applied to the electrodes thereby generating a "silent electric discharge" which leads to the creation of excited states in the gas fill. Coatings are cured in a nitrogen atmosphere and this has advantages and disadvantages. Clearly there are cost implications but these may be offset by being able to use less photoinitiator. The claimed advantages of the water cooled lamps include the following:

- The substrate is not heated during curing and this enables thin plastic films, thermal paper and other temperature sensitive materials to be coated.

- The lamps ignite immediately on applying power i.e. there is no warm up period.

- Curing under nitrogen leads to zero ozone production and the odours from cured formulations reduced.

- The lamp units are compact and easy to install.

A very interesting application of these lamps is to produce matt coatings since use of conventional lamps usually leads to glossy coatings.[13] If a formulation not containing a matting agent is irradiated with 172 nm. radiation only the top surface is cured with the surface taking on a wrinkled appearance which is attributed to shrinkage. It is the wrinkling that gives the matt effect. The wet material beneath the surface can be cured in the conventional way.

Xenon lamps are available as point source and tubular lamps and other configurations. Since the radiation delivered by a xenon lamp is not particularly rich below 400 nm. these lamps have not attracted a great deal of attention. However two developments have restimulated interest. Firstly it is possible to pulse xenon lamps which enables high peak irradiances to be achieved and secondly by altering the gas fill, lamps having an output rich in u.v. are available. Pulsed lamps are available having emission in the u.v. and the visible. Applications of these lamps include medical, electronics, semiconductor production and in fibre optics. The claimed advantages of these lamps include:

- Pulsed lamps enable deeper cure, which is particularly valuable for pigmented coatings.

- Cure is effected in less than a second.

- Heat is controlled thereby minimising damage to substrate and coating.

- Pulsed lamps generate higher peak power than continuous wave lamps enabling faster cure to be acheived at lower average power and lower temperatures.

- No need for nitrogen inertion.

- Blowers not required to reduce air temperature in the curing tunnel.

- No need to install shutters should power failure occur.

Spot cure lamps use short arc lamps together with a focussing system[14] (Figure 16) that concentrates the emitted radiation into a small area - a spot. The light is often transmitted from the lamp housing to the surface to be cured via an optical delivery system such as u.v. transmitting light guide. Energy levels of 2,000 mW/cm^2 can be obtained with a 100W short arc mercury source. Such systems are ideal for curing small areas such as are encountered in assembling small electronic and optical components by means of u.v. curable adhesives.

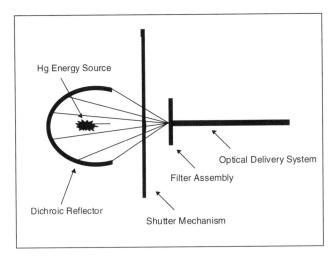

Figure 16: Focussing geometry of a spot cure system [14]

The use of light sources such as light emitting diodes in radiation curing is still very limited but the promised availability of photoinitiators based on borate salts of cyanine and other dyes which will respond to the emission generated by these lamps is expected to enhance their use. Undoubtedly early applications will be in specialised areas such as direct write systems, holography etc. Continous wave lasers are also likely to find more extensive application as the number of initiators available which respond in the visible region increase. Argon ion and helium-cadmium are particularly popular lasers.

(c)   Some Useful Terms

U.v. Irradiance is the radiant power (flux) arriving at surface per unit area i.e the photon flux and is sometimes referred to as "dose rate". It is usually expressed in Watts or milliWatts per square centimetre. Irradiance depends upon the type of lamp, presence of optical filters, efficiency of the reflector system. **Peak irradiance** is the maximum radiant power that a lamp can give at the surface and is influential in determining how effective cure is as a function of the thickness of the coating (an application of the Beer Lambert Law).

U.v. dose is the **total** amount of radiant energy experienced by the surface and is therefore dependent upon the radiant power, the time of exposure to the radiation and number of exposures to the light source. When a u.v. curing tunnel is used, the dose is inversely proportional to the conveyor speed and to the number of passes under the lamp. Dose is expressed in Joules or milliJoules.

Spectral distribution is the radiant energy as a function of wavelength.

To characterise a system in terms of some of the above requires one has to have available a u.v. measuring device. Dosemeter papers are available which change colour as the dose increases but their wavelength sensitivity is restricted to > 300nm. If a conveyor is used to transport the substrate beneath the lamps then a "light bug" can be used. These "bugs" contain a photocell that upon illumination generates an electrical signal, which is proportional to the light intensity. If this is integrated as the "bug" passes through the tunnel then the u.v. dose can be obtained. In those case where it may not be possible to pass the "bug" through the unit, light guides, provided they have the right transmission characteristics, may be used to take light from the illuminated zone to the radiometer. Light "bugs" do not give any spectral information and since the response of the photocell may be limited e.g. to the UVA range, and is not uniform over the entire spectral range of the lamp, some emission lines will make a greater contribution to the derived dose than others. This latter fact makes it very difficult to compare doses delivered by different types of lamps. Spectral radiometers are now available which give radiance values (watts per cm.) as a function of wavelength. (Figure 17). Such equipment can be installed to monitor a lamps performance on a continuous basis as well as to make spot checks.

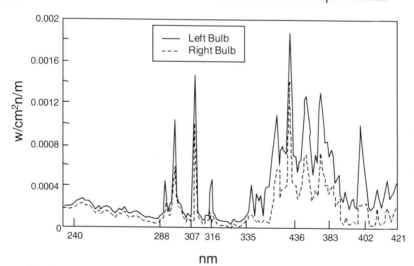

Figure 17: Spectral distribution of two similar lamps on a conveyor line as measured by a Sola-Sensor through a 7" probe.

(vi)   **Electron Beam Curing Equipment**[9, 10, 15, 16,17]

Every television tube contains an electron gun and the electrons so produced are accelerated and guided so that on impact with the phosphors upon the screen an image is produced. Early e.b. curing units worked upon a similar principle but in this case the screen was replaced by a cooled metal foil window which transmitted the electrons so that they could used for initiating of cure. These days the equipment is usually applies the electrons as a curtain (Figure 18). The cathode is powered (applied voltage 120-300kV) so that it emits electrons parallel to the direction of movement of the web and these are accelerated. These processes occur in vacuo and the electrons escape via the metal window, traverse a small gap before impinging upon the coating to be cured. The gap between the electron source and the coating is flushed with nitrogen so that the passage of the electrons is not impeded by oxygen (oxygen scavenges electrons) and also initiation of cure is not deleteriously affects by oxygen scavenging the radical produced by the electron beam.

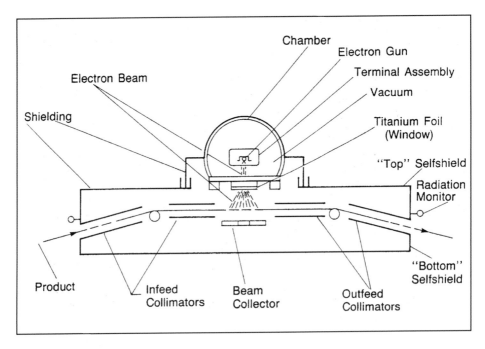

Figure 18a: Electrocurtain[R] processor with selfshield web handling assembly [(17)]

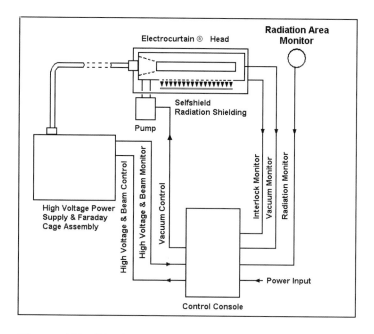

Figure 18b: Block diagram of an Electrocurtain^R unit [17]

Some units are equipped with more than one electron gun (Figure 19).

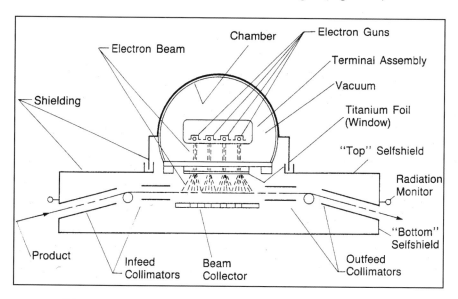

Figure 19: Four filament Electrocurtain^R processor [17]

An alternative to this arrangement is to have multiple short filaments, spaced approximately three inches apart, with their axes parallel to the direction of the movement of the web (Figure 20). Electrons are generated by applying a voltage of ~120-300kV.

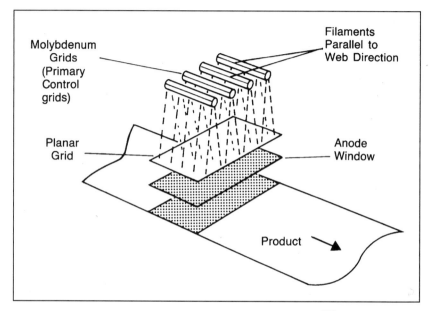

Figure 20:Broadbeam™ Processor [17]

Units composed of several filaments are capable of delivering very high energy doses (1,500 Mrad metres per minute).

A relative newcomer to the field is a unit equipped with a conveyor (6" width) which can sit on top of a relatively small table[18]. Electrons are delivered from small e.b. tubes and to irradiate samples of 5" width it is necessary to have five of these tubes arranged in parallel. The operating voltage for the tubes is 30 - 70 kV. Such a unit has the capacity to cure coatings up to 70μm thick and not in every case is nitrogen inerting required. Such units are going to be very valuable for testing the suitability of formulations for e. b. cure.

The dose delivered to a system is measured in rads or grays with their relationship being shown below.

One megarad = 1 Mrad = 10 joules per gram

One kilogray = 1 kGy = 1joule per gram

i.e. 10 kGy = 1 Mrad

Dose rate is the rate at which energy is absorbed and is expressed as Mrad/s or Mrad/min.

The delivered dose is between line speed and dose.

Dose rate X exposure time = Dose rate/Line speed = Dose
and Dose rate = Beam Current

The accelerating voltage is an important parameter since it determines the extent that the electrons will penetrate the coating but is independent of beam current and hence dose rate.

(vii)   The Relative Merits of U.v. and E.b. Radiation

U.v. curing is undoubtedly the lower cost option since the irradiation units are less expensive, and normally one does not have the added expense of nitrogen inerting. For free radical mediated curing systems, a disadvantage of u.v. curing is the requirement to use photoinitiators since many are expensive and give rise to undesirable effects in the film such as colour and odour. Both these effects can be minimised if nitrogen blanketing is used with u.v. curing. For reasons detailed later, curing of pigmented coatings and in particular thick ones, present problems for u.v. curing whereas the same coatings are cured efficiently by e.b. It is also true that the percentage migratable species present in a u.v. cured coating is higher than that in an e.b. cured coating and this can often be attributed to the presence of unused photoinitiator and initiator residues. Given the regulations concerning food packaging, it would seem that e.b. curing has the definite edge in this market. The coatings formed from similar formulations but cured under u.v. and e.b. often differ in their physical properties such as scratch resistance and solvent resistance since the two curing processes are fundamentally different.

Despite the greater cost of installing and running e.b. units, e.b. curing has many important applications. For processes have a high and continuous throughput e.g. wood coating and for curing thick pigmented coatings and for food packaging, it comes into its own.

(viii)   Coating Methods

Various factors influence the choice of coating method. In the printing industry it is the nature of the process that determines the coating method. The laying down of a curable layer in screen printing is very different to that for flexographic or litho printing. A very important factor is the viscosity of the formulation, which in turn depends upon the application temperature. If a three dimensional article has to be coated spray coating may be used and if so the formulation must have a low viscosity. Coating a substrate for a laboratory investigation can be very different to running a coater associated with a large printing press.

Some application methods will be briefly described and are as follows:

- Use of draw down bars
- Spin coating
- Spray coating
- Screen printing
- Curtain coater
- Slot die

Draw down bars are commonly used in laboratory applications.

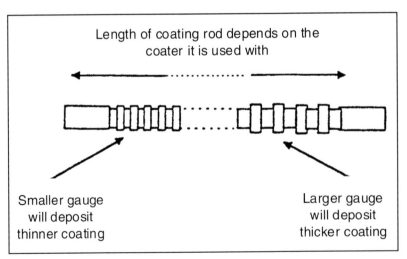

Figure 21: Diagram of a coating rod.

They consist (Figure 21) of a steel rod around which a wire is wound. The dimension of the wire and the tightness with which it is wound, determines the thickness of the film applied. A wide range of coating weights can be applied using these rods although for normal laboratory applications thicknesses which vary from 2 to 80µm are most commonly encountered. The bars may be used manually but equipment is available in which the bars are drawn down mechanically. There is a variety of beds available to support the substrate such as vacuum beds which hold the substrate in a perfectly flat mode, magnetic beds to hold suitable metal substrates in position and heated beds which allow application of films up to a temperature of 200 degrees.

The beds can also be used with applicators other than draw down bars and include a micrometer adjustable applicator.

Spin coating is used to coat surfaces having relatively small dimensions when a very even and often very thin coating is required as in the production of integrated circuits. The substrate e.g. a silicon wafer, is spun and a solution of the curable material in a solvent is applied at the centre. Centrifugal force causes the formulation to run out over the coat. The solvent is removed by evaporation. The thickness of the applied coating is determined by how much material is applied and the rate of spinning.

Coatings may be applied by spraying the formulation onto the substrate and this is particularly valuable for coating three dimensional objects e.g. car headlight components etc. This method has also been used for wood coating. The method lends itself for laying down relatively thick films, but the thickness of the applied film is not particularly uniform. It is essential that the formulation has a relatively low viscosity and in the past it has been common practise to add a little organic solvent which clearly is not desirable. However with the growth of materials available for water based coatings, there is now the possibility of using water as the solvent. The water may be removed by infra red radiation prior to curing or alternatively the heat produced in the curing tunnel may be sufficient to effect removal.

Screen printing, as its name implies, has its origins in the screen printing industry, and is still an important graphic arts process. In the early days, silk screens were "painted" with a negative, and the imaged screen so obtained laid over a substrate and ink applied. The ink flowed, with the aid of an applicator, through the holes in the screen and hence a positive image was obtained (Figure 22).

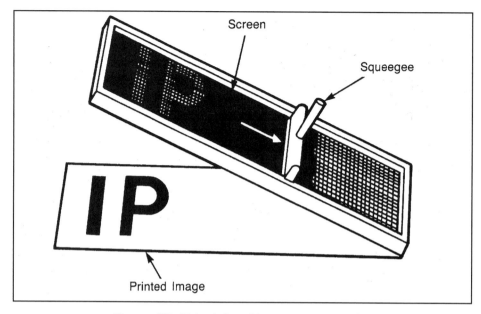

Figure 22: Principle of screen printing [11]

Silk as a sreen material has now been replaced by nylon, polyester and stainless steel. If a photo-sensitive emulsion is applied to the screen it may be imaged by irradiation through a negative or using a direct laser write system. The imaged stencil may be used to lay down a curable resin on a copper clad board as part of the process for production of printed circuit boards. In the normal printing process the curable resin is laid down on non conducting substrates e.g. a plastic surface and then cured in the usual way. Imaging of stencils by means of a projector systems allows the production of very large stencils which are useful for printing large areas as found in advertisement hoardings.

Curtain coating is used by the furniture and electronics industries since it is useful for applying relatively thick films (> 20μm). The formulation is pumped into a trough (Figure 23a and b) which either has a slit in its bottom plate or a suitable arrangement of knife-edges. The liquid flows through the gap and hence a curtain of liquid is produced which falls onto the substrate.

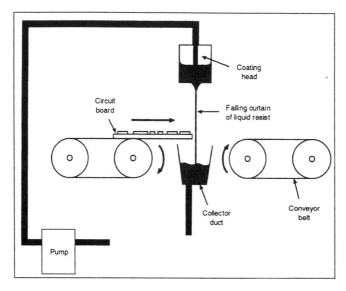

Figure 23a: Curtain coating equipment

C.Lowe in in Formulations for radiation Curable coatings in Chemistry & Technology of UV & EB Formulations for Coatings, Inks and Paints, Vol 4, p 477, ed PKT Oldring, SITA Technology Ltd 1991

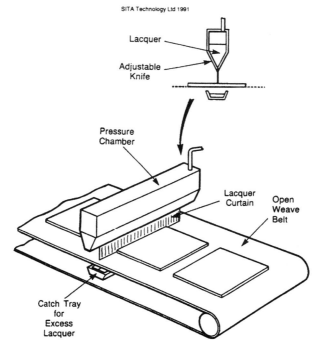

Figure 23b: Diagram of curtain coater [11]

For the liquid to form a curtain it is essential that it has a the correct surface tension. Additives e.g. silicones, can have a drastic effect on surface tension and make it impossible to form a good curtain. The thickness of the deposited film can be controlled by adjusting the speed at which the substrate pass beneath the curtain and by varying the distance between the knife edges. This method of application is good for coatings having an uneven surfaces although, because the formulation viscosity is relatively low, the coating may run subsequent to application and hence raised parts of the substrate may have a thinner coating than the lower ones.

Slot die coaters enable formulations having a relatively high viscosity to be applied and films of thickness >25µm can be applied in this way. The formulation is applied under pressure through a gap between two plates whose separation distance is carefully controlled (Figure 24).

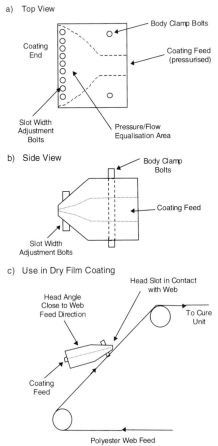

Figure 24: Slot die coater

CHAPTER II

POLYMERISATION SYSTEMS USED IN RADIATION CURING[2, 8,19,21]

CHAPTER II

POLYMERISATION PROCESSES USED IN RADIATION CURING[2, 8, 19,21]

(i)   Free Radical Processes

The free radical reactions commonly used in radiation curing are radical - addition reactions, i.e. a fundamental step is the addition of a radical to a double bond. The type of polymerisable unsaturated system used gives rise to the name of the process, e.g. acrylate or methacrylate, stryrene unsaturated polyester etc. Another feature of the reactions employed in radiation curing is that they are **CHAIN REACTIONS**, i.e. the addition of a radical to a double bond generates another radical which in turn reacts with another double bond and so forth. There are three distinct steps to these reactions:

   (a)   Initiation

   (b)   Propagation

   (c)   Termination

In the first step (a), an initiating radical adds to a double bond, e.g. a mono-substituted double bond $CH_2=CHX$ to give in the main, the most stable radical (Equation 1).

Equation 1

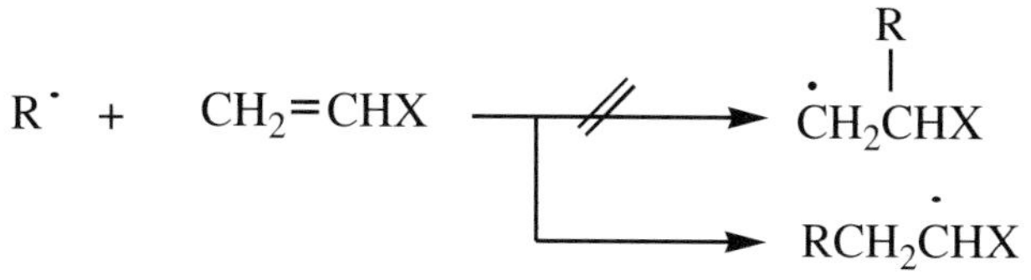

$$R^\cdot \ + \ CH_2{=}CHX \ \longrightarrow\!\!\!/\!\!\!\longrightarrow \ \overset{\displaystyle R}{\underset{\textstyle }{\overset{\cdot}{C}H_2CHX}}$$

$$\longrightarrow \ RCH_2\overset{\cdot}{C}HX$$

The rate constant for this process is dependent upon the nature of R· and X. If X is an electron withdrawing group, reaction is favoured by R· being an electron donating radical i.e. a radical which prefers to generate a positive rather than a negative charge in the transition state (Figure 25).

$$\overset{\delta+\,\cdot}{R----CH_2}\overset{\delta-\,\cdot}{=\!=\!=\!CH-X}$$

Figure 25: Transition state for radical addition to a double bond

A typical electron withdrawing group is the ester group as found in (meth)acrylates and maleates. Typical electron donating radicals include alkyl ($CH_3\cdot$, $R\dot{C}HOR'$) and acyl (RCO·).

Addition of electron withdrawing radicals such as $RCH_2CH\cdot CO_2R'$ is favoured by the substituent X being electron donating such as OR' and $OCOR'$.

A substituent such as phenyl (e.g. as in styrene) can stabilise the incipient radical by delocalisation and consequently the double bond is reactive to both electron donating and withdrawing radicals.

In u.v. curing the radicals are in the main generated photochemically via an initiator system (Type I or II) although radical generated thermally (e.g. peroxidic species) or via hydrogen abstraction from C-H bonds in the diluent or the resin may also play a part.

In the propagation step (b), the radical generated in the initiation step adds to a double bond to generate a radical that undergoes a further reaction (Equation 2).

Equation 2

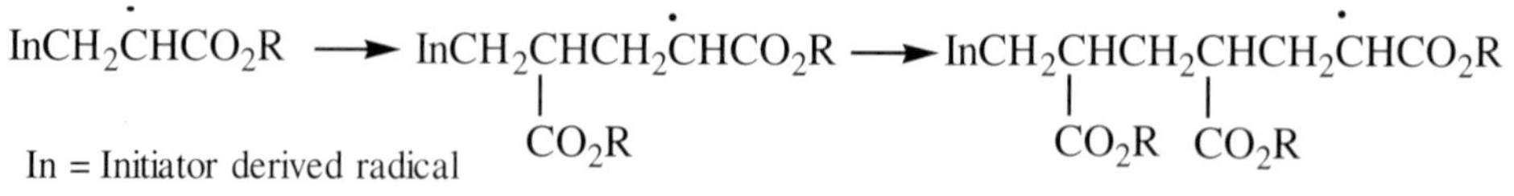

$$InCH_2\overset{\bullet}{C}HCO_2R \longrightarrow InCH_2CHCH_2\overset{\bullet}{C}HCO_2R \longrightarrow InCH_2CHCH_2CHCH_2\overset{\bullet}{C}HCO_2R$$
$$\underset{CO_2R}{|} \qquad\qquad \underset{CO_2R\;\;CO_2R}{|\;\;\;\;|}$$

In = Initiator derived radical

This process leads to the production of a linear homopolymer. If the curing formulation contains a mixture of alkenes there is the possibility for a copolymer being formed. This is particularly true when the reactivity of the two alkenes towards the initiating radical is similar. If the reactivity of the alkenes is very different (e.g. as is the case with acrylates and methacrylates), the more reactive alkene will be used up in preference to the less reactive alkene (e.g polymerisation of an acrylate occurs in preference to the methacrylate). With such systems there is the possibility that a block copolymer may be formed or alternatively that following the polymerisation of one component, the other polymerises thereby giving a mixture of polymers which if conditions are right may produce an interpenetrating network (e.g. as is found with some acrylate - vinyl ether formulations). In some special cases e.g. mixtures of maleate or fumarate esters with vinyl ethers, a 1:1 alternating copolymer is formed.

Use of compounds containing a single polymerisable group gives rise to a linear polymer although secondary reactions may lead to crosslinking. When two polymerisable groups are present in the same compound a branched polymer is formed and when more than two such groups are present a crosslinked structure results.

One might expect the propagation reactions to continue until all the unsaturated groups had been used up. This would be the case if it wasn't for the occurrence of **TERMINATION REACTIONS**. There are two types of termination reactions: (a) Radical - radical combination reactions and (b) Disproportionation reactions. These reactions are depicted in Equations 3 and 4.

$$2 \, RCH_2CH_2^{\cdot} \; \rightarrow \; RCH_2CH_2CH_2CH_2R \qquad \textbf{Equation 3}$$

$$2 \, RCH_2CH_2^{\cdot} \; \rightarrow \; RCH{=}CH_2 \; + \; RCH_2CH_3 \qquad \textbf{Equation 4}$$

Termination reactions consume radicals without generating any other radicals and their rate of occurrence reduces the rate of reaction and the average molecular weight of the polymer produced. Two important factors which favour the participation of termination reactions are (a) a high concentration of radicals and (b) high mobility of radicals which in turn is favoured the medium having a low viscosity.

The progress of radical addition reactions is also affected by the presence of radical scavengers and chain transfer agents. In radiation curing, oxygen is nearly always present during cure and oxygen being a triplet species is a highly efficient radical scavenger. Oxygen reacts with carbon-centred radicals at the diffusion-controlled limit to generate peroxy radicals.

$$R^{\bullet} + O_2 \rightarrow RO_2^{\bullet}$$

The addition of peroxy radicals to double bonds is very inefficient and hence scavenging of initiating and propagating radicals leads to a reduction in the rate of polymerisation and the average molecular weight of the polymer produced. Peroxy radicals will abstract hydrogen atoms from suitable C-H bonds such as $-CH_2OCH_2R$ and may thereby produce radicals capable of initiation.

Chain transfer agents scavenge radicals but in doing so generate radicals capable of initiating polymerisation. Commonly used chain transfer agents contain S-H and P-H bonds since a hydrogen atom is readily abstracted from these bonds. Chain transfer agents are added to formulations to control molecular weight and the crosslink density of the cured formulation.

A study has been made of the addition of thiophenols to the benzoin isopropyl ether initiated polymerisation of methyl methacrylate [20]. The thiols reduced the induction period and led to an acceleration in the rate of polymerisation. It was suggested that these effects can be explained by the consumption of oxygen in the coating to give peroxides which decompose to give species which abstract hydrogen from the thiols to generate initiating radicals.

(a)   Acrylate/Methacrylate Systems

These systems are highly popular finding wide application in a variety of industries. Their popularity is due in part to the ready availability of a large choice of materials thereby making it possible to produce a range of coatings having widely different properties e.g. hard tough coatings to soft, highly flexible coatings.

The curing of acrylates is a chain process and may be considered as an amplification process since one photon producing one initiating radical can in principle lead to the formation of many hundreds of new bonds. When this process is accompanied by crosslinking, very rapid cure ensues and this is important if the high line speeds, which are required by so many coating processes, are to be achieved. Fast cure is also important in many imaging applications such printed circuit board (PCB) manufacture. In the first step of the polymerisation process an initiating radical adds to the acrylate double bond in such a way as to create the most stable radical (Equation 1).

Benzoyl radicals are the most commonly encountered initiating species. Other such radicals include substituted benzoyl radicals and phosphinoyl radicals. Phenyl and alkyl radicals will also initiate polymerisation but, apparently, with lower efficiency. The initiation process is in competition with scavenging the initiator radicals by oxygen (Equation 5)[22] or atom abstraction (usually hydrogen) from the backbones of the reactive diluent or prepolymer (Equation 6).

Equation 5

$$In\cdot \ + \ ^3O_2 \ \longrightarrow \ InOO\cdot$$

An inefficient initiator

Equation 6

$$In\cdot \ + \ H-\overset{|}{\underset{|}{C}}-OR \ \longrightarrow \ InH \ + \ \cdot\overset{|}{\underset{|}{C}}-OR$$

May act as an initiator

If the initiator radicals are generated at high local concentration they may dimerise or disproportionate thereby reducing the efficiency of initiation. Thus in u.v. curing, increasing the light intensity leads to an increase in cure rate but only to a certain level after which it levels off due to occurrence of these termination reactions.

The second phase of the polymerisation reaction is the propagation process which leads to the growth of the chain via intermediate macroradicals (Equation 2). This process is exothermic and as a consequence it is possible for the reaction mixtures to reach quite high temperatures, thereby leading to a thermal contribution to the curing process. These effects contribute to the autoacceleration of the polymerisation process. The extent to which heating contributes to the process is dependent upon such factors as the ratio of the surface coating area to the mass of the coating (thick coatings reach high temperatures than comparable thin coatings), the thermal conductivity of the coating and the substrate and the temperature of the air above coating. As polymerisation proceeds the length of the macroradical increases and crosslinking reactions may occur all of which lead inevitably to an increase in viscosity and this is not without its consequences since it leads to a decrease in the rate of diffusional processes. The mobility of the macroradicals becomes more and more restricted as the viscosity rises and this is far more marked than for the smaller initiator radicals [23,24]. As a consequence the macroradicals are less likely to undergo radical-radical combination and disproportionation (termination reactions) (Equations 3 and 4). The decrease in the termination rate constant leads to an overall increase in rate which leads to autoacceleration. This is known as the Tromsdorf Effect. Eventually the rise in viscosity leads to the system gelling and under these conditions, the conformational mobility of the macroradical is severely restricted.[16, 17] The final phase is when eventually the coating vitrifies, and radical mobility is even further restricted. At all stages of the polymerisation the growing macroradical may also react with dissolved oxygen thereby terminating chain growth (Equation 7).

Equation 7

$$In(CH_2CH)_nCH_2\overset{\bullet}{C}HCO_2R \;+\; {}^3O_2 \longrightarrow In(CH_2CH)_nCH_2\underset{\underset{CO_2R}{|}}{C}HCO_2R$$

with the CO_2R and $OO\bullet$ groups, leading to

$$In(CH_2CH)_nCH_2\underset{\underset{CO_2R \quad OOH}{|}}{C}HCO_2R$$

$$\text{wwww}\overset{\bullet}{C}HCO_2R \;+\; R'\overset{\bullet}{C}H_2CH_2 \longrightarrow \text{wwww}CH_2CO_2R \;+\; R'CH{=}CH_2$$

This radical scavenging by oxygen will also be retarded by a rise in viscosity and will be severely restricted in the gelled and vitrified state.

The propagation process (Equation 2) knits molecules together by forming new carbon-carbon bonds. Thus when two acrylate residues becomes so linked, the distance between the residues is less than when the free acrylate molecules are present in neat solution. A consequence of this effect is that the polymerisation process is accompanied by a decrease in volume and in the case of curing a surface coating shrinkage occurs.[25,26] Although with monoacrylates the extent of shrinkage is not large, it does become very important with multifunctional acrylates and may lead to imperfections in the surface coating (e.g. cracks) and poor adhesion of the coating to the substrate.

The polymerisation of monoacrylates leads to linear polymers being formed whereas diacrylates lead to branching and higher functionality acrylates give rise to the crosslinked structures (Figure 26).

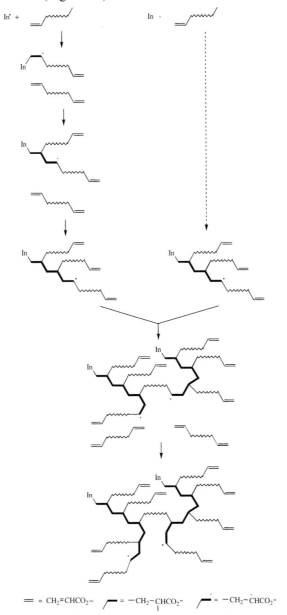

Figure 26: Branching exhibited by a diacrylate

Methacrylates polymerise in a similar manner to acrylates but the polymerisation is slower. As can be seen from Figure 27, polymerisation occurs via a tertiary radical.

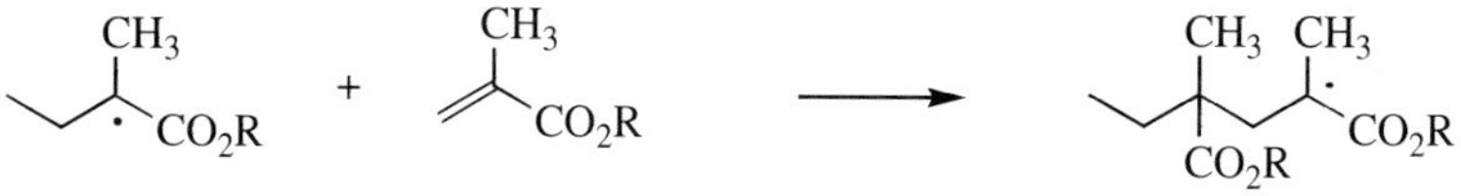

Figure 27: Polymerisation of a methacrylate

Tertiary carbon radicals are more stable than secondary carbon radicals and are more sterically hindered. These factors lead to the propagation reaction of methacrylates being slower than the corresponding reaction for acrylates. Methacrylate systems are more prone to termination via a disproportionation reaction than acrylates (Figure 28)[27,28].

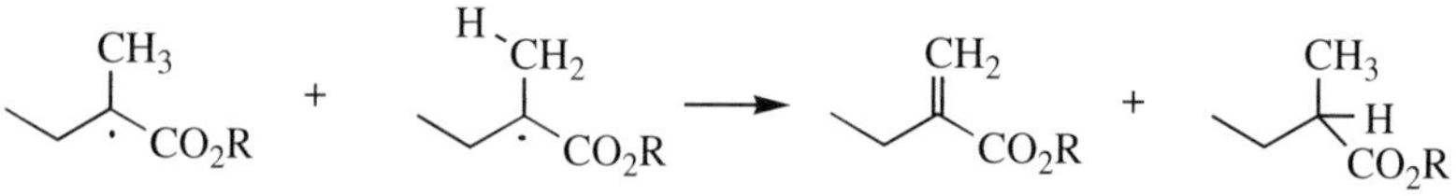

Figure 28: Disproportionation of the macroradicals involved in the polymerisation of methacrylates

Despite the reactivity of methacrylates being lower than acrylates, they are of commercial importance owing to their toxicity (particular irritancy) being lower than acrylates.

(b)   Styrene/Unsaturated Polyesters[29]

The polymerisation of styrene can be initiated by a wide range of thermal and Type I photoinitiators (NB Type II systems cannot always be used since styrene quenches the triplet state of many carbonyl compounds). Styrene is used as a reactive diluent for unsaturated esters prepared from maleic anhydride and fumaric acid (Figure 29).

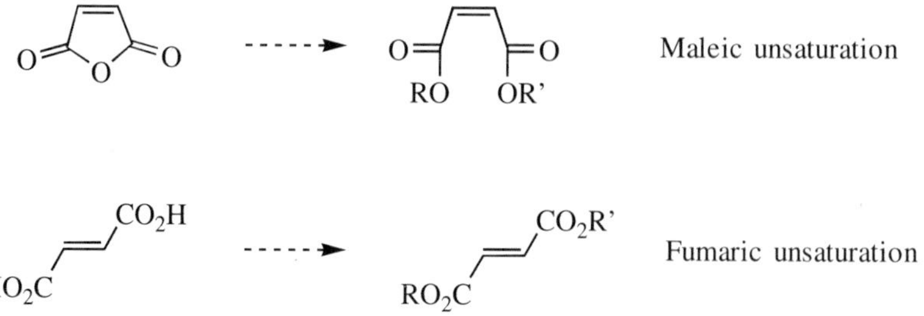

Maleic unsaturation

Fumaric unsaturation

Figure 29: Prepolymer based on maleic anhydride and fumaric acid

Photoinitiated polymerisation of these systems will lead to a styrene-polyester copolymer. Despite the curing process being relatively slow the system has found extensive use in the wood coating industry because of its low cost and because other operations such as sanding and handling require slow line speeds to be used. The system, not surprisingly (because of the slow cure rate), suffers from oxygen inhibition. If allyl ether groups are introduced into the polymers, allylic hydroperoxides are produced and these can be used to introduce further crosslinks by the processes which occur in air drying (Equation 8).

Equation 8

$$RH + X^\bullet \longrightarrow R^\bullet + XH$$

$$2\ R'O_2H \longrightarrow R'O^\bullet + R'OO^\bullet + H_2O$$

$$R^\bullet + R'O^\bullet \longrightarrow ROR' \ \rbrace$$

$$2R^\bullet \longrightarrow R^-R \ \rbrace \quad \text{Crosslinking formation}$$

$$X^\bullet = C \text{ or } O \text{ centred}$$

(c)   The Thiol-ene Reaction [30]

This system is based on a stoichiometric reaction of multifunctional olefins (enes) with thiols i.e. in contrast to the foregoing examples it is a 1:2 addition reaction. The addition reaction can be initiated thermally, photochemically and by e.b. radiation. Thiyl radicals can be generated by the reaction of an excited carbonyl compound (usually in its triplet state) with a thiol (Equation 9) or via radicals e.g. benzoyl radicals, produced by photolysing a Type I initiator reacting with the thiol.

Equation 9

$$Ph_2CO \xrightarrow{\ hv\ } Ph_2CO^* \xrightarrow{\ RSH\ } R\overset{\bullet}{S} - Ph_2\overset{\bullet}{C}OH$$

The thiyl radicals add to olefins and this is the basis of the polymerisation process (Figure 30).

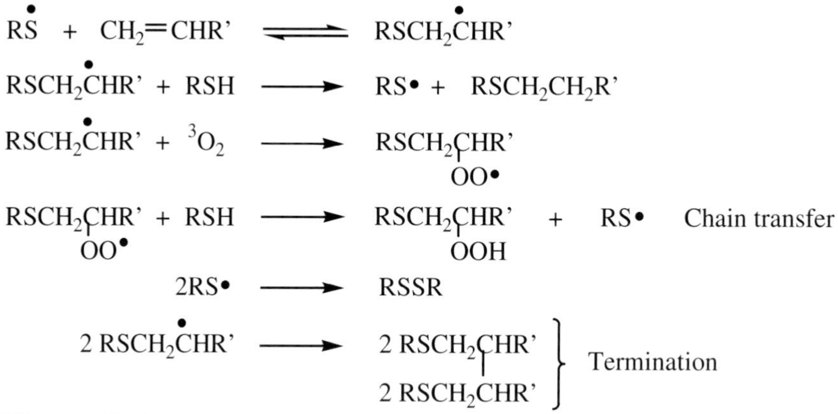

$$RS\bullet \ + \ CH_2=CHR' \ \rightleftharpoons \ RSCH_2\overset{\bullet}{C}HR'$$

$$RSCH_2\overset{\bullet}{C}HR' + RSH \longrightarrow RS\bullet + RSCH_2CH_2R'$$

$$RSCH_2\overset{\bullet}{C}HR' + {}^3O_2 \longrightarrow RSCH_2\underset{OO\bullet}{C}HR'$$

$$RSCH_2\underset{OO\bullet}{C}HR' + RSH \longrightarrow RSCH_2\underset{OOH}{C}HR' + RS\bullet \quad \text{Chain transfer}$$

$$2RS\bullet \longrightarrow RSSR$$

$$2\,RSCH_2\overset{\bullet}{C}HR' \longrightarrow \left.\begin{array}{l} 2\,RSCH_2\underset{|}{C}HR' \\ 2\,RSCH_2CHR' \end{array}\right\} \text{Termination}$$

Figure 30: Reactions participating in the thiol-ene reaction

From a consideration of the mechanism it will be seen that the addition of a dithiol to a diolefin will give a linear polymer. When higher functionality thiols and alkenes are used, crosslinked systems are formed.

Another feature of the thiol-ene system is that the addition of the thiyl radical to the olefin is reversible and as a consequence the stereochemical integrity of the starting olefin is not maintained in the product. The reactivity of alkenes towards thiyl radicals has been shown to the vinyl ether > propenyl ether > allyl ether > unsubstituted alkene > acrylates > styrene. Given that the thiyl radical is an electrophilic radical, this is not surprising. Most of the commercial system are based on compounds containing the allyl group e.g. Figure 31

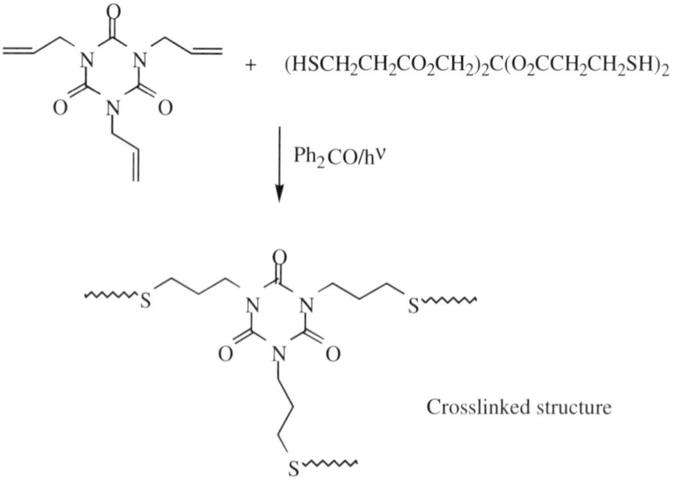

$(HSCH_2CH_2CO_2CH_2)_2C(O_2CCH_2CH_2SH)_2$

Ph_2CO/h^v

Crosslinked structure

Figure 31: An example of a thiol-ene crosslinking reaction.

Commonly used materials are allyl esters, (e.g. of phthalic acid, or unsaturated acids (e.g. maleic acid), allyl ethers (e.g. based upon trimethylolpropane [2-bis(2-hydroxymethyl)butanol]).

Use of the diallyl ester of maleic acid creates the opportunity for dual cure since, after the radical polymerisation has been carried out, base induced crosslinking of thiol residues to the unsaturated ester via the Michael addition reaction can be performed (Figure 32).

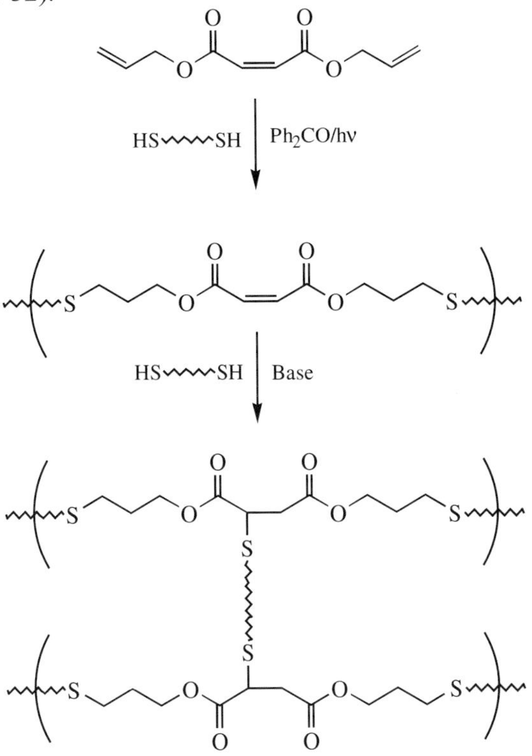

Figure 32: An example of a dual cure thiol-ene system

There is much scope for creating new curing systems based on the thiol-ene reaction. Thus vinyl siloxanes have been used to produce a silicone elastomers. Now that a good range of vinyl ethers is commercially available, the use of vinyl as opposed to allyl ethers opens up further possibilities.[31]

A most important feature of the thiol-ene system is its insensitivity to oxygen i.e. it doesn't suffer from oxygen inhibition. Not surprisingly, the carbon-centred radical (a β-thiylalkyl radical) is scavenged by oxygen to give a peroxy-radical but this in turn reacts with the thiol to generate the thiyl radical which can then initiate further polymerisation. Thus, the overall effect of the oxygen is to promote a chain transfer process. When multifunctional compounds, which give rise to crosslinking are used, cure speeds are very high and this is a further attractive feature. The coatings produced exhibit good adhesion to many different substrates and this is possibly due to the polarisability of the C-S bond. The thioether linkages present in the coating are not so prone to oxidative degradation as are ether linkages. An undoubted disadvantage of the thiol-ene reaction is the smell associated with the thiol component and this is probably the most important factor, which is holding back further exploitation of this valuable reaction.

(d)   Vinyl Ether/Unsaturated Ester Systems [32,33]

Vinyl ethers are attractive polymerisable species due to their low toxicity and now that a good range of these compounds is commercially available, new photopolymerisable systems using these compounds are being sought.

The polymerisation of vinyl ethers initiated by radicals generated from Type I and II initiator systems is a relatively inefficient process but when suitable unsaturated esters (maleate, fumarate, citraconate etc.), imides (maleimides) or N-vinylformamides are present, 1:1 alternating copolymers are formed [34](Figure 33).

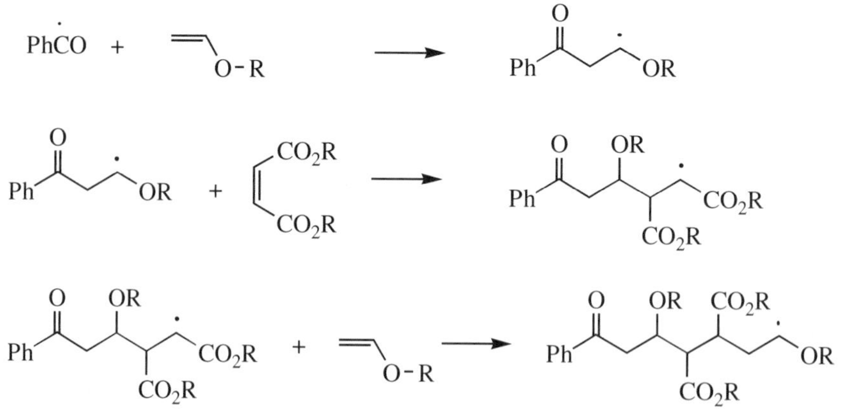

Figure 33: Formation of a vinyl ether unsaturated ester alternating copolymer

Needless to say, this system is susceptible to oxygen inhibition but interestingly not to the same extent as acrylate polymerisations. Photo DSC experiments have shown

(Figure 34) that in the case of the reaction of a divinyl ether with N-(n-hexyl)maleimide oxygen retards the rate of initiation but the overall extent of polymerisation is only slightly less than that observed when polymerisation occurs under nitrogen.

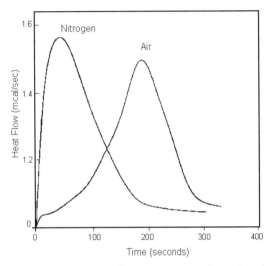

Figure 34: Exotherm curves for exposure of equimolar mixture of Di-(4-vinylglycol) butyl isophthalate and N-hexyl maleimide in nitrogen and air to medium pressure mercury lamp through Pyrex (I~20 mW cm^{-2})

By way of comparison when a 50:50 mixture of n-hexyl acrylate and hexane-1,6-diol diacrylate is irradiated under similar conditions very little cure occurs under an atmosphere of oxygen whereas cure occurs normally under nitrogen[35]. It is not completely clear as to why this is the case but occurrence of hydrogen abstraction reactions which lead to generation of initiating radicals are clearly beneficial. For this reason use of polyethers such as polyethylene and polypropylene glycols reduces the sensitivity of the reactions towards oxygen inhibition (N.B. the rate constant for hydrogen abstraction from ethers ~2 x 10^{5}Ms^{-1} whereas addition of a benzoyl radical to an acrylate is ~ 10^5 to 10^{6}Ms^{-1} which means that hydrogen abstraction reactions may readily compete with the addition reaction provided the concentration of C-H bonds adjacent to oxygen atoms is at least ten times greater than the double bond concentration). In the following schemes (Figure 35), the first shows how hydrogen abstraction reactions can lead to new initiating species, the second shows how the hydroperoxides generated in a polyether chain can via intramolecular hydrogen abstraction from the reactive tertiary C-H bond (via a six membered transition state) can lead to generation of the reactive hydroxyl radical and the third scheme shows the participation of intermolecular hydrogen abstraction reactions[36].

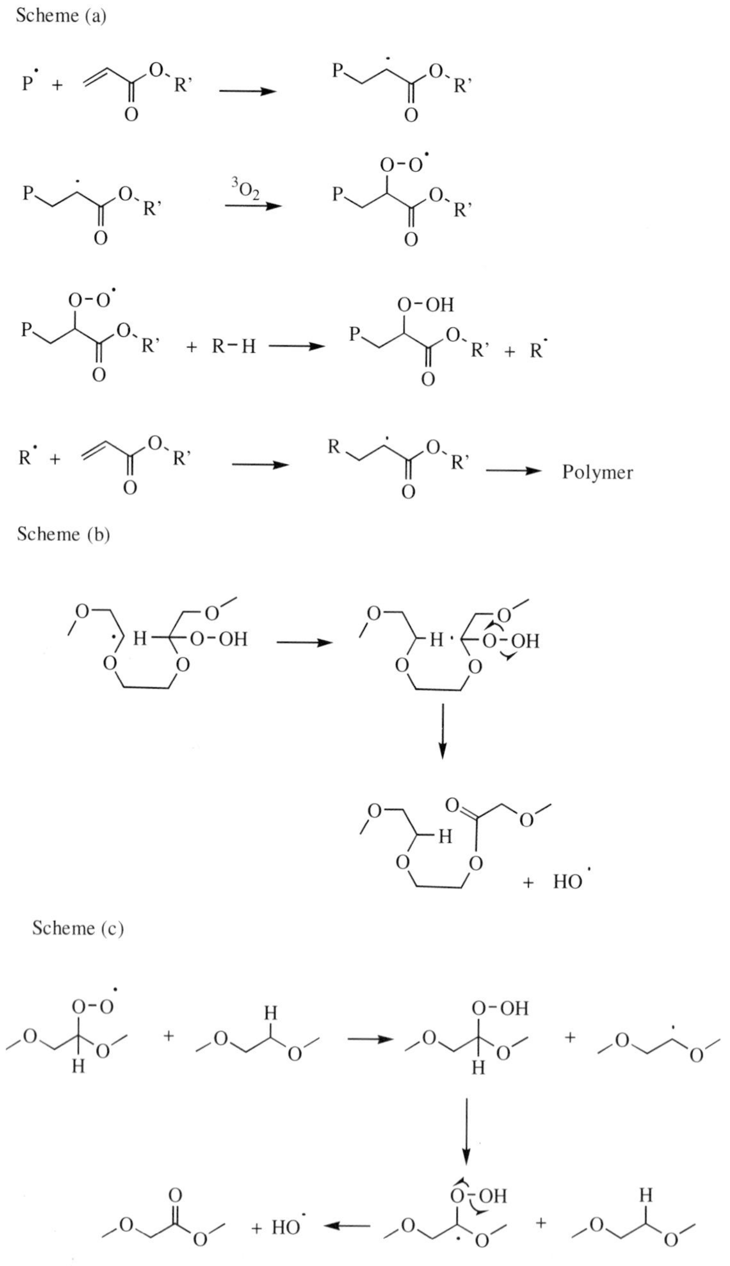

Scheme (a)

Scheme (b)

Scheme (c)

P· - radical derived from photoinitiator
R· - generated radical

Figure 35: Radicals generated during cure via the intervention of oxygen

Another facet is that the system is not very tolerant towards the presence of the tertiary amines such as those commonly used to overcome oxygen inhibition and to act as synergists (N.B. amines are sometimes added to formulations in small concentrations to reduce acid-catalysed hydrolysis of the vinyl ether component which produces odorous acetaldehyde). The deleterious effect of having amines in the formulation is an interesting observation but its origin is not clear. In view of this phenomenon it is not surprising that Type II initiator systems are not particularly efficient. Type I initiator systems such as acylphosphine oxides and non-amine containing acetophenones are very efficient. When the donor and acceptor are correctly matched, new absorption bands due to charge transfer complex formation can be observed and irradiation of the complexes via these bands leads to the formation of the 1:1 alternating copolymer i.e. polymerisation has occurred in the absence of a photoinitiator.[33] Maleimides behave in a similar way to the unsaturated esters and give rise to stronger charge transfer bands due to their lower reduction potential.

The lower susceptibility of the maleimide systems to oxygen inhibition may also be due in part to the ability of maleimides upon excitation (an $n \rightarrow \pi^*$ excited triplet state) to abstract a hydrogen atom from a suitable C-H bond thereby generating another initiating radical (Figure 36).

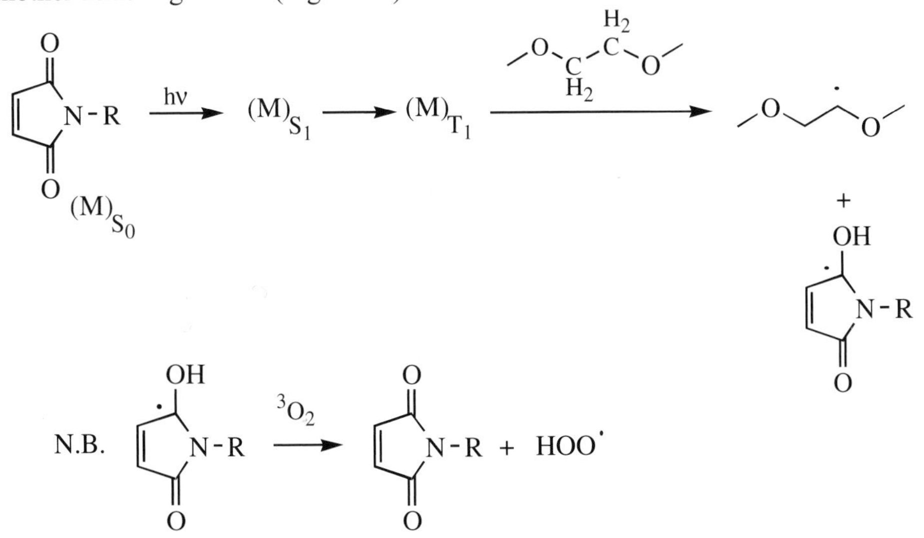

Figure 36: Hydrogen abstraction by maleimides

If the N-(n-alkyl) substituent in the maleimide contains suitable C-H bonds and the excited of the maleimide can interact with them via a six or greater than ten membered transition state then intramolecular hydrogen abstraction may occur [37]. It should also be noted that the presence of oxygen leads to regeneration of the maleimide which means that the hydrogen abstraction process does not reduce the extent to which the alternating co-polymerisation process occurs. Once again polyethers appear to be most suitable for promoting the hydrogen abstraction reactions with unbranched alkyl chains having little effect.

The ability of excited maleimides to hydrogen abstract from polyethers means that they can be used to initiate the polymerisation of acrylates, which contain these groups. N-Aryl imides also undergo the hydrogen abstraction reactions exhibited by their N-alkyl counterparts provided the aryl group contains substituents in the 2 position which is sufficiently bulky as to cause the aryl ring to twist thereby removing its congugation with the imidic nitrogen atom. Substituents which are effective in causing deconjugation include trifluoromethyl, tertiary butyl and isopropyl. Deconjugation leads to the lower triplet state being an $n\pi^*$ rather than a less reactive (lower energy) $\pi\pi^*$ state. The hydrogen abstraction reactions of the N-alkyl and N-arylimides can be sensitised by thioxanthones thereby extending the wavelength sensitivity of this new initiation system. Somewhat surprisingly non-twisted N-aryl maleimides can be induced to undergo hydrogen abstraction if a triplet sensitiser such as thioxanthone is used[38].

(ii)   Cationic Processes[39]

Cationic polymerisation processes are initiated by Lewis and Brønstead acids. In radiation curing these acids have to be generated from a suitable precursor utilising the radiation and such materials are termed cationic initiators.

If we consider a simplistic view of the polymerisation of an epoxide (oxirane), Figure 37, a number of important facts emerge.

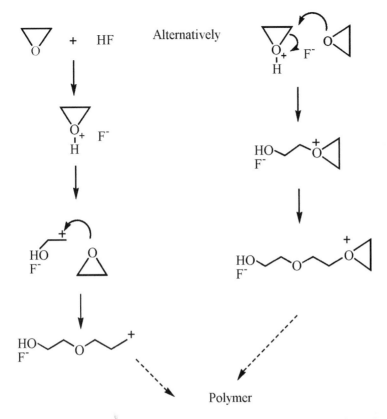

Figure 37: Schematic representation of the acid-catalysed polymerisation of epoxides

The species which initiate and propagate the reaction are cationic and for this process to be efficient it is essential that nucleophilic anions e.g. Cl⁻ or $SO_4^=$ are absent. All the cationic photoinitiators available are salts and as such contain anions (Section III.(v)). To overcome the problem of these anions retarding or preventing cure, anions are chosen which are poorly nucleophilic. Often these are large anions such as the hexafluorophosphate anion in which the negative charge is spread over a large volume. It is also important that other components of the formulation do not contain anions e.g. pigments (many pigments have anions adsorbed on the surface and some are coated with polyamines to aid dispersion in formulations). Other commonly encountered nucleophiles present in formulations are hydroxyl and amino groups. Interaction of an alcohol with a carbocation generates a proton i.e. the alcohol is acting as a chain transfer agent (Figure 38).

The addition of polyfunctional alcohols to cationic curing systems can be most beneficial since it can be used to create crosslinks and a number of such compounds is commercially available for this purpose.

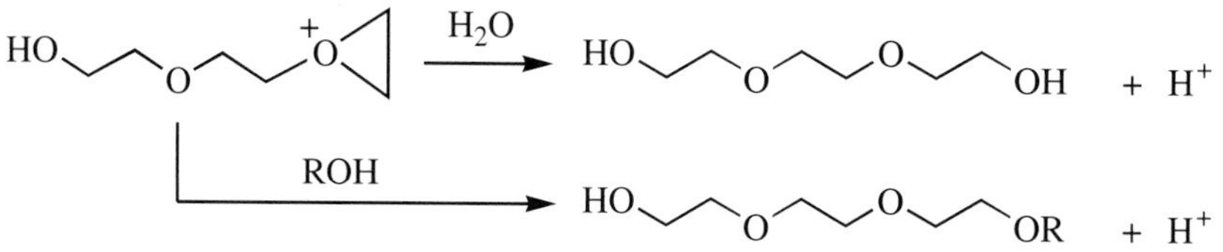

Figure 38: Crosslinking induced by multifunctional alcohols

Thiols react in a similar way to alcohols but this is not the case for amines which react to give ammonium ions and terminate the reaction.

Given that alcohols act as chain transfer agents it is not surprising to find that water acts in a similar way. Water can be tolerated in a number of cationic curing formulations up to quite a high percentage and sometimes with a beneficial effect. The presence of water in the atmosphere can have a deleterious effect and an undoubted downside to cationic curing is the sensitivity of the curing process to humidity. High humidity may lead to total cessation of cure. This profound effect of humidity may be due to the volatile acids generated in the coating, migrating into the moisture-laden atmosphere. Two most positive aspects of cationic systems is that they are not subject to oxygen inhibition and the coatings produced usually exhibit good adhesion to the substrate.

Another important feature of cationic cure is that it is a living polymerisation process i.e when all the polymerisable species has been used up, carbocations and/ or protons are present and therefore if a furher amount of a polymerisable material is added, polymerisation will recommence. Due to the presence of nucleophilic impurities it is unlikely that any carbocations will be present after the coating has been through the curing tunnel but protons will certainly be present. It is the presence of these species that gives rise to the phenomenon of post-cure (see later).

Materials that are available for cationic curing systems are epoxides and vinyl ethers and their derivatives. Recently interest has been shown in the use of oxetanes. Epoxides cure by a ring opening reaction with the driving force being the release of ring strain. Not so much energy is released when oxetanes undergo ring opening but this is to some extent offset by the higher nucleophilicity of the oxygen atom in the oxetane ring compared with that in the epoxide ring.

(a)   Epoxides (oxiranes)[39,40]

Polymerisation of epoxides involves ring opening and the relief in the strain energy contributes favourably to the thermodynamics of the polymerisation process. The reaction can be brought about by Lewis acids (e.g. boron trifluoride, phosphorous pentafluoride) or Brønsted acids (e.g. hydrogen fluoride). A simplistic view of the polymerisation process is shown in Figure 37.

Epoxides which are commonly used include cycloaliphatic epoxides and glycidyl ethers (Figure 39).

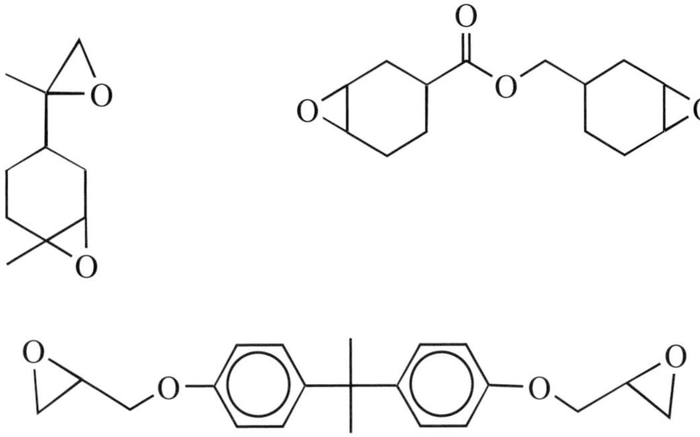

Figure 39: Some epoxides used in radiation curing

The cycloaliphatic epoxides are more reactive than glycidyl ethers.[41] There is good range of glycidyl ethers available since they are readily prepared by reacting epichlorohydrin.with alcohols and phenols. It has been shown that the presence of a carbonyl group in one of the very popular diluents deactivates the compound to cationic cure[42]. A number of explanations for this effect can be put forward but it is undoubtedly true that the lone pair electrons present in the carbonyl group will interact with both protons and carbocations in a reversible process which will effectively lower the concentration of these species available for participating in the cure process.

The ring opening of some epoxides e.g. glycidyl ethers requires input of thermal energy in order to complete the polymerisation process. As a consequence, after the coating has passed under the lamp, polymerisation continues with its progress, being determined by the temperature it is subjected to. This process is termed "postcure".

Most radiation curable formulations contain polyol additives to enhance cure speed by increasing the crosslink density. Increasing the crosslink density also improves the mechanical strength of the films provided the right type of polyol is used. Cure speed is also reputed to be increased by the addition of oxetanes.

Epoxides can be polymerised by e.b. radiation but a cationic photoinitiator must be present so that an acid can be generated.

(b)   Vinyl Ethers [43]

Vinyl ethers can be cured cationically using the photoinitiator systems used for epoxides.

They can also be cured by e.b. at an acceptable dose level if a cationic photoinitiator is included in the formulation.

The mechanism of cure of vinyl ethers by Lewis and Brønsted esters is still a matter of some debate. A simplistic view of the mechanism of cure by a Lewis acid is shown in Figure 40.

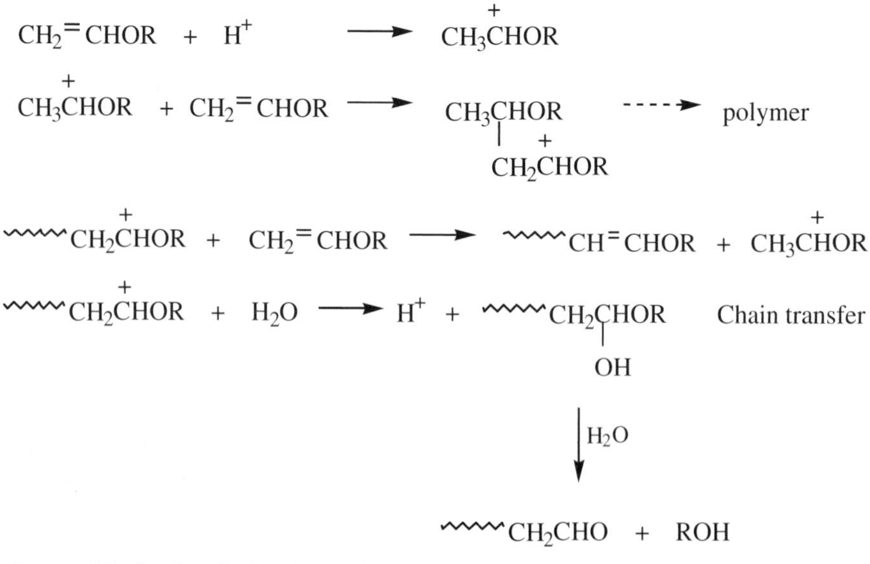

$$CH_2\!=\!CHOR \;+\; H^+ \longrightarrow \overset{+}{CH_3}CHOR$$

$$\overset{+}{CH_3}CHOR \;+\; CH_2\!=\!CHOR \longrightarrow \underset{\underset{CH_2CHOR}{\overset{+}{|}}}{CH_3CHOR} \;\;-\!-\!-\!\rightarrow\; polymer$$

$$\sim\!\!\sim\!\!\sim\!\overset{+}{CH_2}CHOR \;+\; CH_2\!=\!CHOR \longrightarrow \sim\!\!\sim\!\!\sim CH\!=\!CHOR \;+\; \overset{+}{CH_3}CHOR$$

$$\sim\!\!\sim\!\!\sim\!\overset{+}{CH_2}CHOR \;+\; H_2O \longrightarrow H^+ \;+\; \underset{OH}{\overset{|}{\sim\!\!\sim\!\!\sim CH_2CHOR}} \quad \text{Chain transfer}$$

$$\Big\downarrow H_2O$$

$$\sim\!\!\sim\!\!\sim CH_2CHO \;+\; ROH$$

Figure 40: A simplistic view of some of the reactions that can be occur upon the cationic cure of vinyl ethers

The use of polyfunctional vinyl ethers leads to crosslinking. A wide variety of such materials which in the case of di-functional ethers have polyether, polyester and polyurethane linking chains is now available. It was found that aliphatic polyurethane vinyl ethers cured much slower than aromatic urethane vinyl ethers which in turn were slower than polyether divinyl ethers.

From Figure 40 it will have been appreciated that the polymerisation process involves carbocations and that these are essential species in the propagating reactions. The nitrogen atom in urethanes is nucleophilic with the nucleophilicity being higher for aliphatic than aromatic urethanes. Thus these functional groups can impede the reaction by interacting with the carbocation and thereby reduce the rate of cure. Other nucleophiles react similarly, but in the case of water, a hemiacetal is produced which undergoes ready hydrolysis to give acetaldehyde (Figure 40). The presence of this aldehyde in coatings imparts a very objectionable smell.

The occurrence of chain transfer reduces the kinetic chain length. Its occurrence could lead to softer coatings than anticipated being obtained since it leads to a reduction in molecular weight. However, the production of a low molecular weight carbocation (CH_3C^+HOR) which is far more mobile than the macro carbocation from which it was generated, probably leads to more extensive consumption of the vinyl ether groups. The curing of vinyl ethers like epoxides produces a living polymer. Under u.v. curing conditions the carbocations are usually scavenged but the coatings as they emerge from the cure unit will contain acid.

In general the cure of vinyl ethers is extremely rapid being far faster than the cure of epoxides. Interestingly if a hybrid system consisting of a vinyl ether diluent and an epoxide prepolymer is used, the cure of the epoxide in terms of rate and amount consumed is enhanced[44].

Much interest has been shown in the application of substituted vinyl ethers and in particular propenyl ethers. These compounds are far easier to prepare than vinyl ethers being produced by the catalysed isomerisation of readily available allyl ethers. The rate of cure of these compounds is similar to that of vinyl ethers as is the ease of hydrolysis. The number of propenyl ethers commercially available is expected to increase significantly.

Vinylogoues of vinyl ethers are 2 and 4 alkoxystyrenes. These compounds cure at very acceptable rates and are finding application as resist materials.

(c) Hybrid Systems

A number of benefits have been ascribed to the use of hybrid systems such as acrylate diluents plus epoxide prepolymers, vinyl ether diluents plus acrylate prepolymers and acrylate diluents plus vinyl ether prepolymers. In these systems hybrid is used in the context of using mixtures of materials, which polymerise by different mechanisms. Another type of hybrid system is that in which two different types of materials are used but which polymerise by a common mechanism e.g. allyl ethers plus acrylates [45].

When acrylate diluents are used with epoxide prepolymers together with a mixture of a Type 1 initiator and a cationic initiator, coatings are produced having properties that surpass those of either of the individual components[46]. Mixtures of vinyl ether diluents and acrylate prepolymers such as epoxy acrylates and urethane acrylates have been cured using a mixture of a Type 1 initiator plus a cationic initiator[47]. These systems cured very quickly in both air and under nitrogen and were found to be faster than a system in which an epoxy diluent was used in place of the vinyl ether. It was found that the vinyl ether diluent led to a much higher utilisation of the acrylate double bonds than when an acrylate reactive diluent is used. These systems are also less susceptible to oxygen inhibition and this is probably due to the fast cationic cure of the vinyl ether producing a film, which retards oxygen penetration from the atmosphere thereby speeding up the acrylate cure. The films were found to show excellent adhesion to polyester, to show good solvent resistance and they were hard. If an inert atmosphere is used, cure can be effected by the sole use of an onium salt initiator. When this is done, polymerisation of the vinyl ether races ahead of the acrylate and as a consequence the acrylate polymerisation occurs when it is as a solute in a poly(vinylether) solvent. This process leads to the production of an interpenetrating network[48]. Use of acrylate diluents with vinyl ether prepolymers gives fast curing systems and coatings exhibiting good impact resistance and adhesion [49].

(iii)   Anionic Processes

Whilst there are numerous polymerisation reactions that can be catalysed by base, very few have found their way into radiation curable systems. The reason for this lack is that very few suitable photoinitiator systems have been available (see Section 3.6) until recently.

Most commonly, photogenerated amines have been used to induce the crosslinking of diepoxides.[50] A negative working resist based on these reactions has been described (Figure 41)[51]. A recent patent[52] describes initiators that release a very strong base, which can be used to catalyse, the Michael addition of a malonate polyester to a multifunctional acrylate.

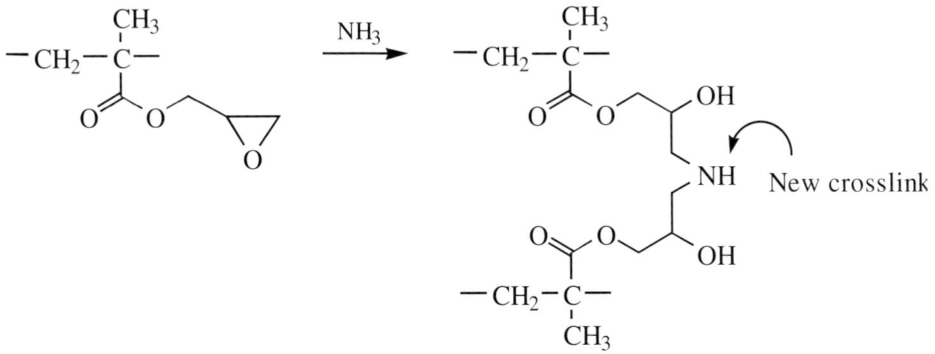

Figure 41: A negative working resist system based upon an anionic polymerisation process

Photogenerated thiocyanate anions generated from a metal complex have been used to initiate the polymerisation of α-cyanoacrylates. Other amine releasing complexes have been used to trigger the anionic polymerisation of multifunctional acrylates [53].

(iv) Cycloaddition Reactions [54,55]

(a) Cinnamate Systems

The use of cycloaddition reactions, and in particular the cycloaddition reactions of cinnamates, is well established particularly for the production of printed circuit boards and lithoplates.[56] When poly(vinylalcohol), PVOH, is esterified with cinnamic acid, a photosensitive polymer is produced. Irradiation leads to the cinnamate residues undergoing a [2+2]-cycloaddition reaction (Figure 42).

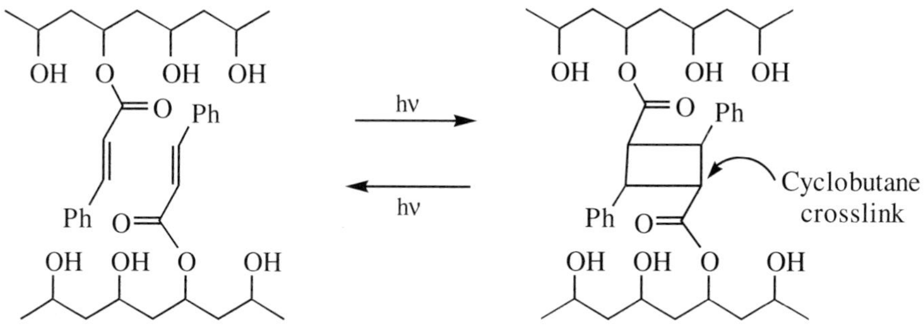

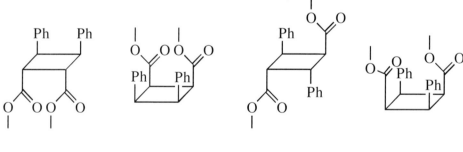

Figure 42: The cycloaddition reaction of cinnamate residues

There are several important facts to recognise about this reaction. If only one cyclobutane crosslink is formed between two linear polymer chains, the molecular weight will be doubled. This increase in molecular weight leads to a decrease of solubility in the solvents used to solubilise the monomer. Thus, the irradiated areas can be distinguished from the unirradiated areas by solvent development. Consequently, if a film of the material is exposed to light through a negative, and the exposed film is washed with the appropriate solvent, an image will remain which corresponds to the irradiated area of the film. A second point to note is that there are four isomeric forms of the cyclobutane formed (Figure 43).

| Head to head | Head to head | Head to tail | Head to tail |

Figure 43: Cyclobutanes produced upon crosslinking
cinnamate residues

The aryl substituted cyclobutane is itself photosensitive and will, upon irradiation, split to generate the cinnamate esters. Since both forward and backward reactions can be driven by light, how can we cause the reaction we wish to occur, to take place selectively? The cinnamate group shows absorption between 300-350nm and this is range where the cyclobutanes do not absorb. Use therefore, of light of >300nm, leads to the desired reactions. Shorter wavelengths (<290nm) can be used to depolymerise the photocrosslinked polymer.

The cinnamoylated PVOH has a high viscosity and therefore little conformational movement of the polymer and pendant ester groups can take place when films are dried down. Irradiation of the cinnamate esters populates the excited singlet state which undergoes intersystem crossing (ISC) to the triplet state. From this state cycloaddition can occur. Deactivation of the triplet state can occur via cis/trans isomerisation or by quenching by oxygen or by undergoing the cycloaddition reaction. For the cycloaddition reaction to occur efficiently the drying down of the film needs to leave cinnamate groups adjacent to the each other. This can be quite difficult to control and attempts have been to engineer new systems in which some of the cinnamate groups contain electron donating substituents whereas others contain electron withdrawing groups [57]. It was hoped that these modifications would lead to donor-acceptor complex formation therefore leading to some pre-organisation of the polymer. Some success was obtained but undoubtedly greater success was attained by the incorporating effective triplet photosensitisers into the formulation such as the ketocoumarins (Figure 44).

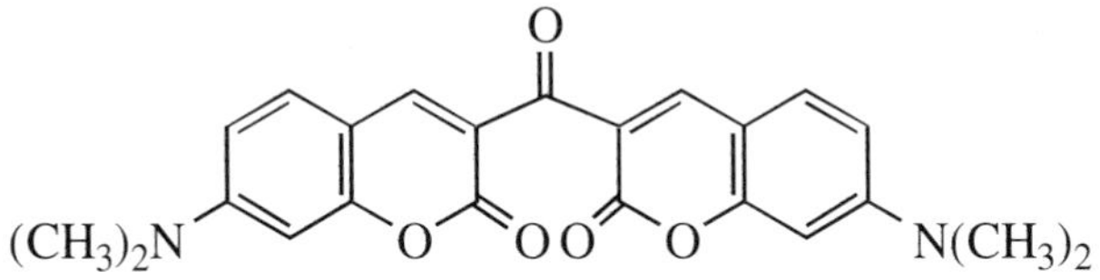

Figure 44: A bis ketocoumarin used to sensitise the cycloaddition of cinnamate residues.

Such sensitisers extend the wavelengths of sensitivity of the poly(vinylalcohol)'s out to almost 500nm.

(b)   Chalcone Systems [54]

β-Aryl α:β-unsaturated ketones are known as chalcones. The chalcone group may be introduced into the polymer backbone or as pendant group (Figure 45).

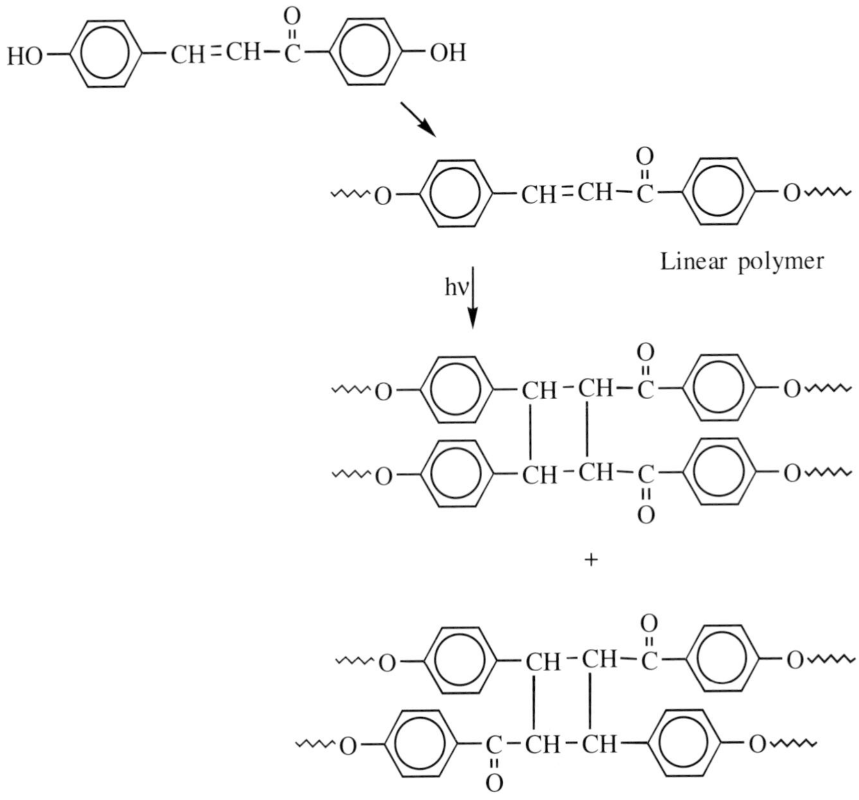

Linear polymer

Chalcone group in the side chain

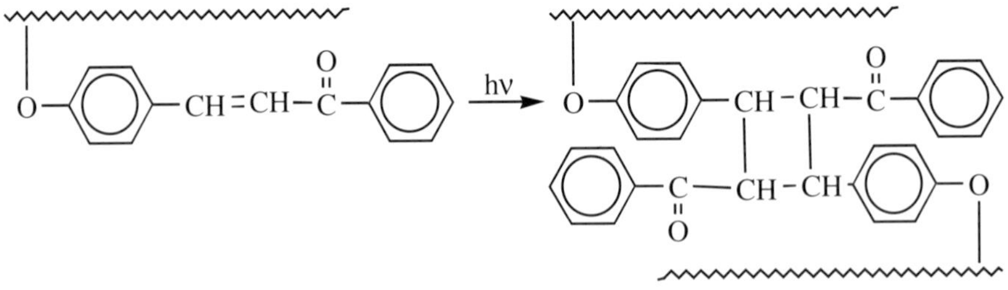

Figure 45: Examples of the chalcone group in the backbone and in the side chain

In both the examples shown, the crosslinking is via the formation of a cyclobutane ring and again there are four isomeric products. As with the cinnamate system, the photosensitive group can undergo little spatial movement during the lifetime of its excited state and consequently it is necessary for the chalcone groups to be close to each other in the dried down film. To increase the probability of reaction chalcones of the type shown in Figure 46 were introduced.

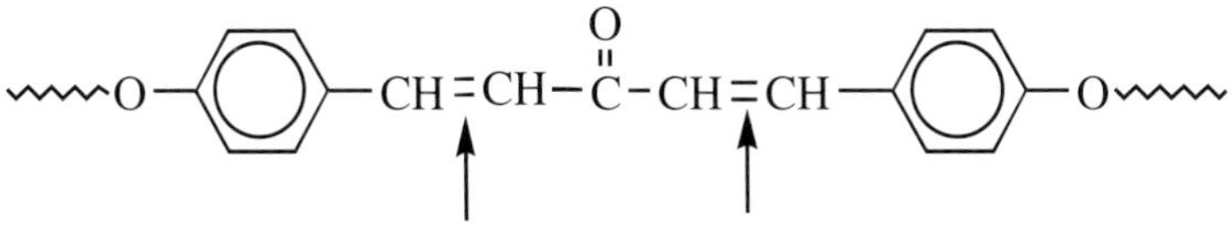

Two potential sites for cyclodimerisation

Figure 46: Chalcone having enhanced reactivity

A statistical model was set up to investigate how the nature of the chalcone would influence the reactivity of the system and the one shown in Figure 46 was found to have the highest predicts reactivity.[58]

(c)   Stilbazolium Systems

Ichimura first described how PVOH can be made photosensitive by the introduction of stilbazolium groups.[59] These donor-acceptor systems are highly coloured, fluorescent and readily undergo [2+2] cycloaddition reactions from their excited singlet states. The key to linking the photosensitive group to the polymer is via acetal formation (Figure 47).

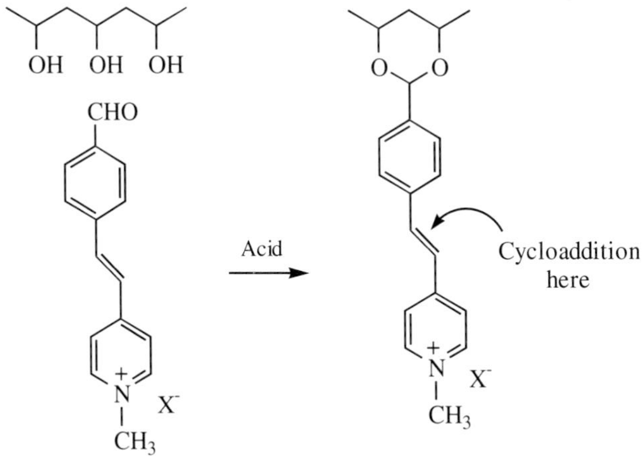

Figure 47: Use of acetalisation to link a stilbazolium group to poly(vinyl alcohol)

The acetal derivative of the stilbazolium compound is fluorescent and the observed fluorescence spectrum is dependent upon the concentration of the photosensitive group. As the concentration of the group is increased, the fluorescence spectrum broadens and moves out to the red. This is indicative of the association of the stilbazolium groups as their concentration is increased. Irradiation of such films made in this way leads to cycloaddition with attendant insolubilisation of the derivatised PVOH in water. After irradiation, the films exhibit fluorescence, but this is typical of unassociated stilbazolium groups. Thus the association of the stilbazolium groups has in fact helped pre-organise the photosensitive groups.[60]

A wide range of other stilbazolium compounds and related compounds have been prepared and examples include the one shown in Figure 48.[61]

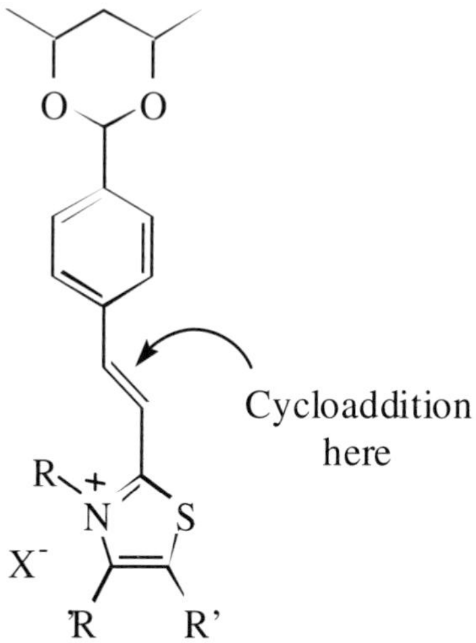

Figure 48: A stilbazolium equivalent

(d)   Other Cycloaddition Systems

Several other crosslinking reactions involving [2+2] cycloaddition reactions of pendant groups have been described (Figure 49).[62] That of maleimides is interesting since this system is insensitive to light of wavelength >300nm, but by the use of triplet sensitisers the wavelength sensitivity can be increased. The cyclodimerisation of anthracene groups proceeds, in contrast to the other systems, via the excited singlet state.

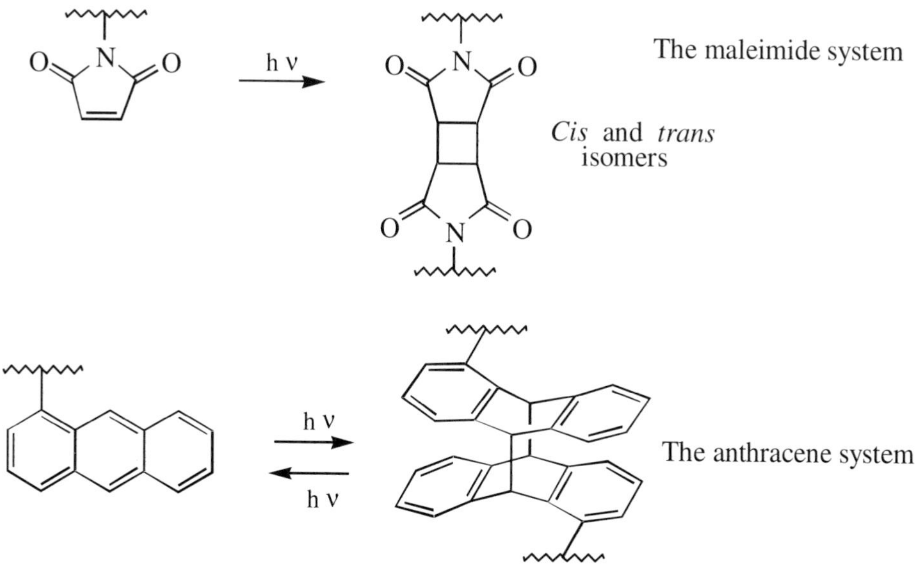

The maleimide system

Cis and *trans* isomers

The anthracene system

Figure 49: Cyclodimerisation of pendant maleimide and anthracene groups.

Use of light of wavelength 300-400nm drives the cyclodimerisation reaction whereas 254nm light causes the anthracenyl photodimer to dissociate thereby regenerating the anthracene system.

CHAPTER III

PHOTOINITIATOR SYSTEMS

CHAPTER III

PHOTOINITIATOR SYSTEMS

(i)   Introduction to Classification

Conveniently, initiators are classed by the type of polymerisation system they initiate i.e. free radical, cationic or anionic.[8, 63, 64, 65, 65, 66.] In a few cases initiators may be used to initiate polymerisation reactions which occur via different processes, e.g. the cationic initiators such as iodonium and sulphonium salts and iron arene complexes will also initiate polymerisation reactions which occur via a free radical mechanism.[67]

Free radical initiators have been subdivided into Type I and Type II systems but nevertheless there are a few systems cannot be so classified e.g the borate salt initiators that depend upon inter/intramolecular electron transfer. Type I initiators or those compounds which upon irradiation undergo a cleavage reaction (α or β-cleavage [68]) to generate two radicals (Figure 50).

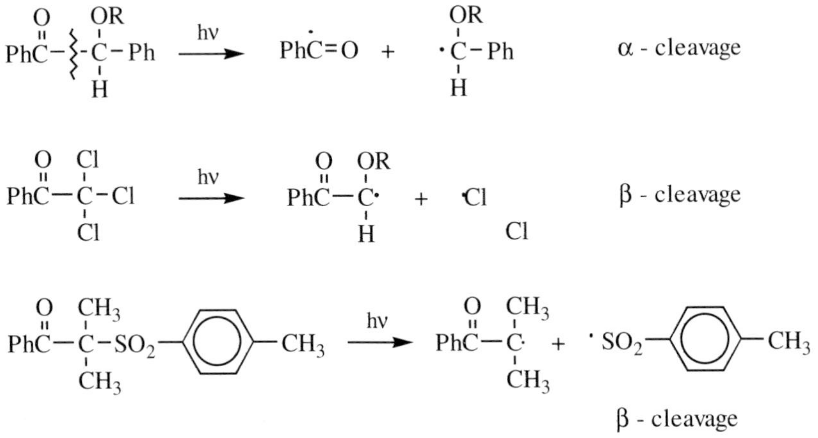

Figure 50: α and β-cleavage reactions

The cleavage reaction generates two radical species and usually (although not always) only one of these is reactive. In general, reaction occurs from the excited triplet state of the ketone. The cleavage reaction is often so facile that it occurs very rapidly ($k_{dissoc} > 10^9$ sec^{-1}) and consequently it is the cleavage reaction, which determines the triplet lifetime of the initiator. Thus many Type I photoinitiators have relatively short triplet lifetimes (~1-50nsec)[69] and as a consequence the cleavage reaction does not suffer from oxygen quenching.

Type II initiator systems are based on compounds which when excited ultimately lead to atom or electron abstraction from a suitable donor molecule (synergist) thereby producing a carbon centred radical which acts as the initiating species for the polymerisation process (Figure 51).

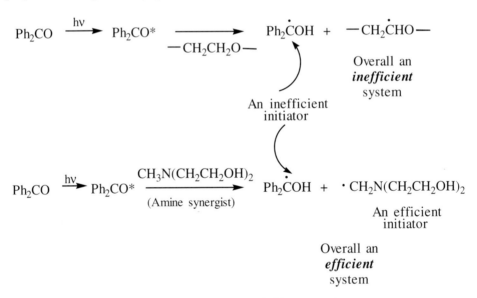

Figure 51: Type II photoinitiator systems

In the examples shown, the photoactive species is benzophenone. This compound has a long triplet lifetime (~10^{-3}sec) and this is reduced by hydrogen or electron abstraction from substrates and also it is deactivated by energy transfer to oxygen (Figure 52).

$$Ph_2CO_{T_1} + {}^3O_2 \longrightarrow Ph_2CO_{S_0} + {}^1O_2 \quad \text{Energy transfer}$$

Figure 52: Deactivation of triplet benzophenone by oxygen quenching

It is a fact that in all Type II systems there is competition between energy transfer to oxygen and reaction with the synergist. Even the acrylate and methacrylate groups and styrene quench high energy triplet states such as those of benzophenone (N.B. this may occur by energy transfer or by reversible biradical formation).

The role of the synergist is very important in the Type II systems. Usually tertiary amines are used since (a) they react very efficiently with the triplet states of low and energy (40-70 kcal/mole) and (b) they serve to retard the inhibition of cure by oxygen.[22]

For readers having more of an interest in the photochemistry of these systems a little more detail concerning the mechanism of these reactions is now given. Triplet ketones will abstract hydrogen atoms from a variety of substrates including alkanes, ethers and alcohols. Compounds containing atoms or groups which have a low ionisation potential may react with excited and singlet states by an electron transfer process. This can lead in turn to a proton transfer reaction which produces radical species which could formally be considered as arriving via hydrogen atom abstraction (Figure 53).[70]

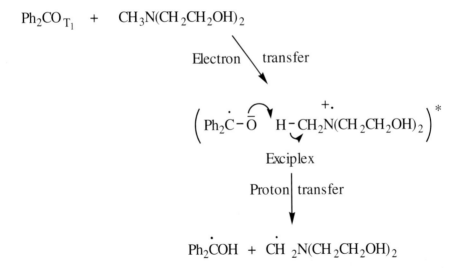

Figure 53: Reaction of triplet benzophenone with an amine synergist via an electron transfer process

It was an appreciation of this mechanism which led to the finding that appropriately substituted 2-aminoalcohols and α-amino acids may also act as synergists (Figure 54)[71]. Furthermore, the mechanism suggested that the triplet states of a range of other species, heterocyclic compounds[72], aromatic nitro compounds[73], dyes[72] etc. should be capable of reacting in a similar way to benzophenone. This proved to be the case and the results helped in the understanding of a number initiating systems developed during the early part of the 1970's.

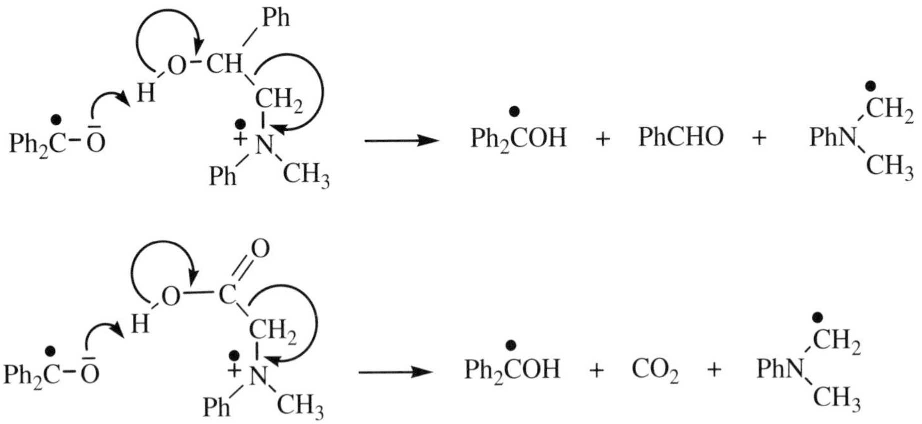

$$Ph_2\overset{\bullet}{C}-\bar{O} \quad + \quad \text{[2-aminoalcohol structure]} \quad \longrightarrow \quad Ph_2\overset{\bullet}{C}OH \quad + \quad PhCHO \quad + \quad PhN\overset{CH_2}{\underset{CH_3}{}}$$

$$Ph_2\overset{\bullet}{C}-\bar{O} \quad + \quad \text{[α-amino acid structure]} \quad \longrightarrow \quad Ph_2\overset{\bullet}{C}OH \quad + \quad CO_2 \quad + \quad PhN\overset{CH_2}{\underset{CH_3}{}}$$

Figure 54: Reactions following electron transfer from a 2-aminoalcohol and an α-amino acid to triplet benzophenone

(ii)   Type I Free Radical Initiators

Benzoin and benzoin ethers were one of the earliest Type I systems to be used in radiation curing. A whole range of techniques e.g. product studies, radical trapping, ^{1}H n.m.r. chemically induced dynamic polarisation etc. have established that homolysis does produce a benzoyl radical and an α-substituted benzoyl radical (Figure 55).[74, 75, 76]

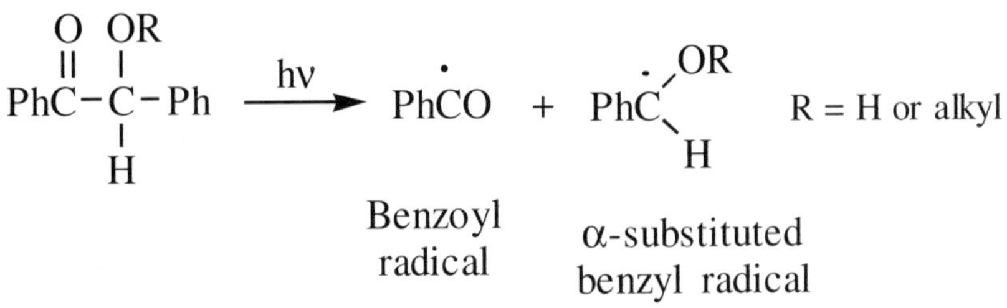

$$\underset{\underset{H}{|}}{\overset{\overset{O\ OR}{||\ |}}{PhC-C-Ph}} \quad \xrightarrow{h\nu} \quad Ph\overset{\bullet}{C}O \quad + \quad Ph\overset{\bullet}{\underset{H}{C}}\diagup^{OR} \qquad R = H \text{ or alkyl}$$

Benzoyl radical   α-substituted benzyl radical

Figure 55: α-Cleavage of a benzoin ether

There is abundant evidence that the benzoyl radical will initiate the polymerisation of acrylates, methacrylates, styrene etc and in many cases rate constants are available. There is considerable debate as to whether or not the α-substituted benzyl radical is an initiator.[77] It seems to be a relatively unreactive radical and this feature means that its most likely role in the curing of acrylates etc. is as a chain terminator. This has been shown to be the case in the benzoin methyl ether photoinitiated polymerisation of methyl methacrylate since the polymer produced was shown by gas chromatography/mass spectrometry to have the structure shown in Figure 56.[63]

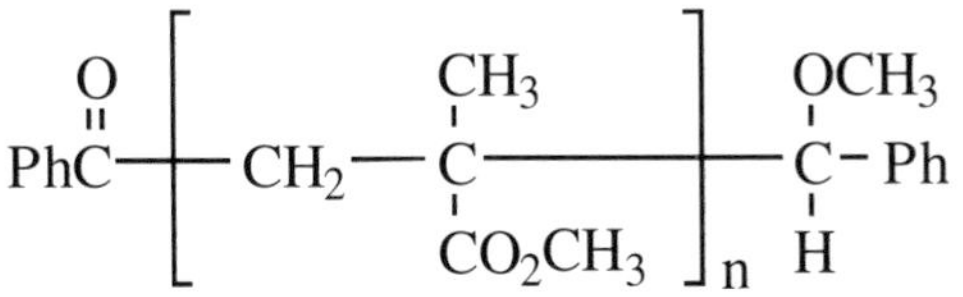

$$PhC \overset{O}{\underset{}{\|}} \left[CH_2 - \overset{CH_3}{\underset{CO_2CH_3}{\overset{|}{\underset{|}{C}}}} \right]_n \overset{OCH_3}{\underset{H}{\overset{|}{\underset{|}{C}}}} - Ph$$

Figure 56: Structure of the polymer produced by benzoin methyl ether photoinitiated polymerisation of methyl methacrylate

This finding sets the stage for understanding the reactions which occur with a wide range of initiating systems.

The aryl ethers of benzoin, although not used extensively, do have some interesting photochemical properties. These compounds fragment both by α and β-cleavage reactions (Figure 57)[78].

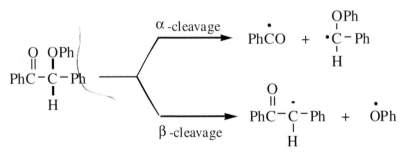

Figure 57: α and β-Cleavage reactions of an aryl ether of benzoin

In the case of the compounds shown in Figure 58 α-cleavage is suppressed (since this mode of cleavage does not produce a resonance-stabilised radical) and β-cleavage dominates. CIDNP studies have revealed that, unusually, cleavage occurs from the excited singlet state.[79]

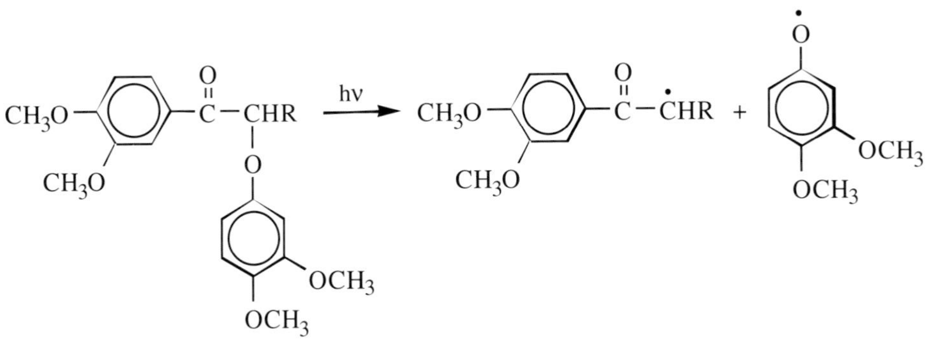

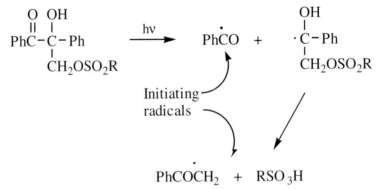

Figure 58: β-cleavage of a β-aryloxyacetophenone

Reactions, similar to this, occur during the photoyellowing of lignin.

Before leaving the simple benzoin ethers it is interesting to note that benzoin ethyl ether behaves as photobleaching initiator (see page 82) and has been used for curing composites.[80]

Benzoin will undergo the aldol reaction with formaldehyde to give a product possessing a primary alcohol group (Figure 59). Sulphonate esters of the alcohol are excellent photoinitiators, and upon irradiation yield two active radicals and a sulphonic acid.[81, 82]

Figure 59: Photoinduced fragmentation of a sulphonate ester of α-methylolbenzoin.

NB: The type of radical which fragments, releasing a sulphonic acid can also be generated by a Type II system (Figure 60).[83]

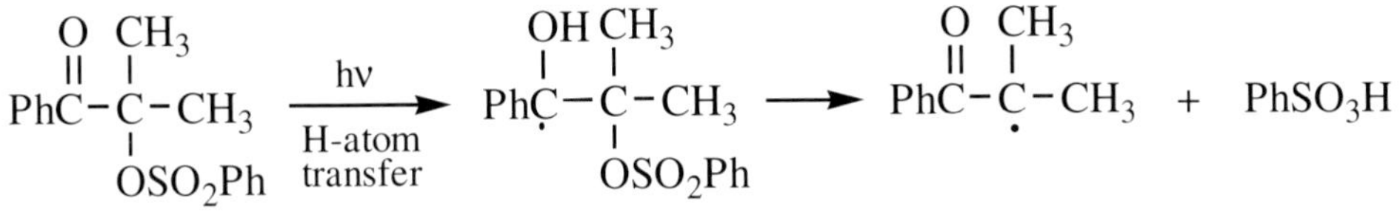

$$\underset{\underset{\displaystyle OSO_2Ph}{\overset{\displaystyle O \quad CH_3}{\underset{|}{\overset{||\ \ |}{PhC-C-CH_3}}}}}{} \xrightarrow[\text{transfer}]{\overset{\displaystyle h\nu}{\text{H-atom}}} \underset{\underset{\displaystyle OSO_2Ph}{\overset{\displaystyle OH\ CH_3}{\underset{\bullet}{\overset{|\quad |}{Ph\overset{\bullet}{C}-C-CH_3}}}}}{} \longrightarrow \underset{}{\overset{\displaystyle O \quad CH_3}{\underset{\bullet}{\overset{||\ \ |}{PhC-C-CH_3}}}} + PhSO_3H$$

Figure 60: Generation of a sulphonic acid via a Type II reaction

Before looking at other Type I photoinitiators, it is worthwhile considering the following which relates to cleavage of benzoin ethers. Cleavage of these compounds occurs from an n-π* triplet state (energy 68 kcal/mole). The energy of this state has to exceed the energy of the bond broken if the reaction is to occur with any degree of efficiency. The energy of the bond broken is related to the stability of the radicals produced. The benzoyl radical is a σ radical i.e. the electron is not delocalised over the aromatic system. On the other hand the alkoxybenzyl radical is resonance stabilised and the lone pair electrons of the oxygen play an important part in this stabilisation. When the alkoxy group is replaced by an ester group, the oxygen is far less effective in stabilising the radical due to the lone pairs interacting with the π system of the carbonyl group and consequently the presence of such a substituent reduces the efficiency of the Type I process (Figure 61).

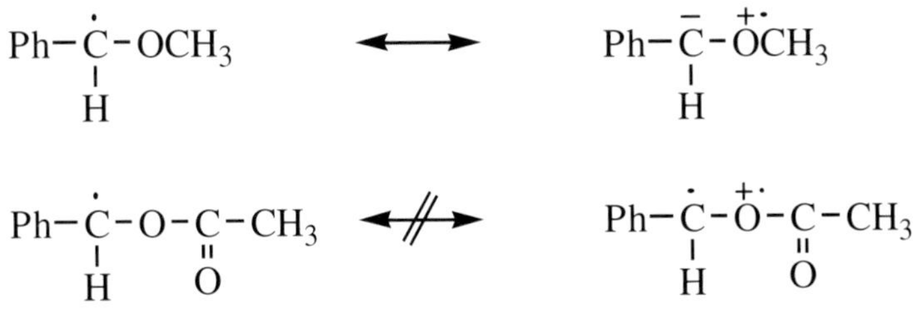

$$\underset{\displaystyle H}{\overset{\bullet}{\underset{|}{Ph-C-OCH_3}}} \quad \longleftrightarrow \quad \underset{\displaystyle H}{\overset{\displaystyle -\ +\bullet}{\underset{|}{Ph-\overline{C}-\overset{+\bullet}{O}CH_3}}}$$

$$\underset{\displaystyle H \quad\ O}{\overset{\bullet}{\underset{|\ \ ||}{Ph-C-O-C-CH_3}}} \quad \overset{/\!/}{\longleftrightarrow\!\!\!\!\!} \quad \underset{\displaystyle H \quad\ O}{\overset{\bullet \quad +\bullet}{\underset{|\ \ ||}{Ph-C-\overset{+\bullet}{O}-C-CH_3}}}$$

Figure 61: Resonance stabilisation of substituted benzyl radicals

Having recognised these factors it is easy to see why it is important to have the right type of substituent present in the benzyl radical if sufficiently low bond energies are to be achieved which will enable α-cleavage reaction to occur from the triplet state. What happens if two alkoxy groups are present in the benzylic radical? The dimethyl ketal of benzil is a very popular and efficient initiator of this type (Figure 62) showing the beneficial effect of the type of substitution.

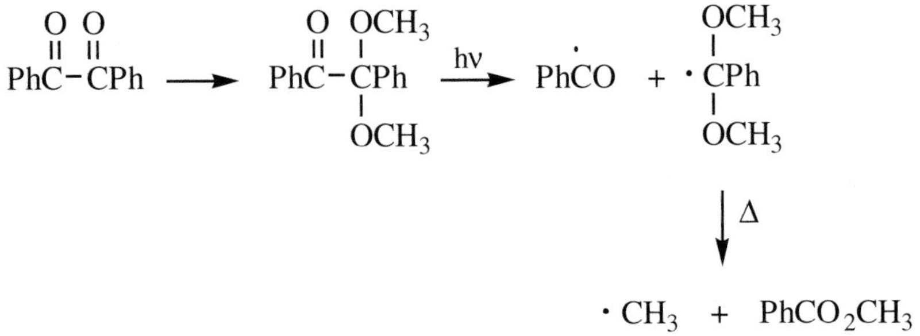

$$PhC-CPh \longrightarrow PhC-CPh \xrightarrow{h\nu} PhCO \cdot + \cdot CPh$$

(with O,O; O,OCH$_3$; OCH$_3$ substituents)

$$\downarrow \Delta$$

$$\cdot CH_3 + PhCO_2CH_3$$

Figure 62: The photochemical fragmentation of benzil dimethyl ketal

The dimethoxybenzyl radical produced in the fragmentation, however, undergoes a thermally activated fragmentation to give methyl benzoate.[75] This ester has a distinctive odour and hence the initiator cannot be used in the printing of packaging materials.

A related system, which has not been yet exploited, is based upon derivatives of Fdibenzoylmethane (Figure 63).[84]

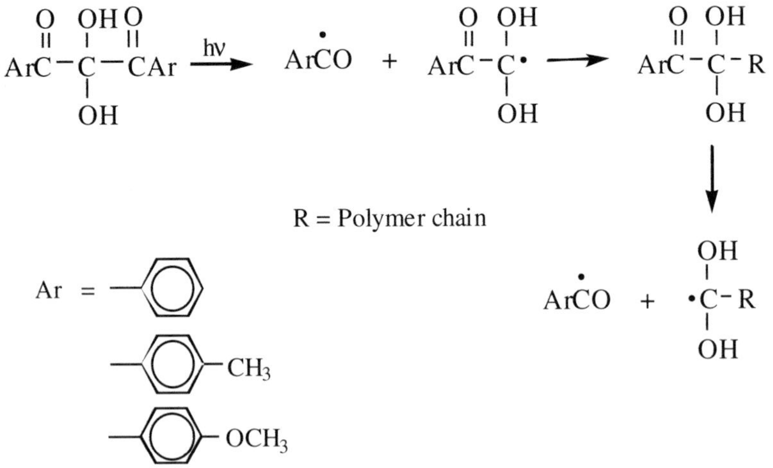

$$ArC-C-CAr \xrightarrow{h\nu} ArCO \cdot + ArC-C \cdot \longrightarrow ArC-C-R$$

(O,OH,O / OH; O,OH / OH; O,OH / OH substituents)

R = Polymer chain

$$\downarrow$$

$$ArCO \cdot + \cdot C-R$$ (OH, OH substituents)

$$Ar = -C_6H_5$$

$$-C_6H_4-CH_3$$

$$-C_6H_4-OCH_3$$

Figure 63: α-Cleavage reaction of a substituted dibenzoylmethane

This system has the potential to produce two reactive radicals and one unreactive radical per molecule of initiator.

Whilst undoubtedly the stability of the α-alkoxybenzyl radicals is due to the stabilisation of the carbon centred radical by interaction with the lone pair of electrons on oxygen. Some stabilisation must also accrue from overlap of the carbon centred radical with the aryl group. If this latter type of stabilisation is not too important, could initiators be formulated which produce alkoxymethyl rather alkoxybenzyl radicals? This has been shown to be the case. Thus 2,2-diethoxyacetophenone is an excellent initiator and has the added bonus for formulators in that at room temperature it is a liquid.[85] It is interesting to note that this compound can undergo a Norrish Type II reaction (not to be confused with Type II as applied to the classification of photoinitiators) (Figure 64).[74]

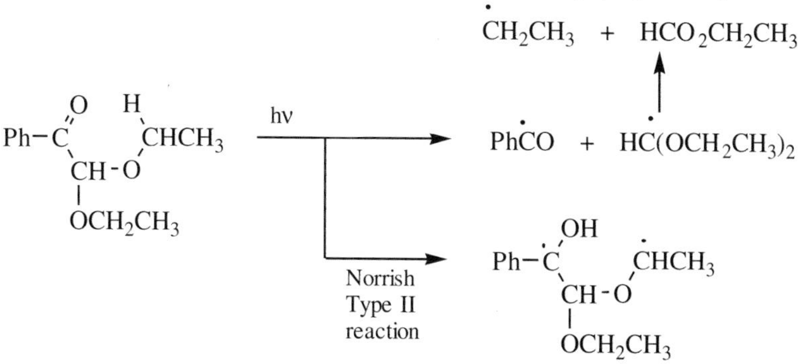

Figure 64: Photoreactions of 2,2-diethoxyacetophenone

A range of photoinitiators is available which undergo α-cleavage to give tertiary hydroxyalkyl radicals (Figure 65).[65, 69]

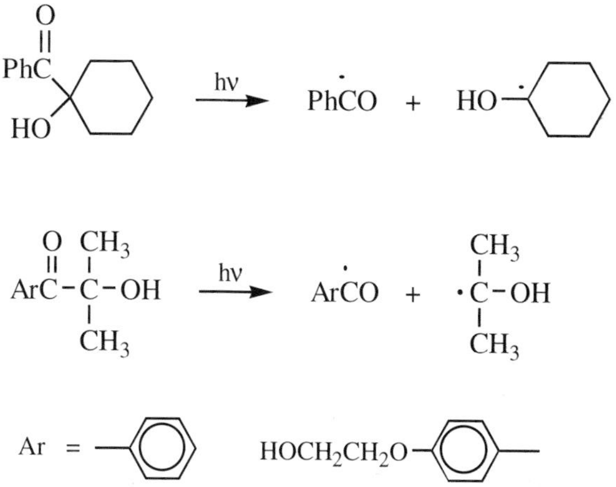

Figure 65: α-cleavage reactions of some 2-hydroxyacetophenones

Recently a series of Type I photoinitiators has becomes available which yield α-aminoalkyl as well as substituted benzoyl radicals (Figure 66).

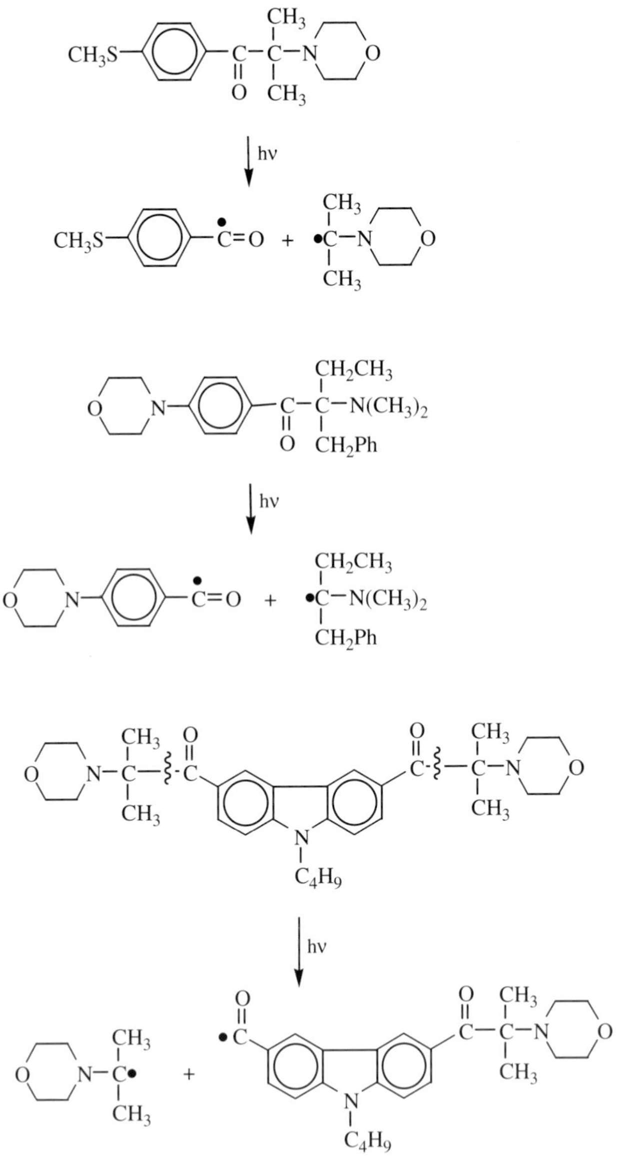

Figure 66: Type I photoinitiators producing α-aminoalkyl radicals

The ability of a nitrogen atom to stabilise an adjacent carbon centred radical is greater than that of oxygen. Consequently, the amino group probably reduces the strength of the bond which undergoes α-cleavage to a greater extent than an alkoxy group. This in turn means less excitation energy is required to cause cleavage.

Sensitisers e.g. thioxanthones, having triplet energies of >60 kcal/mole are able to cause cleavage. Furthermore, the triplet states of the initiators are $\pi\pi^*$ triplets and have relatively long lifetimes. This increase in lifetime makes them more prone to oxygen quenching and to undergo bimolecular reactions with such species as amine synergists.

So far all the α-scission reactions have involved cleavage of C-C bonds. Examples are known of C-S bond cleavage as shown in Figure 67.[89]

$$\text{ArCSR} \xrightarrow{\text{hv}} \text{Ar}\overset{\bullet}{\text{C}}\text{O} + \overset{\bullet}{\text{S}}\text{R}$$

Figure 67: α-cleavage of thiobenzoic S-aryl esters

Some photoinitiators have been commercialised which rely on the cleavage of C-P bonds.[90] Thus the acylphosphine oxides shown in Figure 68 cleave to give substituted benzoyl radicals and phosphorus centred radicals.[91] Both radicals are capable of initiating polymerisation of acrylates and methacrylates.

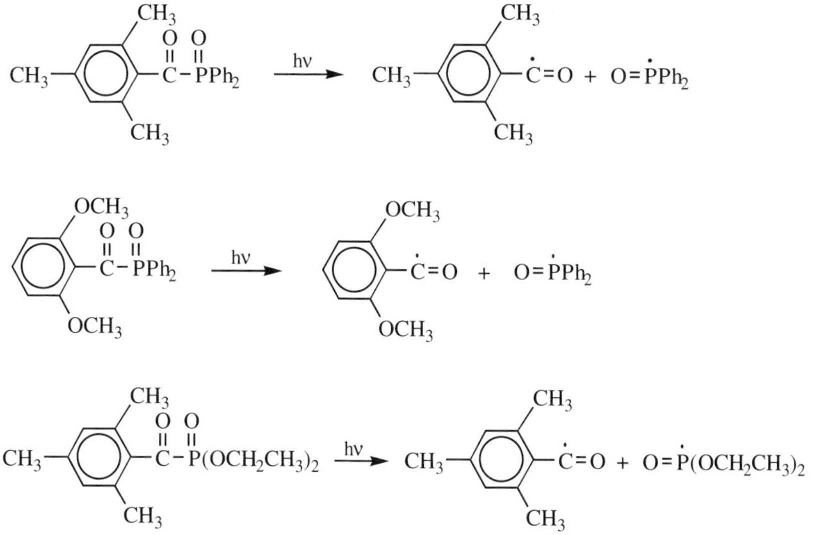

Figure 68: α-cleavage of acylphosphine oxides and an acyl phosphonate

The compounds shown in Figure 68 exhibit absorption around 380 to 390nm and are consequently yellow in colour. This colour is due to the -C(O)P(O)- chromophore which is destroyed upon irradiation. Consequently, upon irradiation the compounds shown in Figure 68 yield colourless products and therefore they are known as photobleachable initiators. This is a particularly useful feature since it enables thick sections to be cured. As is shown in Figure 69, continued irradiation leads to the gradual penetration of the photolysing irradiation. The cleavage of a number of acylphosphine oxides can be sensitised using a range of optical brightening (fluorescent brightening) agents whose absorption spectra extend more into the red than the initiators[92]

Light beam

t_1 t_2 t_3 t_4 t_5

Figure 69: Principle of curing thick sections using a photobleachable initiator ($t_5 > t_4 > t_3 > t_2 > t_1$)

A recent addition to the family of initiators relying upon C-P bond cleavage is the bis-acylphosphine oxide shown in Figure 70.[93] These materials absorb even further into the red and have proved useful in curing thick sections, composites and pigmented systems. Because of their expense they are often used with a less expensive Type I initiator.

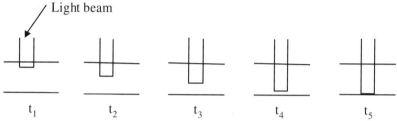

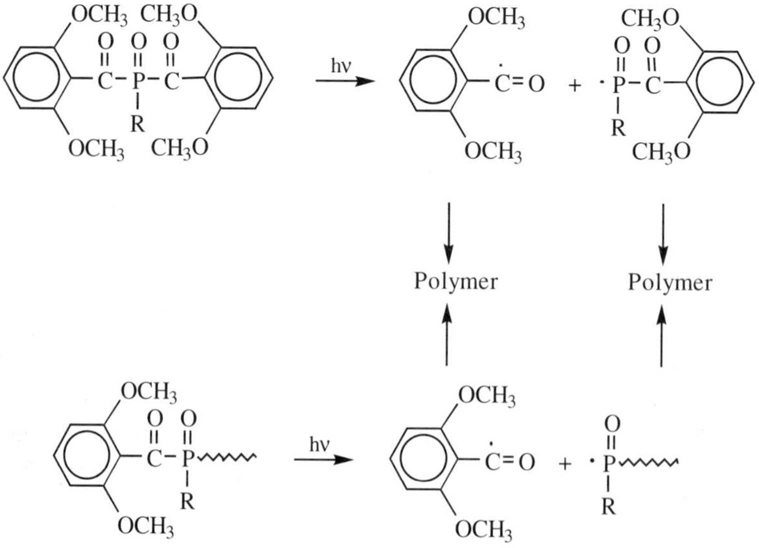

Polymer   Polymer

Figure 70: Photodecomposition of a bis-acylphosphine oxide

From Figure 70 it can be seen that three initiating radical species per mole can in principle be produced. Even more recently triacylphosphine oxides have been described.

The utility of any photoinitiator is dependent upon a number of factors which include how efficiently they absorb radiation. Given that the light source used is a medium pressure mercury lamp, it is essential that light of wavelength 254, 302, and 313nm.is absorbed. If a pigment such as titanium oxide (e.g. rutile) is present it is more important that light of >380 nm is absorbed. The absorption spectra of some of the initiators discussed is shown in Figure 71.

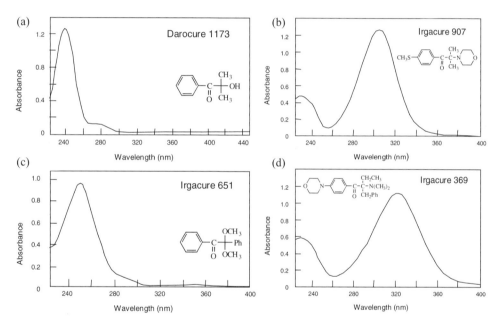

Figure 71: Absorption spectra of some commonly used photoinitiators

It will be noticed that introduction of a sulphur substituent at the 4 position in the benzoyl group moves the absorption a little more to the red. This effect is even more pronounced with the morpholino substituent. However, the biggest shift is observed with the acylphosphine oxides. The initiators whose absorption spectra are shown in Figure 71 b and d are of considerable value for initiating the cure of pigmented systems.[94]

When highly transparent coatings are required (e.g. for fabrication of optical fibre gratings), simple aliphatic ketones which are suitably substituted so as to undergo the α-cleavage cleavage reaction have been recommended.[95]

Before considering Type II systems it should be stated that some of the Type I initiators when used in a clear varnish can give rise to yellowing of the film.[96] The origin of colouration is not fully understood but factors which may contribute have been unravelled. Thus benzoyl radicals undergo combination in the curing formulation to give benzils which are yellow in colour. Coloured products can also be formed via the alkoxybenzyl radicals (Figure 72).

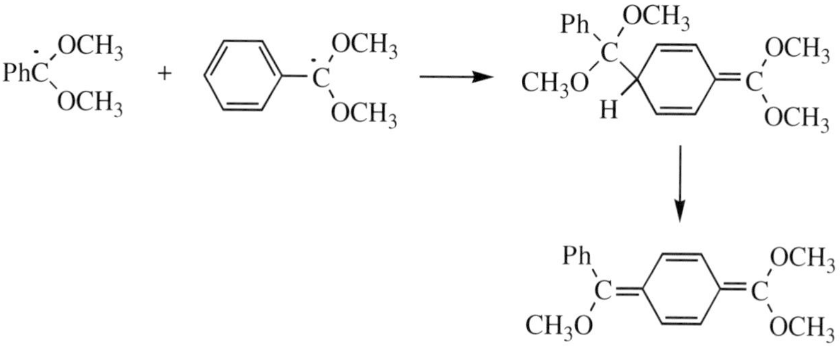

Figure 72: Possible route for formation of coloured products via ketyl radicals

Another source of coloured products is amino groups, which may be present in the initiator or as the amine synergist. The most reactive of amino groups in this respect are (di)methylamino groups. Tertiary amines undergo a variety of photo-oxidation processes may of which lead to highly coloured products (usually unidentified).[22]

(iii)   Type II Free Radical Initiators [8, 63, 64, 65, 66]

The most common (and least expensive!) system is a combination of a benzophenone and a tertiary amine. Usually an aliphatic amine is used as a synergist and ones which contain an N-methyl group are usually the most reactive. Introducing substituents into the aromatic rings of benzophenone shifts the absorption spectrum further out to the red. Alkoxy substituents in the 4 position cause a small red shift as is the case with 4,4'-diphenoxybenzophenone for which exceptionally good cure rates and depth of cure have been reported[97]. Introduction of a sulphur substituent moves the main absorption band even further out to the red (Figure 73) and a dimethylamino group has an even more profound effect[98].

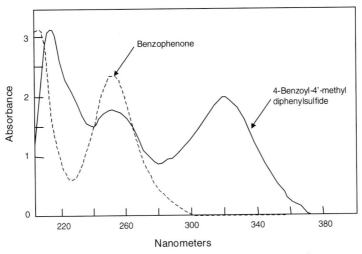

Figure 73: Absorption spectra of some benzophenones

Bis(4,4'- dimethylamino)benzophenone (Michlers ketone) is an excellent photoinitiator (being both an initiator and amine synergist rolled into one) but unfortunately its use is restricted on toxicological grounds.

The closely related compound, bis(4,4'- diethylamino)benzophenone although less toxic is also less reactive.

Compounds which exhibit strong absorption at ~350nm are thioxanthones and a number of these are used in radiation curing systems. Some of the compounds are shown in Figure 74.[99]

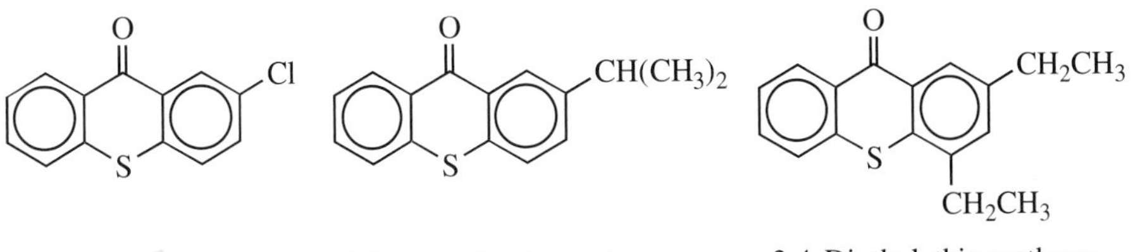

2-Chlorothioxanthone
(CTX)

2-Isopropyl thioxanthone
(ITX)

2,4-Diethyl thioxanthone
(DETX)

Figure 74: Some thioxanthones used in conjunction with an amine synergist for radiation curing

More recently thioxanthones have been produced which show absorption out at 400nm. As shown in Figure 75.[100]

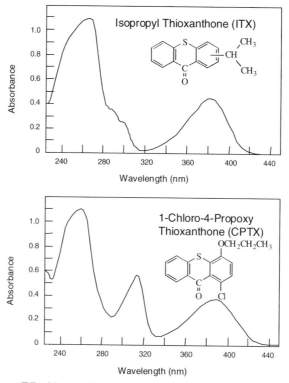

Figure 75: Absorption spectra of some thioxanthones

The thioxanthones can be used with an aliphatic amine synergist but aromatic amine synergists may also be used. Ethyl 4-dimethylaminobenzoate and related esters are commonly used as the synergist (Figure 76).

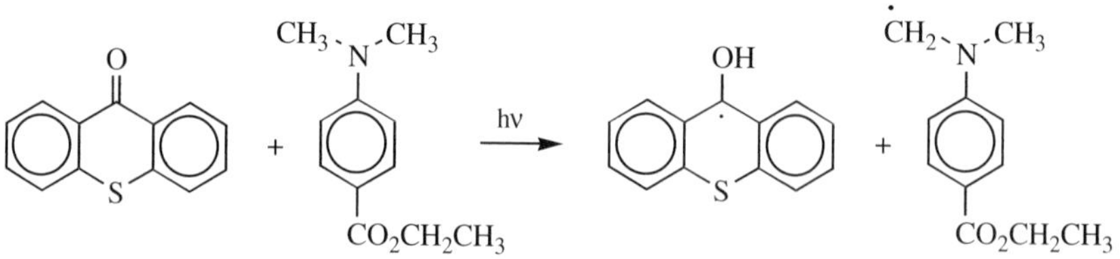

Figure 76: The photoreaction of thioxanthone with ethyl
4-dimethylaminobenzoate

The amine derived radical is an efficient initiating radical.

Anthraquinones[101, 102], such as 2-ethylanthraquinone can be used as initiators and have found use in the production of printed circuits. Other dicarbonyl compounds can be used e.g. benzil, methyl phenylglyoxalate, phenanthraquinone and camphorquinone. Benzil is a low cost initiator. It should be noted that it is not a Type I initiator.[103] (However, benzil does undergo cleavage by a 2-photon process (Equation 10)[104] To attain 2 photon absorption very high light intensities are required.)

Equation 10

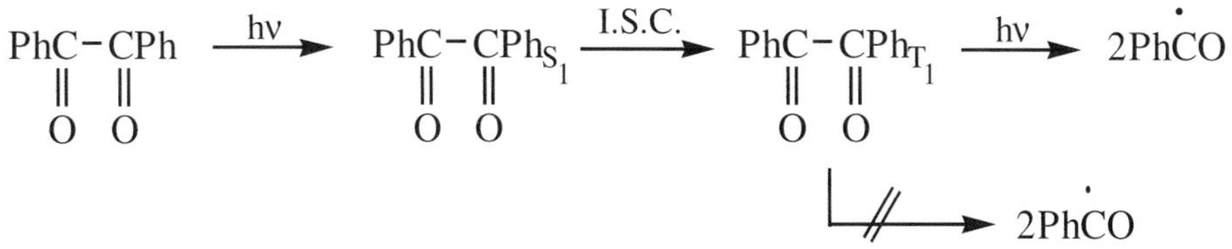

$$PhC-CPh \xrightarrow{h\nu} PhC-CPh_{S_1} \xrightarrow{I.S.C.} PhC-CPh_{T_1} \xrightarrow{h\nu} 2Ph\dot{C}O$$

with the T_1 species also shown:

$$\xrightarrow{} 2Ph\dot{C}O$$
crossed: $\xrightarrow{//} 2Ph\dot{C}O$

In the process of reduction by an amine synergist, benzil produces benzoin which can then produce, on irradiation, a benzoyl radical (Figure 77).

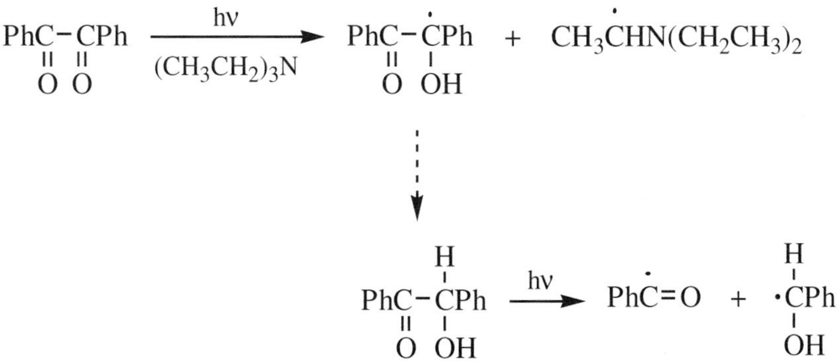

$$PhC-CPh \xrightarrow[\text{(CH}_3\text{CH}_2)_3\text{N}]{h\nu} Ph\dot{C}-\overset{|}{C}Ph + CH_3\dot{C}HN(CH_2CH_3)_2$$

$$PhC-\overset{H}{\underset{OH}{C}}Ph \xrightarrow{h\nu} PhC=O + \cdot\overset{H}{\underset{OH}{C}}Ph$$

Figure 77: Photoreactions of benzil with triethylamine

Methyl phenyglyoxalate is a liquid Type II initiator of medium reactivity[105]. Camphorquinone is an initiator, which absorbs out as far as 480nm (Figure 78). It has to be used with an amine synergist and finds application in the dental industry.[106]

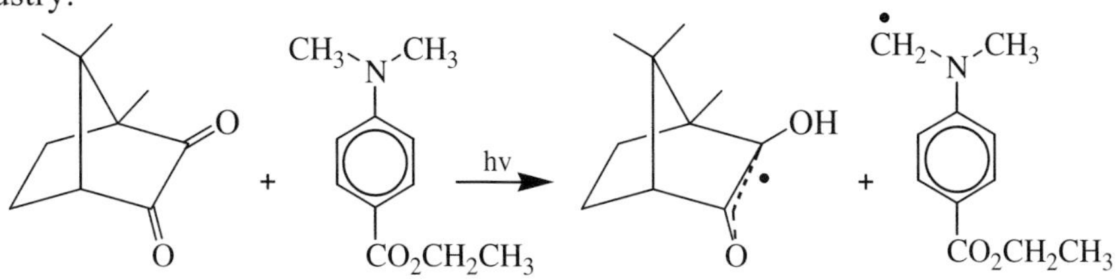

Figure 78: Photoreduction of camphorquinone

The amine-derived radical initiates polymerisation. In all cases the reaction of the carbonyl compounds give ketyl radicals which in turn lead to the production of coloured compounds e.g. thioxanthyl ketyl radicals can react with other radicals to yield coloured products (Figure 79).[107]

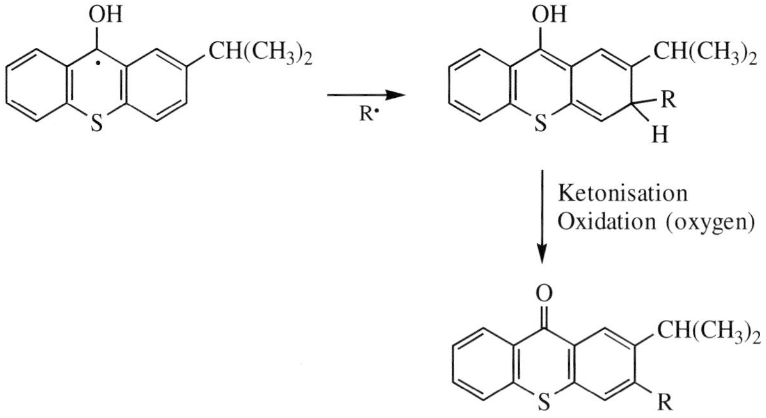

Figure 79: Production of coloured products from the ketyl radical derived from 2-isopropylthioxanthone

When R equals the macroradical produced in the polymerisation reaction, the thioxanthone is incorporated into the polymer.

Ketocoumarins were originally synthesised with a view to using them as photosensitisers for the [2+2] cycloaddition reactions of cinnamate esters. They not only served their purpose well but also proved, when used with an amine synergist, to be excellent Type II initiators.[108] With their excellent absorption properties (e.g. bis- ketocoumarins absorb out to 500nm) they are of great potential for use in pigmented and in direct laser write systems.

So far, all the Type II initiator systems have contained carbonyl compounds as the reactive species. It became clear from a study of electron transfer reactions that many other systems could be used in place of carbonyl compounds. An interesting class of such compounds is the quinoxalines and these are readily prepared by condensing aromatic 1,2-diketones with aromatic 1,2-diamines. A large number of aromatic 1,2-diketones is available thereby facilitating the preparation of a range of compounds having a wide range of absorption properties. Some of the compounds studied are shown in Figure 80 as is the mechanism for formation of the initiating species.[109]

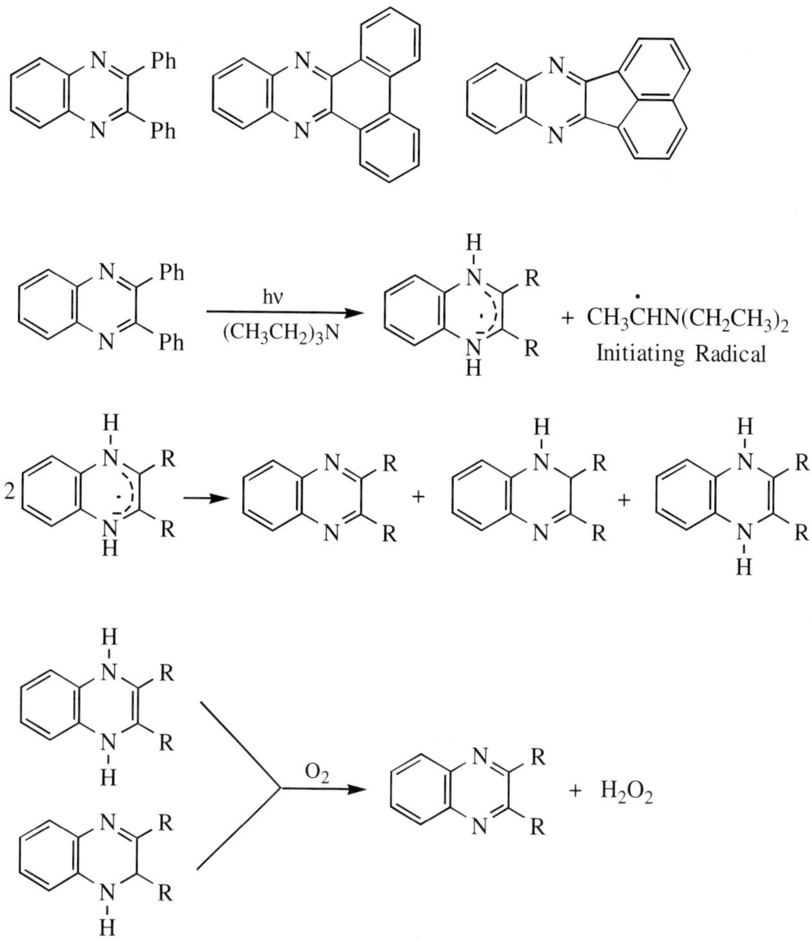

Figure 80: The photoreduction of quinoxalines by a tertiary amine

The presence of dissolved oxygen plays an important part in the reaction as it leads to the regeneration of the photoinitiator. Many dyes such as eosin, methylene blue, chlorophyll and riboflavin react in a similar way to the quinoxalines.

(iv)   Other Radical Initiating Systems

O-Acyl α-oximinoketones are an interesting class of photoinitiator (Figure 81) although not used extensively by industry.[110] CIDNP experiments have shown that fragmentation occurs from the triplet state of the initiator.

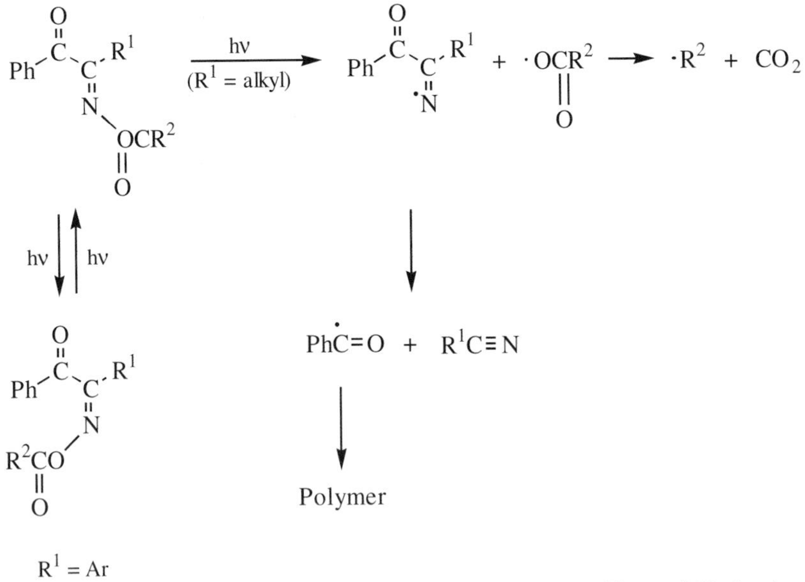

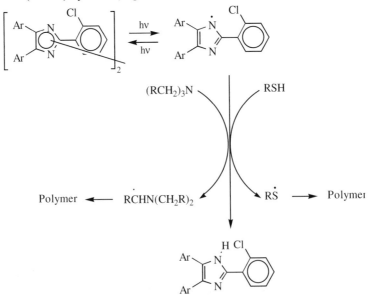

R^1 = Ar

Figure 81: Photoisomerisation and decomposition of O-Acyl
α-oximinoketones

Another class of initiators which fragment upon irradiation is the hexaaryl
bisimidazole (HABI) system (Figure 82).[111]

Figure 82: Photoinitiated polymerisation via a HABI system

Cleavage of the HABI gives a radical which of itself is incapable of initiating polymerisation and importantly is not scavenged by oxygen. However, the radical will abstract a hydrogen atom from thiols and tertiary amines to yield initiating species.[112] Although the HABI's absorb out as far as 375nm, they can be made to operate into the visible by use of sensitisers such as those shown in Figure 83.[113]

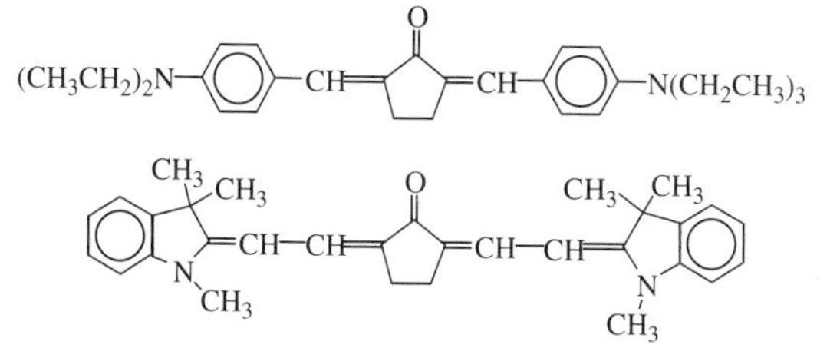

Figure 83: Sensitisers used in combination with HABI's

These systems are being championed for use in direct laser systems and have also found use in curing composites in combination with near i.r.dyes.

Trichloromethyl s-triazines undergo photolysis to generate chlorine atoms which will initiate polymerisation.[114] The decomposition can be sensitised both inter- and intramolecularly (Figure 84).

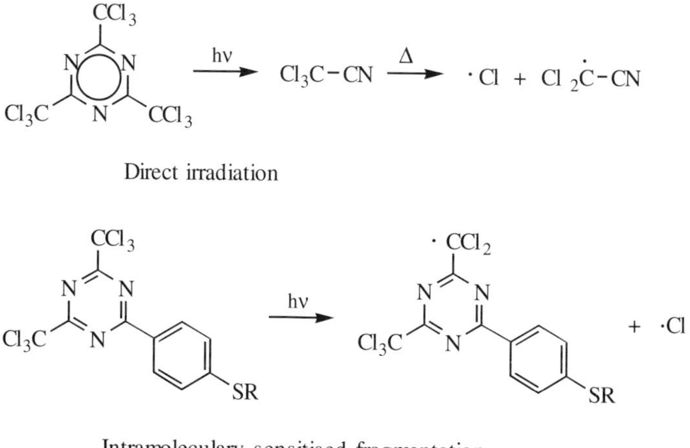

Direct irradiation

Intramoleculary sensitised fragmentation

Figure 84: Decomposition of trichloromethyltriazines

With these systems there is a possibility that the chlorine atom will abstract a hydrogen atom to give hydrogen chloride. Formation of the acid may be a nuisance (e.g. leading to corrosion where coatings are applied to metals) or may be of value for initiating polymerisation of acid hardenable systems.

A system which was designed for a specific purpose utilises cyanine borates (Figure 85).[115]

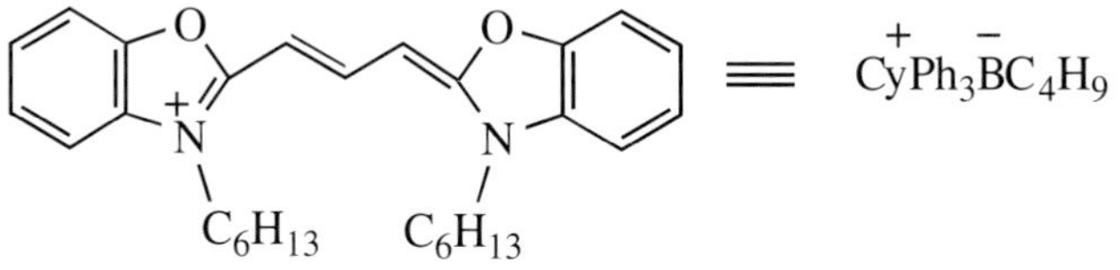

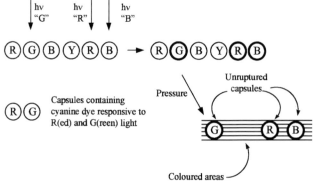

$$CyPh_3\overset{+}{B}C_4H_9 \quad\overset{h\nu}{\longrightarrow}\quad \overset{\cdot}{Cy} \;+\; Ph_3\overset{\cdot}{B}C_4H_9$$

$$Ph_3\overset{\cdot}{B}C_4H_9 \quad\longrightarrow\quad Ph_3B \;+\; \overset{\cdot}{C}_4H_9$$

$$\cdot C_4H_9 \;+\; Acrylate \quad\longrightarrow\quad Polymer$$

Figure 85: Photoinitiated polymerisation of an acrylate using a cyanine borate as initiator

The reaction occurs via electron transfer from the borate anion to the excited cyanine dye to give a boron centred radical which fragments to give an alkyl radical. For an electron transfer process to be efficient it is necessary for the salt to exist in the medium as an intimate ion pair.

There is a large number of known cyanine dyes and by appropriate selection one can find dyes which absorb the primary colours. Capsules were prepared containing a single cyanine dye with the coating of the capsule containing free acrylate groups. Exposure of the capsules lead to decomposition of the cyanine borate in those capsules which contains the cyanine that was responsive to the particular wavelength of the incident radiation (Figure 86).

Figure 86: Use of cyanine borates in colour imaging

The acrylate groups present in the capsule where photodecomposition of the dye occurred were crosslinked. In this way capsules which had been illuminated could be differentiated from non illuminated capsules. By subjecting the coating to pressure, the non-irradiated capsules were broken open and the contents which included a colour former were released into the medium where they reacted with a reagent to generate the appropriate colour.

The mechanism of the cyanine dye borate initiation process suggests that the cyanine dye could be replaced with a range of other cationic species provided that in their excited states (either singlet or triplet) they have sufficient oxidising power to remove an electron from the borate anion. It is therefore not surprising to find that the borate salts of many other dyes such as methylene blue behave in a similar way to the cyanine salts. Of particular interest is the finding that borate salts of near i.r. absorbing dyes such as 1,5-tetraarylpentadienyl cations (Figure 87) behave similarly. Such initiators are finding application in the curing of heavily pigmented systems and composites.

BuB^-Ph_3

Figure 87: Structure of an i.r. dye

In the case of clear wood coatings it has been claimed that the use of such compounds is beneficial since they do not give rise to photoinitiator fragments which act as prodegradants and therefore the coatings exhibit good outdoor durability[116].

Iron arene complexes, normally used as cationic initiators, will also initiate radical polymerisation processes when the counterion is a borate anion, albeit inefficiently[67] and this probably reflects the difficulty in reducing the excited state of the iron arene cation.

Iodonium salts having butyltriphenylborate anions are also efficient initiators for acrylates[117] and such compounds break down upon irradiation by electron transfer from the anion to the excited iodonium ion. For such a process to be efficient it is necessary for the salts to be present as intimate ion pairs and this may put some constraints upon the use of these compounds since as the polarity of the formulations is increased so the degree of dissociation of the salt will increase. From studies using methyl methacrylate, in which the products of the reaction were identified, it is clear that loss of an electron from the borate anion leads to an unstable species which rapidly fragments to give a butyl radical which is responsible for initiating polymerisation. The triplet state of iodonium salts can be created by using admixtures of the sensitiser with the borate salt and by using such a strategy the wavelength response of the salts can be increased. When thioxanthones are used as sensitisers excitation wavelengths of 400nm and above can be used. It is well known that the triplet states of many aromatic ketones are readily reduced and borate anions have been found to be suitable reductants. By substitution of appropriate groups (e.g. ammonium or phosphonium) into the ketones it is possible to make borate salts e.g. butyltriphenylborate salts. Phenacyltrialkylammonium borates decompose upon irradiation to yield phenacyl radicals which are excellent initiators of for acrylate and methacrylate polymerisation[118, 119]. Further work has shown that these systems are very versatile and that naphthacyl and other groups having better light absorption properties than the unsubstituted phenacyl group can be used. In addition the ammonium group may varied and trialkylammonium and imidazolium groups have been used[120]. The decomposition of these salts not only generates an initiating radical but also an amine and therefore they can be classed as anionic photoinitiators (Equation 11).

Equation 11

$$\overset{+}{ArCOCH_2NR_3} \quad \overset{-}{BuBPh_3} \quad \xrightarrow{h\nu} \quad ArCOCH_2{}^{\bullet} + R_3N + \overset{\bullet}{Bu} + Ph_3B$$

Such compounds have been used to initiate the anionic crosslinking of an epoxy resin.

If the mechanism is considered further one may ask "Is it necessary to have a photoactivatable cation since using a mixture of the appropriate tetraalkyammonium borate salt with a neutral compound may accomplish the same end?". This has been shown to be the case. When a mixture of a neutral dye such as 2,4-diodo-6-butoxy-3-fluorone and a tetraalkyl ammonium borate salt is used the polymerisation of acrylates can be initiated effectively[121]. An advantage of this system is that reduction of the dye leads to its bleaching and therefore the system can be used for curing thick sections. It is worth mentioning that formulations containing the borate initiators described so far may not exhibit a good shelf life due to thermally initiated electron transfer occurring on storage. Use of more stable borate anions may increase shelf life stability at the expense of initiating ability. By careful choice of the substituents present in the borate anion, reactivity, shelf life stability and stability towards acids can also be attained [122]. One such anion is the n-hexyl tris(m-fluorophenyl)borate anion.

One of the driving forces for developing an efficient visible light driven system is to carry out direct laser imaging e.g. produce a lithoplate that can be imaged using a laser beam the movement of which reproduces the text which is held on computer (Figure 88)[123]. Such a process would do away with the necessity for using a negative.

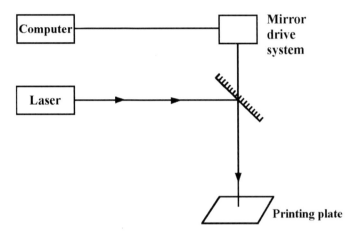

Figure 88: Direct laser imaging of a printing plate

In order for such systems to be of any value, high writing speeds are necessary which in turn means that the polymerisation process must be highly efficient. Such efficiency can only be attained by use of an amplification system e.g. a free radical promoted chain reaction. Initiators of some promise for polymerisation of methacrylates appear to be the dialkyltitanocenes. Most of these compounds are, however, not suitable for use in formulations which are required to have along shelf life. Eventually a compound of suitable stability was discovered i.e. bis((η^5-cyclopentadienyl) bis(2,6-difluoro-3-(1H-pyrryl-1-yl)phenyl titanium (Figure 89).[64, 124]

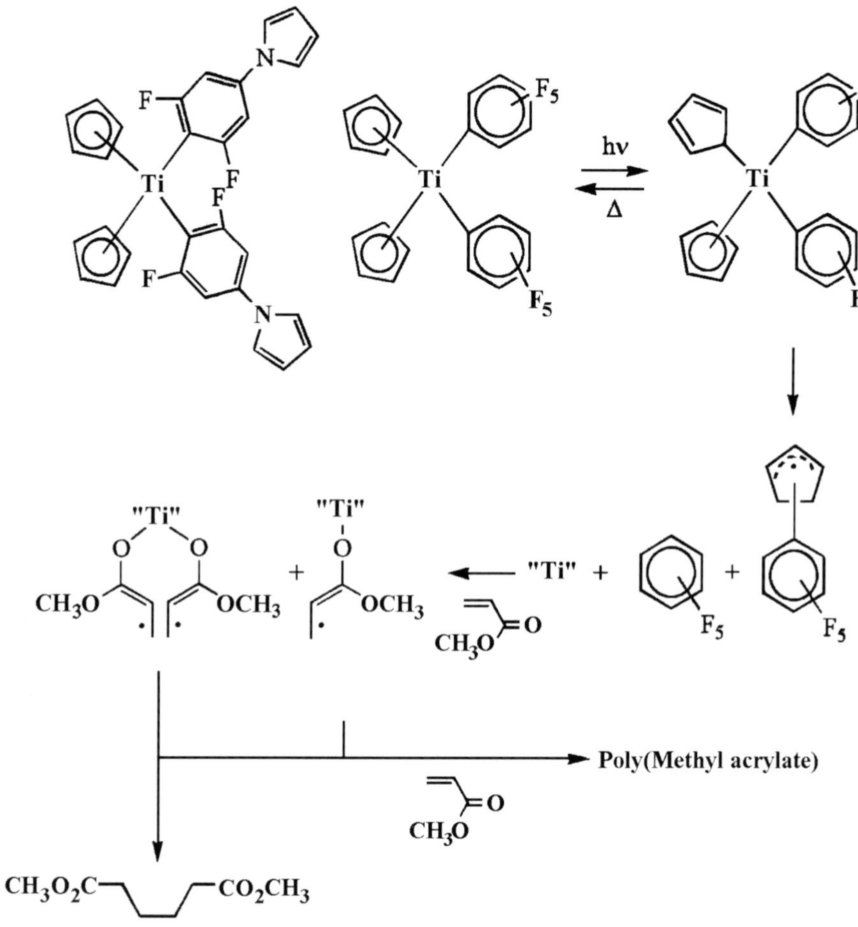

Figure 89: Polymerisation of acrylates initiated by titanocenes

The absorption spectrum of the titanocene renders it most suitable for use with an argon ion laser (strong lines at 488 and 514nm). Since the initiators decompose destroying the chromophores responsible for the absorption of visible light, they are classed as photobleachable initiators. Currently the exact mechanism of initiating polymerisation is not known and Figure 89 sums up the current knowledge of a closely related system.

Recently interest has been shown in photoinitiators which contain a group capable of photosensitising the homolysis of a peroxide bond. (Figure 90) [125].

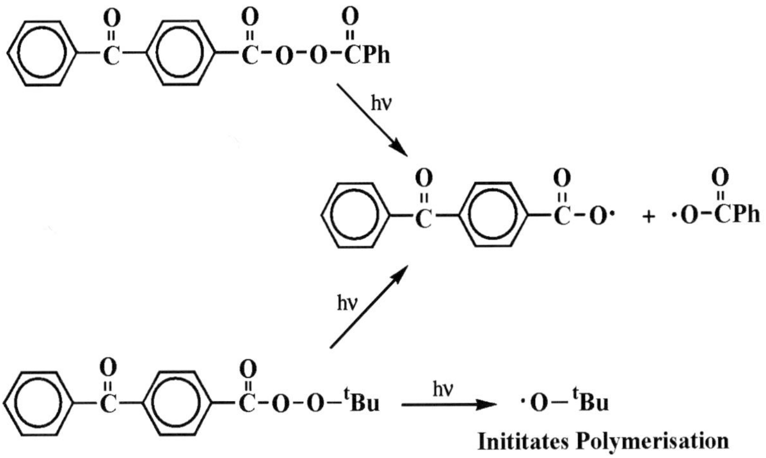

Figure 90: Photoinitiators which produce oxygen centred radicals

Production of the t-butoxyl radical was found to initiate the polymerisation of methyl methacrylate and styrene. Peresters have also been made of xanthene dyes and with these compounds visible light can be used to homolyse the O-O bond. The shelf life of formulations containing these compounds is likely to be short.

Before leaving this topic it should be pointed out that the inclusion of a tertiary amine in the formulation may generate useful radicals if it absorbs radiation[126]. It is believed that radicals are generated by reaction of the excited amine with oxygen. It is well known that aromatic amines form charge transfer complexes with oxygen and irradiation of these species leads to radical production.

(v)   Cationic Photoinitiators [39, 127, 128, 129, 130]

Cationic initiators are compounds which, under the influence of u.v. or visible or e.b. radiation lead to the release of acid which catalyses the desired polymerisation process. The term latent acid initiators has been used to describe some compounds which generate sulphonic acids upon irradiation.[81] In reality, all cationic photoinitiators are latent acid generators.

One of the earliest systems to be used was based on diazonium salts possessing non-nucleophilic counterions such as tetrafluoroborate, hexafluorophosphate, hexafluoroarsenate and hexafluoroantimonate. Irradiation of these salts leads to the elimination of nitrogen (Equation 12).

Equation 12:   Photodecomposition of a diazonium salt

$$ArN{=}\overset{+}{N}\overset{-}{B}F_4 \xrightarrow{\ h\nu\ } ArF \ + \ N_2 \ + \ BF_3$$

By varying the aryl group it proved possible to tailor the absorption spectrum of the initiator to overlap with the emission lines of lamps in the visible u.v. and visible part of the spectrum. Important disadvantages of this type of initiator included poor thermal stability and the evolution of nitrogen gas upon irradiation which can lead to the appearance of pin holes in the cured films.

To overcome the disadvantages exhibited by the diazonium salts diaryliodonium and triarylsulphonium salts were introduced. For both classes of compound it proved essential that the positive charge was counterbalanced by the presence of a large non-nucleophilic anion as was the case with the diazonium salts. The mechanism of fragmentation of onium salts is remarkably complex and the main pathways for decomposition of a triphenylsulphonium salt are shown in Figure 91.

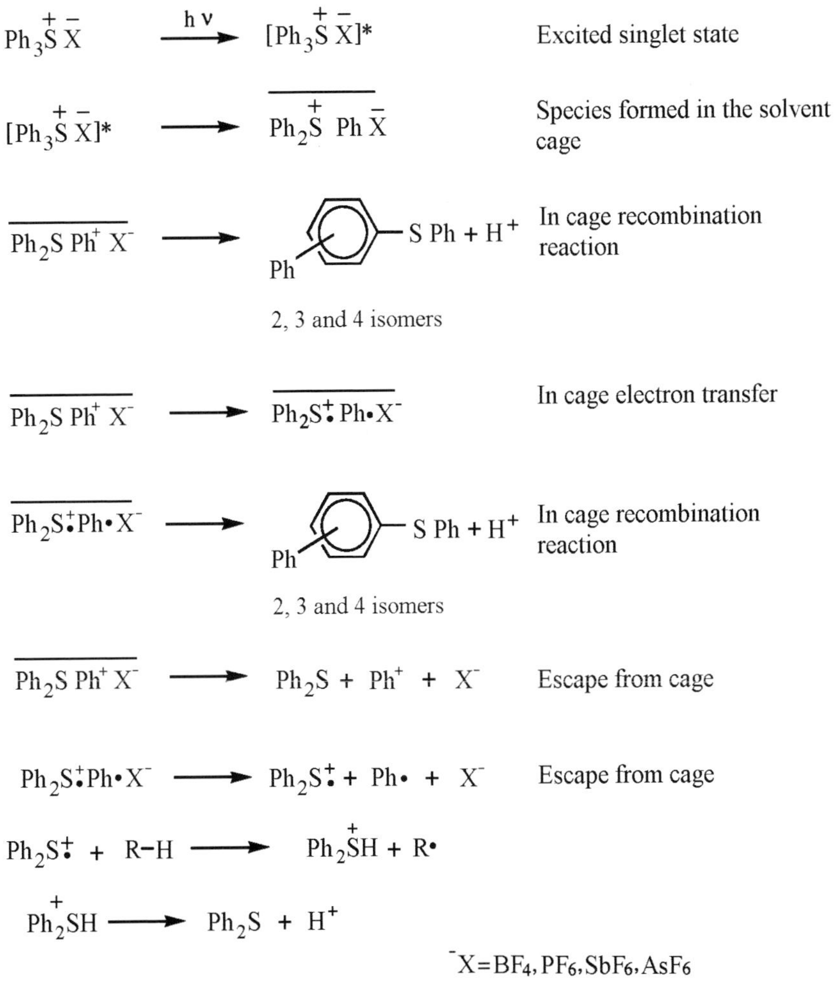

$$Ph_3\overset{+}{S}\ \overset{-}{X} \xrightarrow{\ h\nu\ } [Ph_3\overset{+}{S}\ \overset{-}{X}]^* \qquad \text{Excited singlet state}$$

$$[Ph_3\overset{+}{S}\ \overset{-}{X}]^* \longrightarrow \overline{Ph_2\overset{+}{S}\ Ph\ \overset{-}{X}} \qquad \text{Species formed in the solvent cage}$$

$$\overline{Ph_2S\ \overset{+}{Ph}\ X^-} \longrightarrow$$

$$\text{S Ph} + \text{H}^+ \qquad \text{In cage recombination reaction}$$

2, 3 and 4 isomers

$$\overline{Ph_2S\ \overset{+}{Ph}\ X^-} \longrightarrow \overline{Ph_2\overset{+\bullet}{S}\ Ph\bullet X^-} \qquad \text{In cage electron transfer}$$

$$\overline{Ph_2\overset{+\bullet}{S}Ph\bullet X^-} \longrightarrow$$

$$\text{S Ph} + \text{H}^+ \qquad \text{In cage recombination reaction}$$

2, 3 and 4 isomers

$$\overline{Ph_2S\ \overset{+}{Ph}\ X^-} \longrightarrow Ph_2S\ +\ Ph^+\ +\ X^- \qquad \text{Escape from cage}$$

$$Ph_2\overset{+\bullet}{S}Ph\bullet X^- \longrightarrow Ph_2\overset{+\bullet}{S}\ +\ Ph\bullet\ +\ X^- \qquad \text{Escape from cage}$$

$$Ph_2\overset{+\bullet}{S}\ +\ R{-}H \longrightarrow Ph_2\overset{+}{S}H\ +\ R\bullet$$

$$Ph_2\overset{+}{S}H \longrightarrow Ph_2S\ +\ H^+$$

$$^-X = BF_4, PF_6, SbF_6, AsF_6$$

Figure 91: Mechanism for the photodecomposition of a triarylsulphonium salt

It will be noted that "in cage" and "escape from cage" processes have been identified. Photolysis generates reactive species within close proximity i.e. within the solvent cage. There will be, as in all homo- and heterolytic reactions, competition between recombination of the fragments to regenerate the starting material, reaction between the fragments and escape of the fragments from the cage so that they are truly free. A further point of interest is that proton generation can occur in cage and out of cage by very different processes. The in cage process for proton generation from the diphenylsulphonium radical cation is shown in Figure 92.[131]

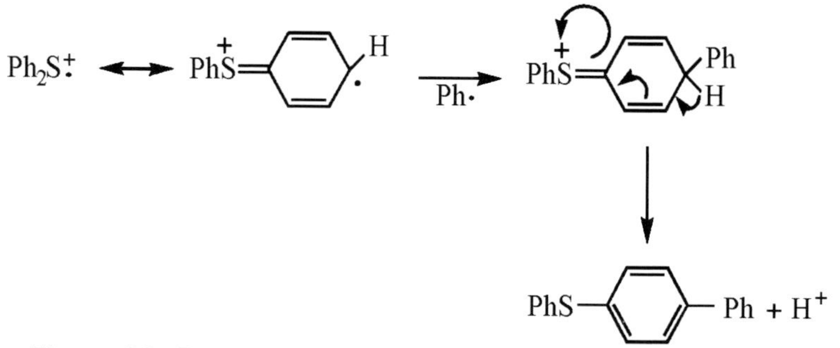

Photinitiator Systems

Figure 92: Proton generation via the cage in reaction of a diphenylsulphonium radical cation and a phenyl radical

The out of cage reaction process for proton production is via hydrogen atom abstraction by the diphenylsulphonium radical cation.

For the mechanism shown in Figure 91, no distinction has been made for processes which occur via the excited singlet and triplet states. Sensitisation studies using high energy triplet sensitisers e.g. acetone and acetophenone, proved that the triplet sulphonium salt leads only to out of cage products (Figure 93) i.e. no protons are produced within the solvent cage.

$$\text{Sens}_{S_0} \xrightarrow{h\nu} \text{Sens}_{S_1} \xrightarrow{\text{I.S.C.}} \text{Sens}_{T_1}$$

$$\text{Sens}_{T_1} + \text{Ar}_3\text{S}^+\text{X}^- \longrightarrow \text{Sens}_{S_0} + [\text{Ar}_3\text{S}^+\text{X}^-]_{T_1}$$

$$[\text{Ar}_3\text{S}^+\text{X}^-]_{T_1} \longrightarrow \overline{^3 \text{Ar}_2\text{S}^+ \text{Ar} \cdot\text{X}^-}$$

$$\overline{^3 \text{Ar}_2\text{S}^+ \text{Ar} \cdot\text{X}^-} \longrightarrow \text{Ar}_2\text{S}^+ + \text{Ar}\cdot + \text{X}^-$$

$$\text{Ar}_2\text{S}^+ + \text{R}-\text{H} \longrightarrow \text{Ar}_2\overset{+}{\text{S}}\text{H} + \text{R}\cdot$$

$$\text{Ar}_2\overset{+}{\text{S}}\text{H} \longrightarrow \text{Ar}_2\text{S} + \text{H}^+$$

Figure 93: Triplet sensitised decomposition of a triarylsulphonium salt

The mechanism for decomposition of diaryliodonium salts is very similar to that for the triarylsulphonium salts.

What lessons can be learned from these mechanistic studies? The in cage reactions are likely to become increasingly important as the viscosity of the medium is raised.[132] Since the in cage products absorb over a similar wavelength region to the starting onium salts, they will lead to an inner filter effect, thereby decreasing the efficiency of the breakdown of the onium salt. The availability, in the substrate to be polymerised, of C-H bonds that are reactive towards radicals is essential if out of cage process for proton production is to occur efficiently.

So far we have considered proton production, but what part does the counterion play? If X$^-$ = methane sulphonate (CH$_3$SO$_3^-$), methanesulphonic acid is produced. With the complex anion, hexafluorophosphate anion, it is reasonable to suppose that hexafluorophosphoric acid is formed. This acid is in reality composed of a molecule of phosphorus pentafluoride hydrogen bonded to a molecule of hydrogen fluoride. In organic solvents the acid is unstable and dissociates into free hydrogen fluoride and phosphorus pentafluoride. Thus, there are two potential initiators a Lewis and Bronsted acid. If water is present in the medium there is also the possibility of some hydrolysis of phosphorus pentafluoride occurring, thereby generating more hydrogen fluoride[133, 134]. Another important fact is that the reactivity of the onium salt is dependent upon the counterion with the observed order reactivity being SbF$_6^-$ > AsF$_6^-$ > PF$_6^-$ > BF$_4^-$. This result probably reflects in part the stability of the anions and the initiating ability of their corresponding Lewis acids ie SbF$_5$ > AsF$_5$ > PF$_5$ > BF$_3$. It also reflects the ability of the anions to form an ion pair with the propagating carbocation. If the anion is strongly associated with the carbocation, nucleophilic attack will be inhibited compared with the situation where the carbocation is essentially free. As the anion size increases, so the degree of association decreases and hence the greatest reactivity is observed with the hexafluoroantimonate anion.

A relative newcomer to the field is diphenyliodonium tetra(pentafluorophenyl)borate which has found particular use in the curing of epoxy silicones[135] due to its more ready solubility in silicone formulations than the classical onium salts. The initiator has been used to cure standard epoxide formulations including some pigmented systems.

When an epoxide is polymerised using an onium hexafluorophosphate as the photoinitiator what are the initiating species? In addition to those already mentioned, there is evidence that the sulphonium and iodonium radical cations can also participate (Figure 94) [136]. Kinetic studies indicate that the iodonium radical cation is particularly reactive towards epoxides and vinyl ethers [137].

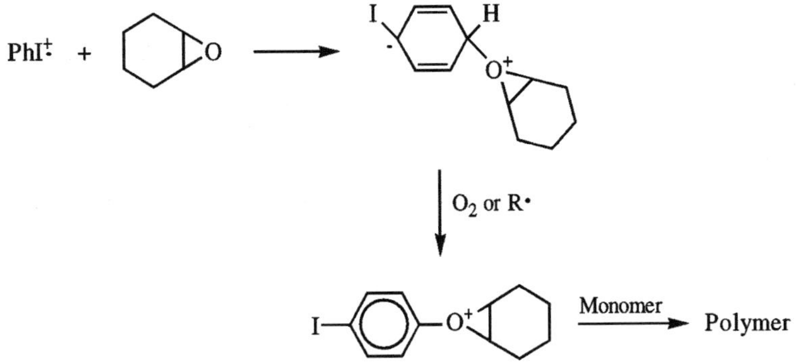

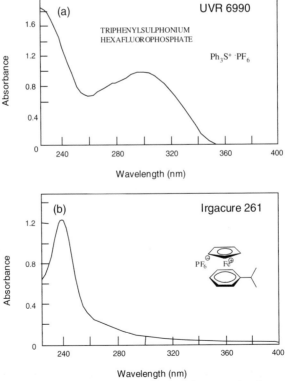

Figure 94: Reaction of the phenyliodonium radical cation with cyclohexene epoxide

The onium salts, although excellent photoinitiators in many ways, suffer in that those which are commonly available only show substantial absorption below 350nm (Figure 95).

Figure 95: Absorption spectra of an onium and a ferrocenium salt

Can the spectral sensitivity of the onium salts be extended? A number of compounds have been found to act as sensitisers but the system is a little more complicated than usual. Some sensitisers energise the onium salts by energy transfer whereas others induce decomposition via electron transfer. It is not always easy to distinguish between the two mechanism. Table 1 reports some of the sensitisers which include decomposition of diaryliodonium and triarylsulphonium salts.

Table 1[a]: Photosensitiser/onium salt combinations for cationic polymerisation of a diepoxide [b, c 27]

Photosensitiser	Ar_2I^+	Ar_3S^+
Anthracene	Yes	Yes
Perylene	Yes	Yes
Phenothiazine	Yes	Yes
Michlers ketone	Yes	Yes
Xanthone	Yes	No
Thioxanthone	Yes	No
Benzophenone	Yes	No
Acetophenone	Yes	No[d]

(a) Taken from S. P. Pappas in Photopolymerisation and Photoimaging Science & Technology (1989) ed. N. S. Allen, Elsevier Applied Science, Essex, UK

(b) The diepoxide used was 3,4-epoxycyclohexylmethyl-3,4-epoxycyclohexane

(c) Yes signifies that polymerisation was observed

(d) Note that it has been shown by Hacker[131] that acetophenone sensitises the decomposition of the sulphonium salt

Intramolecular sensitisation has been achieved by linking a diarylsulfonium group to a thioxanthone[138]. It has also been shown that dyes such as 2,4-diodo-6-butoxy-3-fluorone sensitise the decomposition of iodonium salts.

Iodonium salts are more easily reduced than triarylsulphonium salts and are therefore more prone to decomposition by an electron transfer process (Equation 13). It is assumed that in this process polymerisation is induced by the radical cation of the donor.

Equation 13:   Electron transfer sensitised decomposition of diaryliodonium salt

$$D \xrightarrow{\ h\nu\ } D*$$

$$D* + Ar_2I^+X^- \longrightarrow D^{\bullet+} + ArI + Ar^\bullet + X^-$$

$$D^{\bullet+} + monomer \longrightarrow Polymer$$

D = Electron donor

Electron transfer induced decomposition of onium salts occurs in other systems. Many Type I radical initiators cleave to give ketyl radicals and Type II initiator systems lead to the production of ketyl radicals. Ketyl radicals are known, from radiolysis studies, to be powerful reducing agents since they yield, upon oxidation, highly stable carbocations. Ketyl radicals generated from Type I initiators and from the reduction of aromatic ketones (N.B. for the current purpose amines cannot be used since they form salts with the liberated acid) have been shown to induce decomposition of onium salts thereby initiating polymerisation of epoxides (Figure 96).[139]

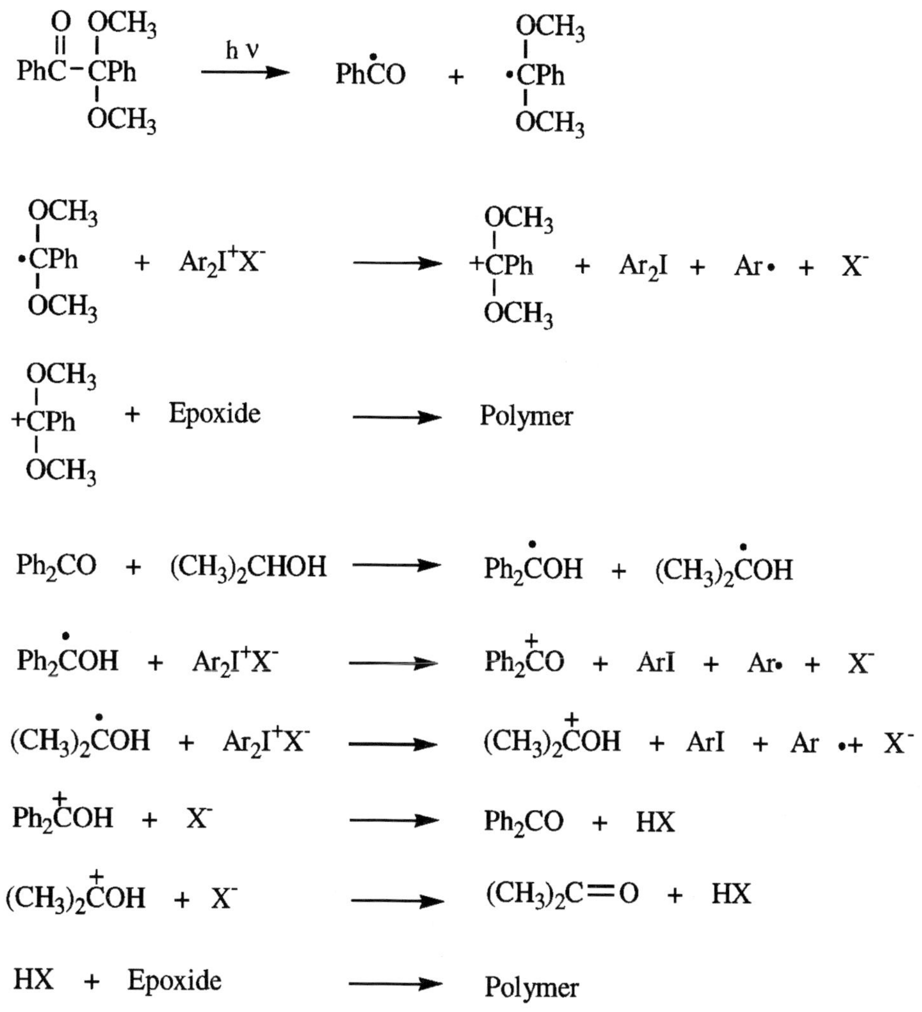

$$\underset{\substack{\text{O} \ \text{OCH}_3 \\ \| \ | \\ \text{PhC}-\text{CPh} \\ | \\ \text{OCH}_3}}{} \xrightarrow{\text{h}\nu} \quad \text{Ph}\overset{\bullet}{\text{CO}} \ + \ \underset{\substack{\text{OCH}_3 \\ | \\ \bullet\text{CPh} \\ | \\ \text{OCH}_3}}{}$$

$$\underset{\substack{\text{OCH}_3 \\ | \\ \bullet\text{CPh} \\ | \\ \text{OCH}_3}}{} + \text{Ar}_2\text{I}^+\text{X}^- \longrightarrow \underset{\substack{\text{OCH}_3 \\ | \\ +\text{CPh} \\ | \\ \text{OCH}_3}}{} + \text{Ar}_2\text{I} + \text{Ar}\bullet + \text{X}^-$$

$$\underset{\substack{\text{OCH}_3 \\ | \\ +\text{CPh} \\ | \\ \text{OCH}_3}}{} + \text{Epoxide} \longrightarrow \text{Polymer}$$

$$\text{Ph}_2\text{CO} + (\text{CH}_3)_2\text{CHOH} \longrightarrow \text{Ph}_2\overset{\bullet}{\text{COH}} + (\text{CH}_3)_2\overset{\bullet}{\text{COH}}$$

$$\text{Ph}_2\overset{\bullet}{\text{COH}} + \text{Ar}_2\text{I}^+\text{X}^- \longrightarrow \text{Ph}_2\overset{+}{\text{CO}} + \text{ArI} + \text{Ar}\bullet + \text{X}^-$$

$$(\text{CH}_3)_2\overset{\bullet}{\text{COH}} + \text{Ar}_2\text{I}^+\text{X}^- \longrightarrow (\text{CH}_3)_2\overset{+}{\text{COH}} + \text{ArI} + \text{Ar}\bullet + \text{X}^-$$

$$\text{Ph}_2\overset{+}{\text{COH}} + \text{X}^- \longrightarrow \text{Ph}_2\text{CO} + \text{HX}$$

$$(\text{CH}_3)_2\overset{+}{\text{COH}} + \text{X}^- \longrightarrow (\text{CH}_3)_2\text{C}=\text{O} + \text{HX}$$

$$\text{HX} + \text{Epoxide} \longrightarrow \text{Polymer}$$

Figure 96: Electron transfer induced decomposition of diaryliodonium salts by a photoinitiator system

The mechanisms shown in Figure 96 have not been proven in their entirety.

An electron is the simplest form of a radical and not surprisingly, under e.b. radiation the iodonium and sulphonium salts are decomposed provided they are contained in an ionisable medium. The mechanism of decomposition by e.b. radiation is thought to involve both the slow electrons and highly oxididisable radicals (Figure 97).[140, 141, 142]

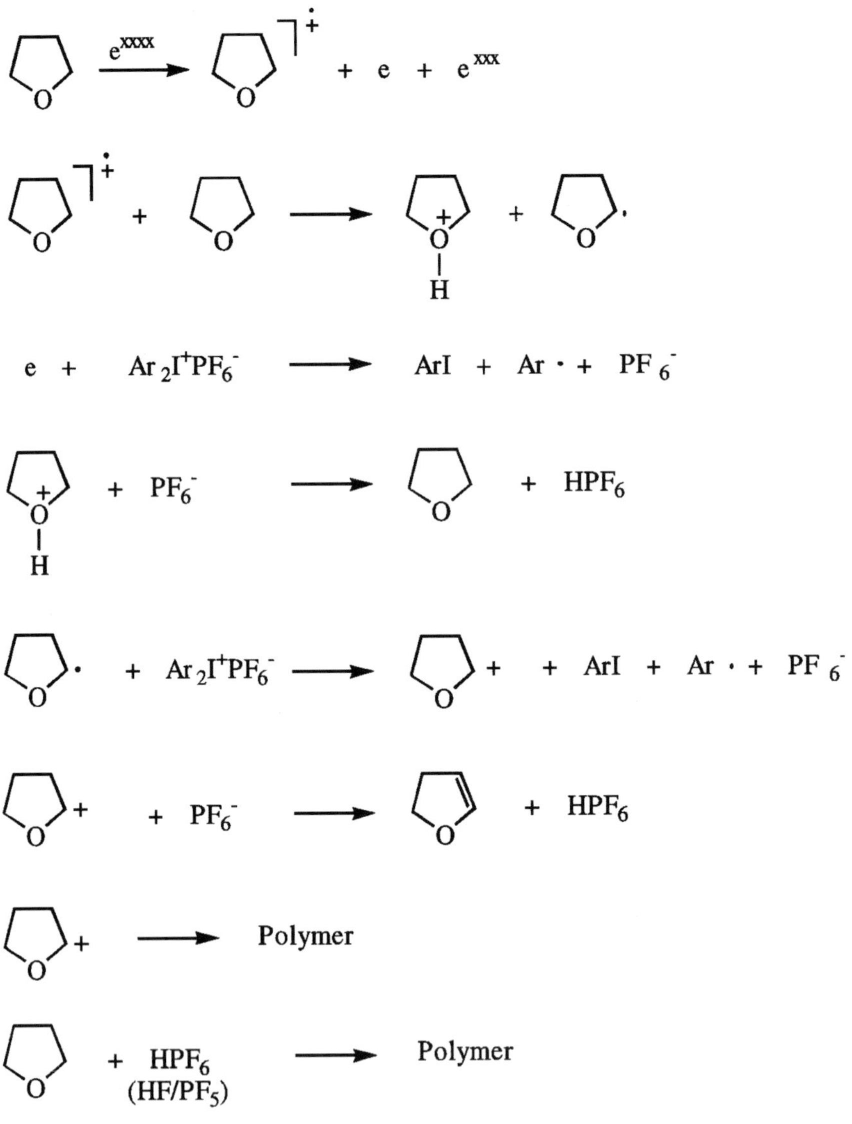

Figure 97: Decomposition of diaryliodonium salts upon e.b. radiation

That the counterion (PF_6^-) plays an important role in these reactions and is in fact consumed in the reactions has been shown by following the reactions by i.r. spectroscopy (Figure 98).

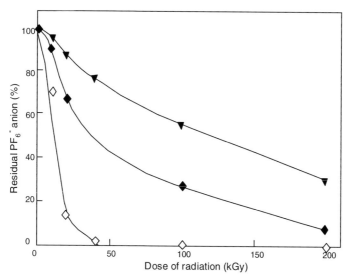

Figure 98: Percentage residual PF_6^- anion in a diepoxide for various initiators (0.05 mole/kg), ($\Diamond$) Ph_2IPF_6 ($\blacklozenge$) Ph_3SPF_6 ($\blacktriangle$) iron complex, as a function of radiation dose

The extent of decomposition of the cationic initiator and its counterion closely follows the extent of cure of the epoxide (Figure 99).

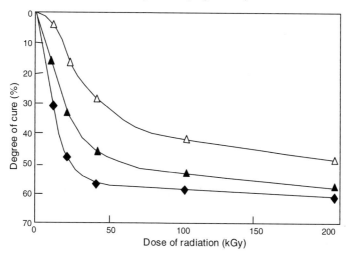

Figure 99: Percentage degree of cure of a diepoxide for various initiators (0.05 mole/kg), ($\blacklozenge$) Ph_2IPF_6 ($\blacktriangle$) Ph_3SPF_6 ($\triangle$) iron complex, as a function of radiation dose

These findings are in accordance with the view that hexafluorophosphoric acid undergoes decomposition releasing hydrogen fluoride and phosphorus pentafluoride.

The decomposition of the onium salts not only releases acidic species but also results in the formation of an aryl radical which should open up the way for radical induced polymerisation. That this can occur was shown using compounds which contained an epoxide and an acrylate group (Figure 100). When irradiated (u.v or e.b.) in the presence of an onium salt under nitrogen, cure via both groups occurs. U.v. irradiation where oxygen is not excluded leads to cure only via the epoxide group.[142]

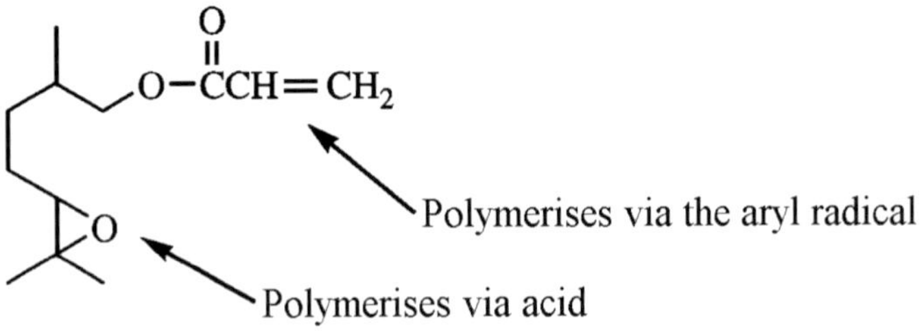

Figure 100: A polymerisation compound containing an acrylate and an epoxide group

This result is important when devising dual cure systems based on a combination of cationic and radical cure.

A variety of other cationic initiators have been described. Phenacylsulphonium and 4-hydroxyphenylsulphonium salts release acid irradiation and concomitantly produce an ylide (Figure 101).[39]

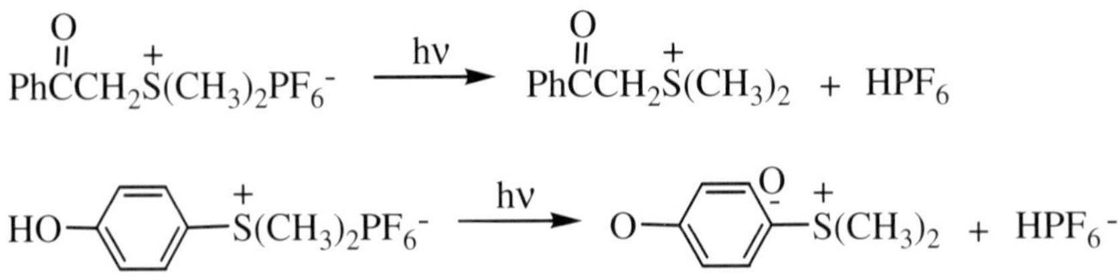

Figure 101: Photon induced decomposition of phenacylsulphonium and 4-hydroxyphenylsulphonium salts

With these systems the acid can be scavenged by the ylide and this process will compete with the initiation of polymerisation. This scavenging also reduces the extent of postcure.

A totally different cationic initiator system utilises iron arene complexes.[143] These compounds initiate the polymerisation of epoxides and the reactions have been proposed as occurring via the mechanism shown in Figure 102.

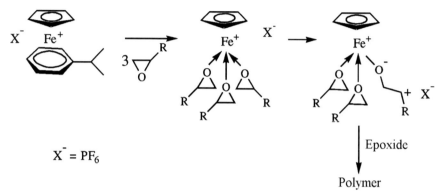

$$X^- = PF_6$$

Epoxide

Polymer

Figure 102: Polymerisation of an epoxide initiated by an iron arene complex

This mechanism does not take into account the role of the anion. The initiator also decomposes under e.b. radiation and as can be seen from Figures 100 and 101 although less efficiently than the iodonium and sulphonium salts and in addition the counterion is decomposed.

The absorption spectra of the arene complex is dependent upon the structure of the aromatic residue. By varying the aromatic residue the absorption spectra can be moved out into the visible. Unfortunately, the extinction coefficients of these visible absorption bands are fairly small and therefore if visible light curing is required, relatively high initiator concentrations have to be used. The relatively low solubility of the iron arene complexes in commonly used curing systems is a limitation of these materials. Some newer onium salts, which are likely to be of some commercial importance are those which carry groups which aid the solubilisation of the onium salt in the curing formulation (Figure 103).[127]

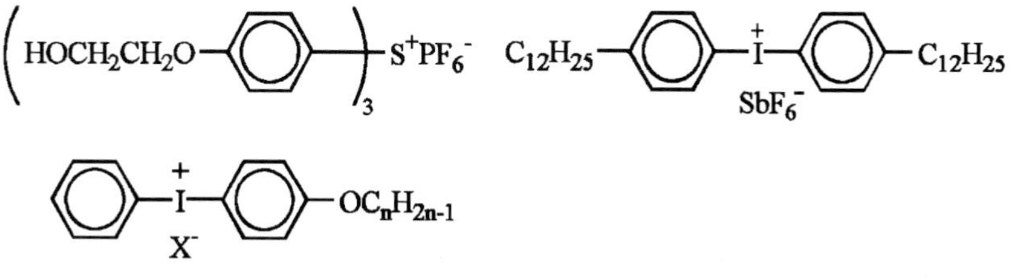

Figure 103: Onium salts carrying solubilising groups

Very interestingly and usefully, the onium salts carrying alkoxy groups containing 8 or more carbon atoms are essentially non toxic (LD_{50} >5000mg/kg in rats). A further benefit of having alkoxy group present is that it red shifts the main u.v. absorption band of the salt by about 10nm. This small shift increases the efficiency of the initiator when conventional medium pressure mercury lamps are used.

Pyrylium and thiopyrylium (Figure 104) salts bearing non-nucleophilic anions have been used to initiate cationic polymerisation. The lack of thermal stability has apparently retarded the development of these compounds. Currently there is much interest in the closely related and more thermally stable alkoxypyridinium compounds which undergo sensitised (via electron transfer) decomposition.[144]

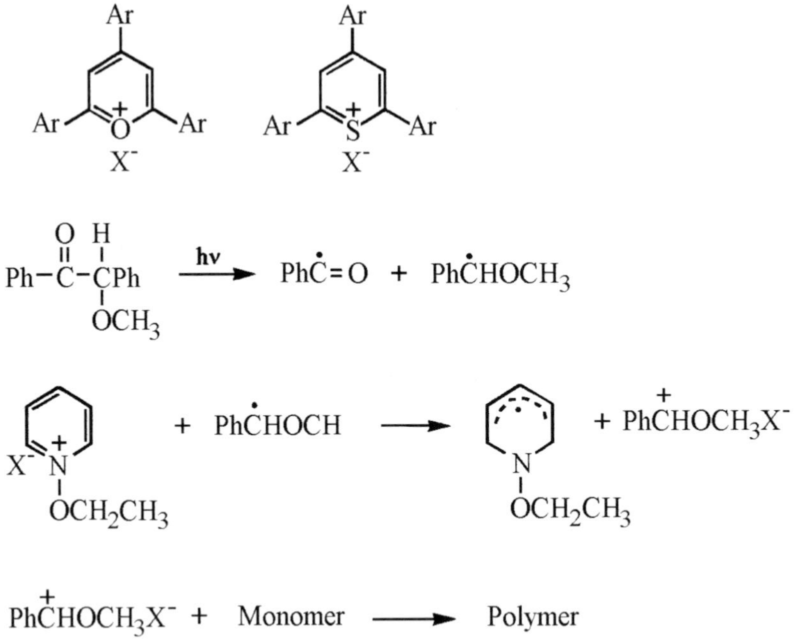

$$Ph-\overset{\overset{O}{\|}}{C}-\overset{\overset{H}{|}}{\underset{\underset{OCH_3}{|}}{C}}Ph \xrightarrow{\text{hv}} Ph\overset{\bullet}{C}=O + Ph\overset{\bullet}{C}HOCH_3$$

$$Ph\overset{+}{C}HOCH_3X^- + \text{Monomer} \longrightarrow \text{Polymer}$$

Figure 104: Pyrylium, thiopyrylium and N-alkoxypyridinium compounds used as cationic initiators

It has been found that the onium salts and iron arene complexes undergo decomposition upon irradiation in the solid state. Decomposition leads to the production of acid and when hexafluorophosphate salts are used, and the acid was shown by infrared spectroscopy to be hydrogen fluoride. This finding led to the development of the "remote" cure system (Figure 105).[134, 145]

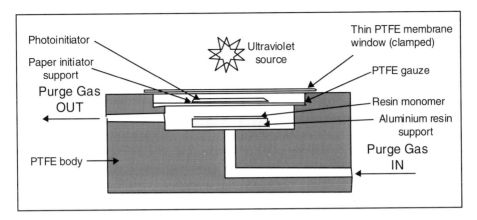

Figure 105: Remote curing equipment

The solid initiator, on a solid support is irradiated and the released hydrogen fluoride used to cure the polymerisable material which is held in close proximity. This system lends itself to dual cure. Thus a mixture of an epoxide and an acrylate containing a Type I initiator is irradiated leading to cure of the acrylate. The coating can then be shaped and curing completed via the epoxide using the remote cure system.

A number of initiators have been described which release a sulphonic acid upon irradiation e.g. those shown in Figure 106.[146]

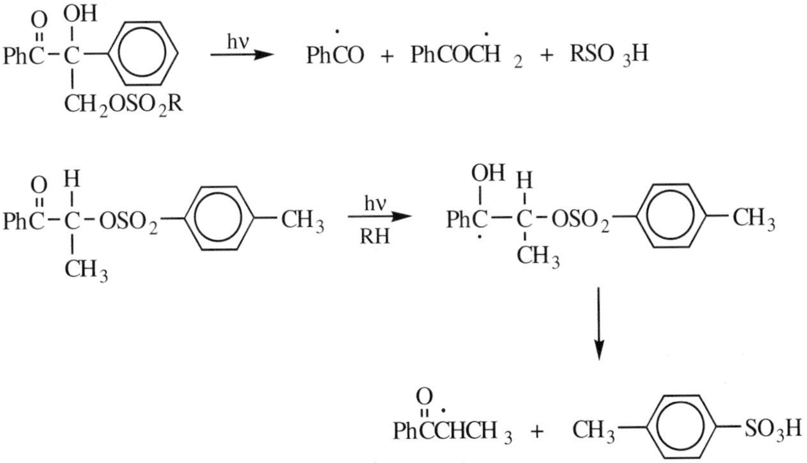

$$PhC\overset{O}{\overset{\|}{C}}-\overset{OH}{\underset{CH_2OSO_2R}{\overset{|}{C}}}-\bigcirc \xrightarrow{h\nu} Ph\overset{\cdot}{CO} + Ph\overset{\cdot}{COCH}_2 + RSO_3H$$

$$PhC\overset{O}{\overset{\|}{C}}-\overset{H}{\underset{CH_3}{\overset{|}{C}}}-OSO_2-\bigcirc-CH_3 \xrightarrow[RH]{h\nu} Ph\overset{OH}{\underset{\cdot}{\overset{|}{C}}}-\overset{H}{\underset{CH_3}{\overset{|}{C}}}-OSO_2-\bigcirc-CH_3$$

$$Ph\overset{O}{\overset{\|}{C}}\overset{\cdot}{CHCH}_3 + CH_3-\bigcirc-SO_3H$$

Figure 106: Photoinitiated leading to the production of sulphonic acids

Various acid catalysed systems (e.g. those based on melamines) have been examined and in most cases heating at around 100° is necessary to cause polymerisation and particularly when sulphonic acid generating systems are used. Other acid generating are those which generate hydrogen halides e.g. decomposition of trichloroacetophenones, trichloromethyl s-triazines and dihalobenzoylmethanes[147] (Figure 107).

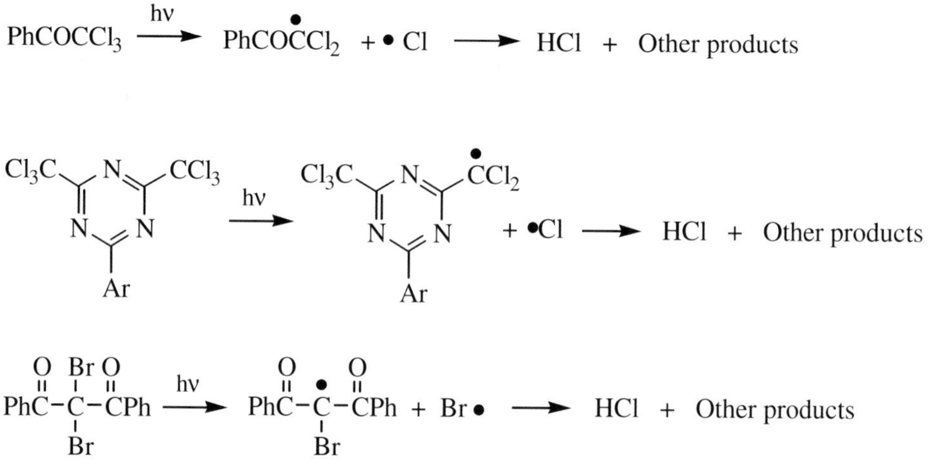

$$PhCOCCl_3 \xrightarrow{h\nu} PhCO\overset{\bullet}{C}Cl_2 + \bullet Cl \longrightarrow HCl + \text{Other products}$$

Figure 107: Hydrogen halide generating systems

Some less well known acid generating systems include those which generate silicic and boric acid. The acidity of these compounds has to be increased by complexation with metal acetoacetonates (Figure 108).[148]

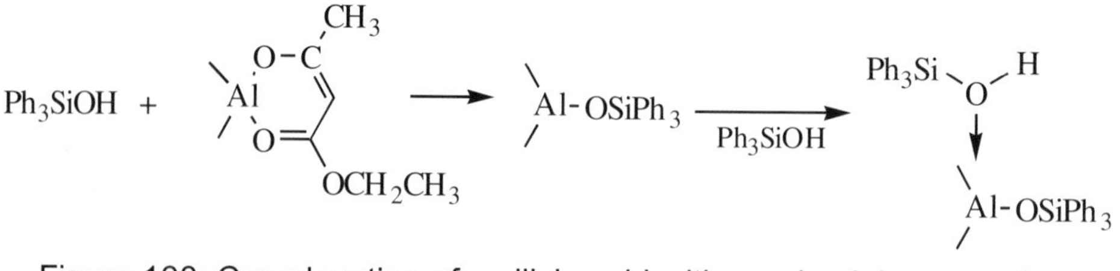

Figure 108: Complexation of a silicic acid with an aluminium complex

(vi)   Anionic Photoinitiators

Very few initiators of this type are available. The first anionic initiator to be described was based on tertiary amine salts of α-ketocarboxylic acids[149] (Figure 109).

$$\underset{\substack{H}}{\overset{\substack{OO \\ \parallel \parallel - + \\ PhCCONR}}{}} \xrightarrow{h\nu} PhCHO + CO_2 + R_3N$$

Figure 109: Photodecomposition of an amine salt of an
α-ketocarboxylic acid

More recently systems have been devised which are based on peptide chemistry. Carbamates have been used in peptide chemistry for the protection of amino groups. Irradiation of suitably substituted carbamates (urethanes) has also been shown to release amines (Figure 110).[150]

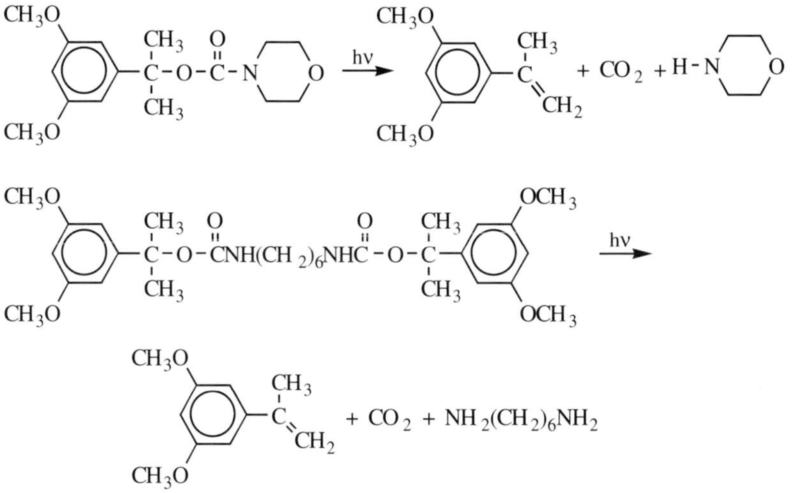

Figure 110: Photogeneration of amines from carbamates (urethanes)

The carbamates are sensitive to irradiation at wavelengths <300nm. Other carbamates based upon the o-nitrobenzyl groups exhibit photosensitivity around 300nm. (Figure 111)

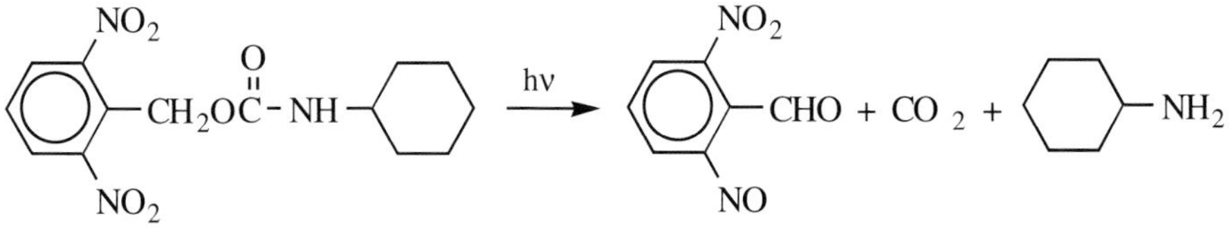

Figure 111: Photodecomposition of an o-nitrobenzyl carbamate

As previously discussed (Section III.iv), phenacylammonium n-butyltriphenylborate salts and related compounds decompose on irradiation to release an amine and this system has been used to catalyse the polymerisation of an epoxy formulation[118]. Other phenacylammonium compounds have been used to generate strong bases capable of catalysing Michael addition reactions[151]

Metal ammine salts have been shown to release ammonia upon irradiation with 254nm. The released ammonia can be used to polymerisation epoxides. Such a system has been described in a formulation for a deep u.v. negative resist.[51, 152]

(vii)   Water Compatible Initiators[153]

Various polymerisation processes occur in the presence of water e.g. suspension, emulsion and interfacial polymerisation[154]. Other processes, although occurring in organic medium, have to tolerate the presence of water. To make a photoinitiator water compatible/soluble it is necessary to append a hydrophilic group e.g. polyethylene oxide, a sulphonic acid or ammonium group. Such groups have been successfully introduced into many aromatic ketones e.g. benzophenone, thioxanthone, benzils etc.[155,] (Figure 112). Hydrophilic groups have been introduced into some Type I photoinitiators but these compounds are less readily available (Figure 113).[156]

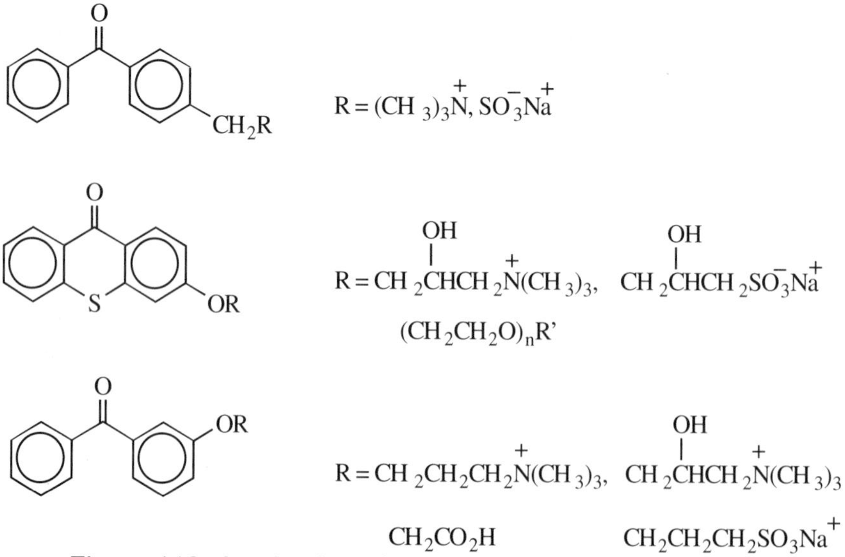

$R = (CH_3)_3\overset{+}{N}, \ SO_3^-\overset{+}{Na}$

$R = CH_2CHCH_2\overset{+}{N}(CH_3)_3, \ CH_2CHCH_2SO_3^-\overset{+}{Na}$
(OH above each CH)

$(CH_2CH_2O)_nR'$

$R = CH_2CH_2CH_2\overset{+}{N}(CH_3)_3, \ CH_2CHCH_2\overset{+}{N}(CH_3)_3$
(OH above second)

$CH_2CO_2H \qquad CH_2CH_2CH_2SO_3\overset{+}{Na}$

Figure 112: A selection of aromatic ketones carrying water solubilising groups

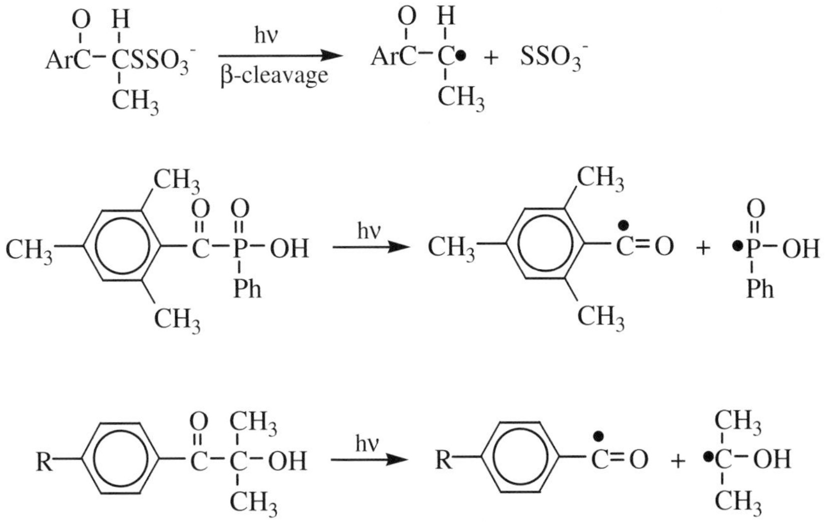

R = OCH$_2$CO$_2$H

Figure 113: A selection of water compatible Type I photoinitiators

(viii) Polymeric, Polymerisable and Multifunctional Photoinititiators[157,158]

Polymeric photoinitiators are currently enjoying much popularity and are the subject of much research. There is the hope that polymeric photoinitiators may be more effective than their monomeric counterparts e.g. via the antennae effect (as observed in photosynthesis), reducing the effectiveness of chain termination, enhancing the effectiveness of light absorption by hyperchromism [159]and eliminate odours from cured coatings which emanate from initiator residues.[160] A more pragmatic reason for assessing their potential is that such initiators will be of value in printing food packaging. Printed food packaging is subject to increasing legislation[161] which is particularly aimed at reducing the concentration of migratable species in cured inks. It is likely that the limits of migratables may be set as low as 50ppb.

Polymeric photoinitiators may be of two types: (I) where the initiator is part of the backbone of the polymer and (ii) where the photoinitiator is pendant to the main chain (Figure 114).

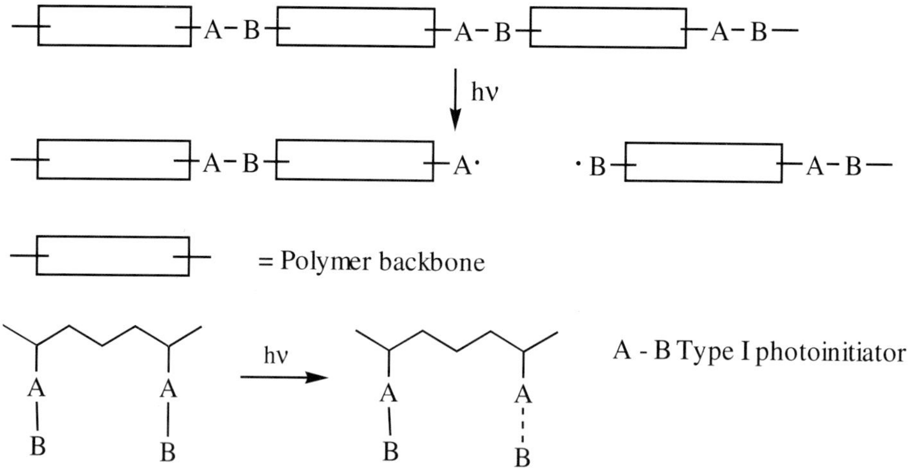

= Polymer backbone

A - B Type I photoinitiator

Pendant polymer, Type I photoinitiator

Figure 114: Two ways of incorporating a cleavage photoinitiator into a polymer

Considering Type I photoinitiators, there are very few examples of them being incorporated into a polymer backbone. There are two examples of benzoins being incorporated (Figure 115).[162, 163]

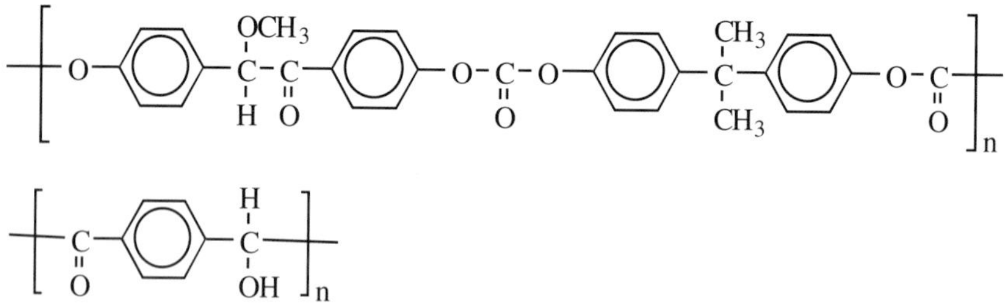

Figure 115: Polymeric benzoins

The performance of these systems has not been disclosed.

Examples in which the initiators are pendant are more abundant and one such system has been commercialised[164,165] (Figure 116).

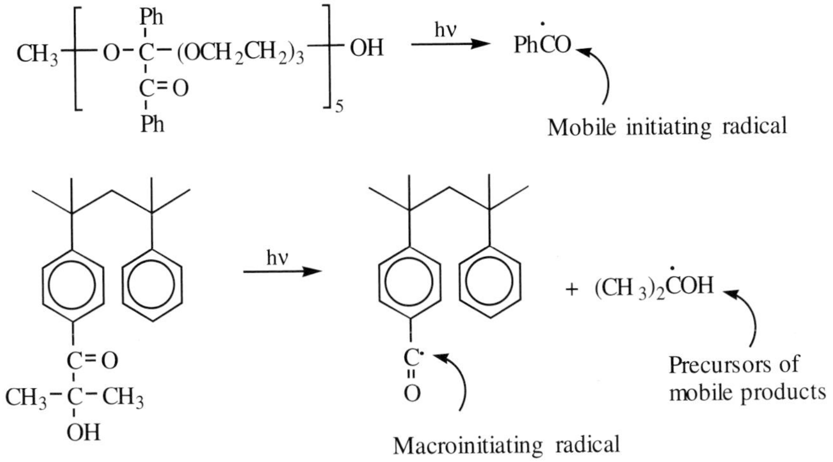

Figure 116: Some polymeric Type I photoinitiators in which the initiator is pendant to the chain

It exhibits good reactivity but is an intractable gum which gives formulators a few headaches.

A number of polymeric ketones have been described with one of the earliest being a polymeric fluorenone.[166] Several polymeric benzophenones have also been described (Figure 117).[167]

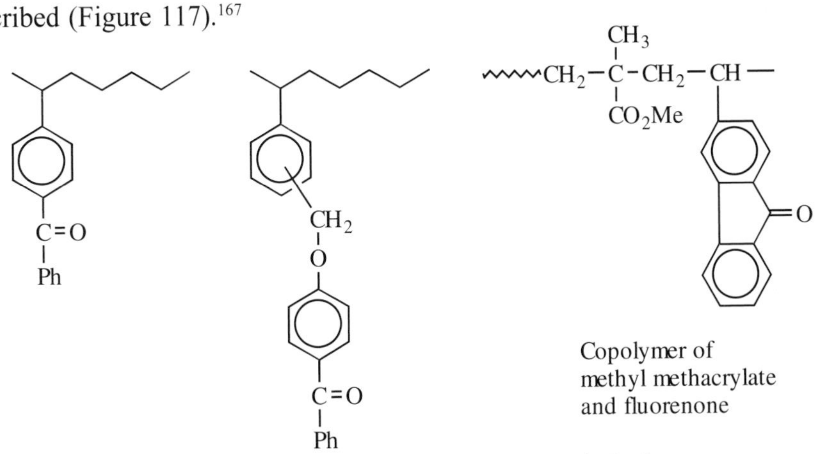

Figure 117: Some polymeric aromatic ketones

Having polymeric aromatic ketones is of no value in overcoming the problem of migratables if a low molecular weight amine synergist has to be used with them.

The interaction between polymeric aromatic ketones and amines is not efficient and this is probably due to the lack of mobility of polymer chains. Compounds have been synthesised in which the aromatic carbonyl and amine are pendant groups on the same polymer backbone (Figure 118).[167, 168] Unfortunately these systems displayed low reactivity. Reactivity was improved when the lengths of the chain linking the aromatic carbonyl group and amine to the polymer backbone were increased. In another system a benzophenone group was incorporated into the polymer backbone and the polymer chain group end capped with a tertiary amino roup. This system also proved to be less reactive than a standard benzophenone-amine mix.[169]

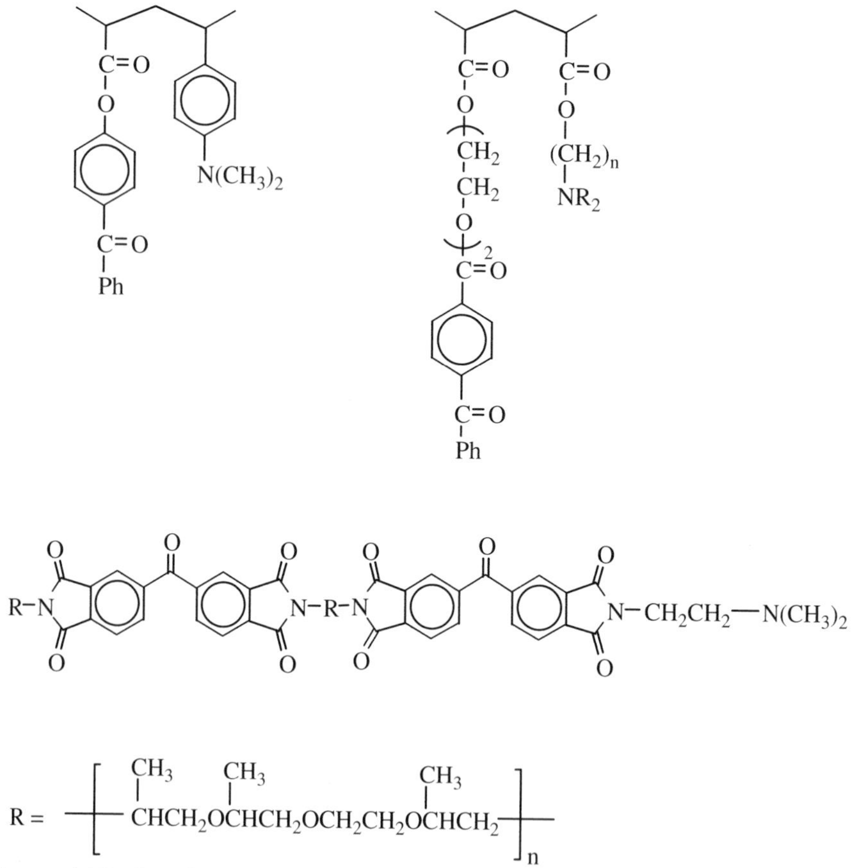

Figure 118: A polymeric benzophenone end-capped with tertiary amine.

Some interest has ben shown in the polymeric cationic photoinitiators. Several compounds, having this potential, have been synthesised for possible use as resists (Figure 119).[170, 171, 172, 173]

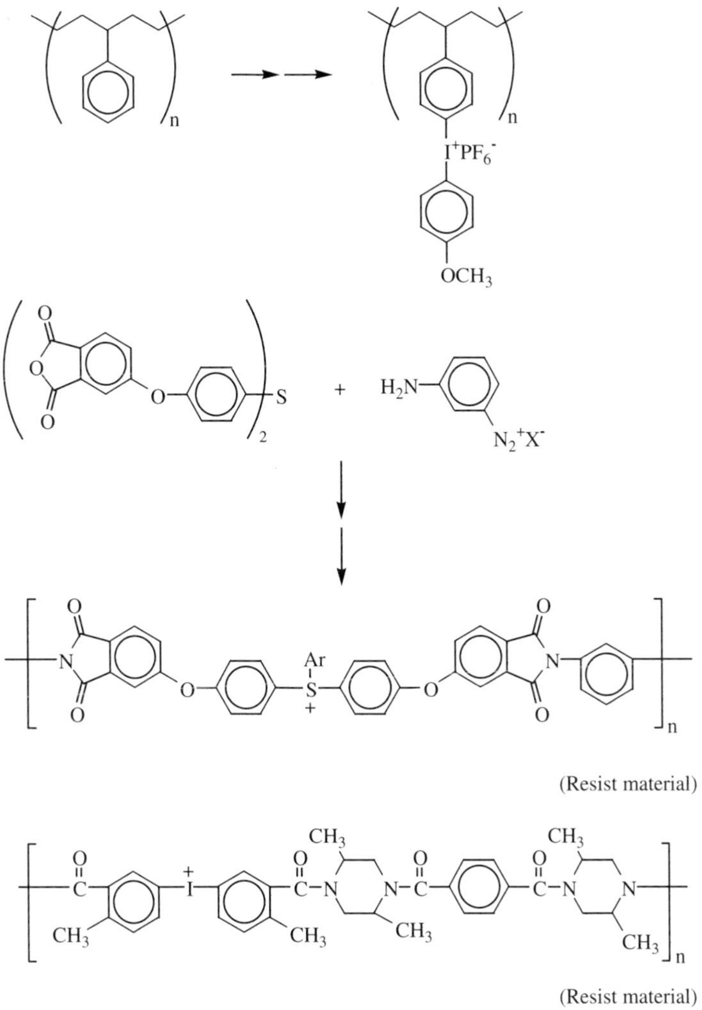

Figure 119: Some polymeric onium salts

From the above results it can be seen that polymeric photoinitiators have several potential disadvantages. Addition of a polymeric photoinitiator to a formulation may also undesirably, increase its viscosity. If the reactivity of polymeric initiators is lower than their monomeric counterparts they may have to be used at a higher level which has an adverse effect on cost. A possible solution to all these problems could be in the "autocurables".[174] Such compounds have the initiator, synergist and prepolymer backbone built into the same molecule (Figure 120). These compounds have been found to exhibit excellent reactivity.

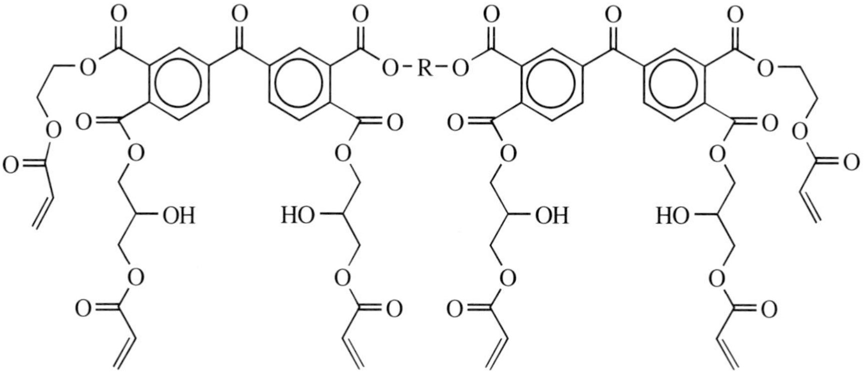

Figure 120: An example of an autocurable benzophenone

Apart from the autocurable system, the polymeric photoinitiator systems show at best, a marginal improvement in reactivity and in addition are going to prove far more expensive to produce than their monomeric counterparts.

In another approach, initiators and synergists have been attached to polyethylene and polypropylene glycol residues[175]These chains confer a number of important properties upon the initiators and synergysts. Some examples are shown in the Figure 121.

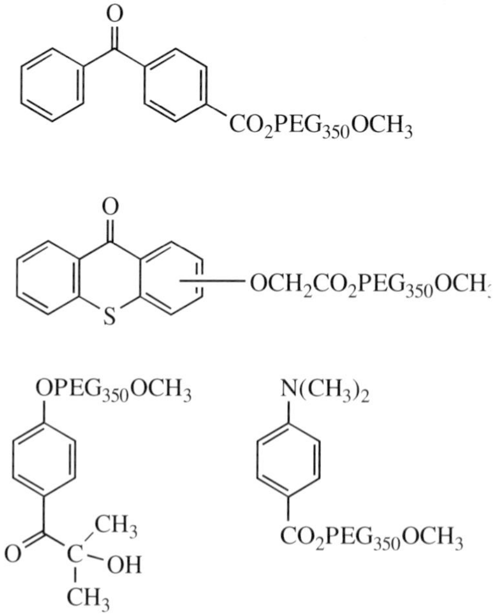

Figure 121: Some photoinitiators having polymer tails.

The effects that these chains have is to some extent determined by their molecular weight. The polyethylene and polypropylene chains impart water compatibility and both chains improve reactivity because they contain reactive C-H bonds which via hydrogen abstraction lead to crosslinking and initiation of polymerisation of acrylates and methacrylates. These latter reactions lead to immobilisation of the initiators and synergysts, and hence appending of the chains reduces the percentage of migrateable species in the cured coating and eliminates odour due to initiator residues. In some cases the appending of these polymer tails transforms a solid into a liquid initiator e.g. as is found for thioxanthones. There are also examples of the 2-ethylhexyl chain causing the same effect. An interesting and valuable finding is that the reactivity of the initiators is not diminished by appending these polymer tails and consequently these materials may be used at the same weight percentage in formulations as the unmodified materials. Thus a polyethyleneglycol ester of N,N-dimethylaminobenzoic acid could be used in a formulation at the same level as the ethyl ester and as a consequence the u.v. screening effect of the aromatic residue is markedly reduced and the percentage migrateables in the cured coating is reduced.

An attractive alternative to polymeric photoinitiators is to use a polymerisable photoinitiator i.e. an initiator to which the appropriate polymerisable group has been covalently attached. Thus a number of acrylated Type I photoinitiators which are aromatic ketones have been developed (Fig 122).[157, 176-181]

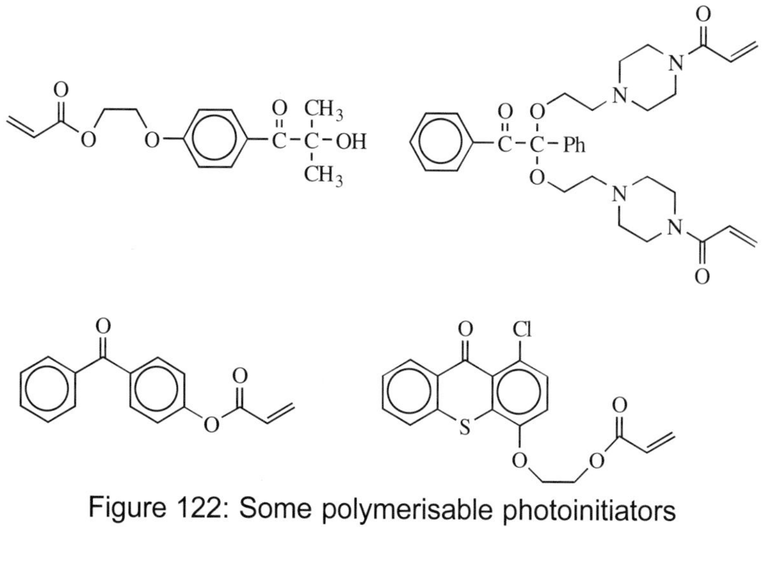

Figure 122: Some polymerisable photoinitiators

Provided the acrylate is introduced into the initiators in a manner that will not affect the photophysics of the initiator, excellent performance is usually observed. However, if the aim is to produce a system in which migratables are present at only very low levels, these initiators are not likely to fulfil the bill. It is very rare to find in a cured acrylate system that all the acrylate double bonds associated with the photoinitiator have been utilised. This being the case, and with the consideration of the low statistical probability that all the initiator will be polymerised into the system, it is highly unlikely that all the initiator will be rendered immobile. Factors that have not been included in the discussions are the extent to which crosslinking in the surface coating and the structures of the prepolymers will affect the percentage of unpolymerised initiator. These aspects will undoubtedly affect the degree of migration of small molecular species.

Some highly reactive α-aminoacetophenones have been functionalised by introducing a 3-mercaptopropylthio group at the 4 position[182]. The terminal mercapto group can be used to introduce the initiator into multifunctional acrylates using the Michael addition reaction.

Having recognised that a major problem of using high molecular weight initiators is that their use increases the viscosity of the formulation and that they have to be used at a higher level than their monomeric counterparts, and that polymerisable photoinitiators are not completely immobilised in the cured coating an alternative approach was sought. Compounds in which several photoinitiator molecules were tied to a central core were synthesised (Figure 123).

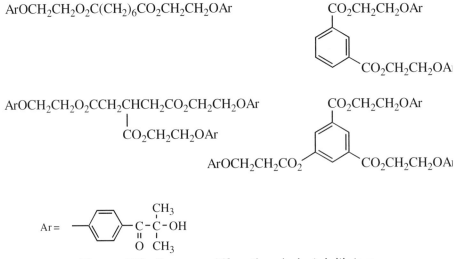

Figure 123: Some multifunctional photoinitiators

These compounds have been given the name multifunctional photoinitiators. If decomposition of one initiator residue failed to initiate polymerisation it was argued that provided one of the other residues was successful, immobilisation of initiator decomposition products would be achieved. This approach has been used with success with both Type I and II initiators. Since the molecular weight of the compounds is relatively low their addition does not increase the viscosity of formulations and their chance of being incorporated into the cured coating is much higher than for initiators carrying one polymerisable group. Recently 4-(2-hydroxyethoxy)-2-hydroxy-2-methyl propiophenone has been reacted with hexamethoxymethyl melamine in a trans etherification reaction leading to a multifunctional initiator. By introducing 2-hydroxyethyl acrylate into the reaction mixture, the initiator was additionally rendered polymerisable[183].

CHAPTER IV

ELECTRON BEAM CURING

CHAPTER IV

ELECTRON BEAM CURING

(i)   Interaction of Electron Beams with Matter

In an earlier section (Section I(iii)) it was pointed out that the interactions of high energy electrons with matter leads to ionisation. Ionisation results from inelastic collisions of fast electrons with the medium and in the process the electrons lose energy. An empirical relationship which links the energy of the electrons to the depth of penetration was obtained by Grun:[184]

$$R_G = 4.57 \, E_0^{1.75}$$

R_G = Grun range in µm; E_0 = energy of electron in keV

This relationship holds for a wide variety of materials e.g. polystyrene and aluminium. As the energy of the electrons increases, so is the penetration depth and as can be seen from Figure 124, for high energy electrons the amount of energy dissipated is small and constant over a large depth.

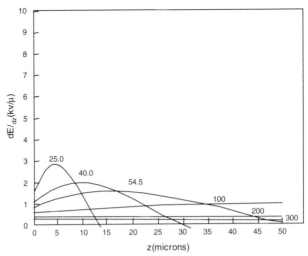

Figure 124: Penetration depth as a function of electron energy

Figure 125 shows a plot of the fractional loss in incident beam energy as a function of film thickness, for electrons accelerated at various stages. Most commercial e.b. accelerators work in the region of 150-300kV. This figure may be a bit misleading since the electrons will lose energy passing through the window (i.e. from the electron gun into the atmosphere above the coating,) and in traversing the layer of inerting gas above the coating. The purity of the nitrogen gas above the coating.

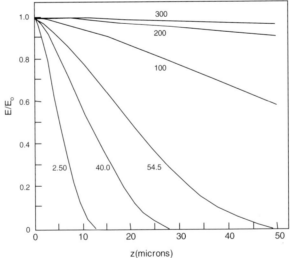

Figure 125: Fractional loss of an incident beam energy as a function of film thickness

The purity of the nitrogen gas above the coating can have a dramatic upon the cure efficiency (Figure 126).[16]

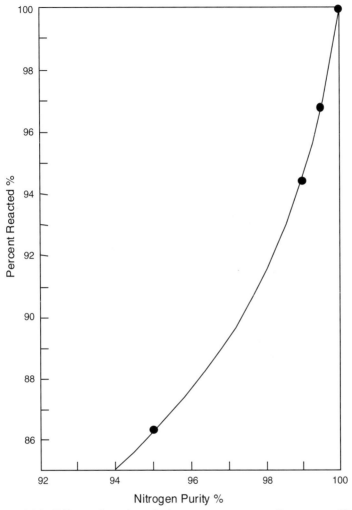

Figure 126: Effect of purity of nitrogen gas upon the cure efficiency

To attain through cure of any coating, it is essential to take account of energy losses in the window and in the passage through the inerting gas and in the coating itself. Factors which influence the latter are its thickness and its composition[185]. The stopping power (dE/ds) which is the energy loss per unit path length of an incident electron is related to the density of the medium and to the relative concentrations of the components and the molecular weights of these components.

Some of these factors will become important when pigments are incorporated since they will slow down the incident electrons without yielding useful species.[185] However, the "slowed down electrons" will more readily interact with the organic species.[186]

From the above discussion it will be appreciated that initiation of polymerisation by e.b. radiation is very different to that caused by u.v. radiation. Figure 127 shows that u.v.radiation leads to most events occurring near the surface of the coating (due to u.v. absorption being governed by the Beer Lambert Law), whereas with e.b., radical production occurs randomly throughout the coating.

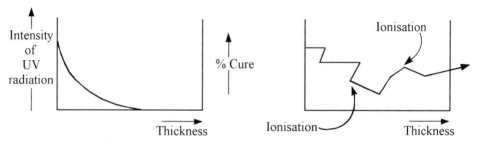

Figure 127: A comparison of absorption of u.v. light in a coating with e.b. radiation.

There is another important distinction between the two processes. In u.v. curing, reaction is brought about via the photoinitiator which causes reaction via the polymerisable group. Further crosslinking is caused by groups such as benzoyl (from the photoinitiators) introduced into the polymer during polymerisation but this occurs at a late stage i.e. at a high u.v. dosage. With e.b. radiation, ionisation is non specific and thus radicals are generated in the backbone of both the diluent and the prepolymer. As a consequence, crosslinking, other than that due to polymerisable groups, is occurring at a much earlier stage in e.b. than in u.v. cured coatings. These effects can influence the properties of a cured film in important ways. Figure 128[185] shows that e.b. radiation of a mixture of a urethane acrylate and diluents leads to increasing hardness as the concentration of diluent is increased, whereas the opposite is true for the u.v. cured coatings.

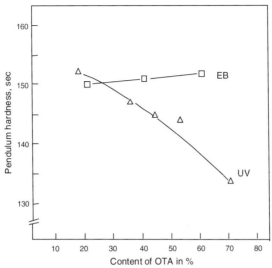

Figure 128: Differences in coating properties in films cured by e.b. and u.v. radiation (diluent OTA in a prepolymer)

For e.b. radiation to be effective it is necessary for the coating to contain ionisable groups. Alkanes ionise to give cation radicals and these may decompose to give hydrogen atoms and carbon centred radicals or may lead to fission of the alkane chain (Figure 129).

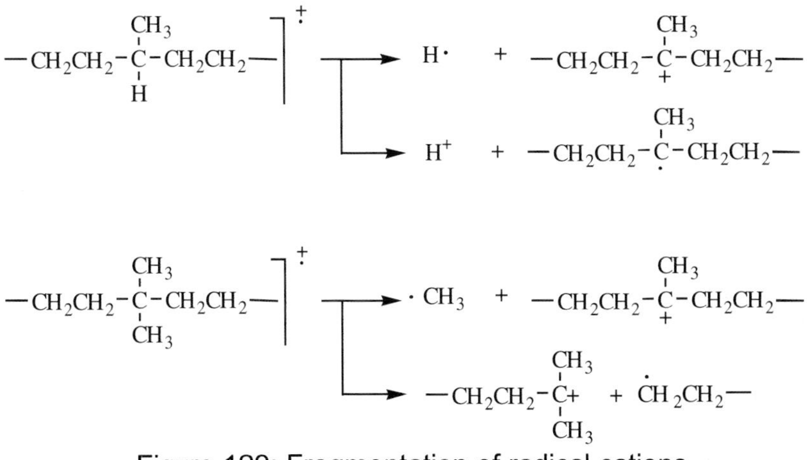

Figure 129: Fragmentation of radical cations

Groups which aid ionisation include ether groups and these can give rise to α-alkoxyalkyl radicals. Thus the presence of poly(ethyleneoxy) and poly(propyleneoxy) groups can often increase the sensitivity of the formulation towards e.b. radiation. Aromatic groups have an obvious potential for ionisation. Electron rich aromatics can be tolerated in e.b. formulations and in some cases can be of positive benefit. However, aromatics containing groups (usually electron withdrawing) which stabilise radical anions can have a deleterious effect since such groups scavenge the low energy electron. Examples of this phenomenon include aromatic nitro and azo compounds. For this reason the presence of azo pigments will slow down the rate of cure.

(ii)   Utilisation of Free Radical Curing Systems

For the production of surface coatings, acrylates are most commonly used because of their availability and speed of cure. The closely related methacrylates are not used as frequently because of their slow cure speed. Acrylates are polymerised via acrylate groups scavenging the low energy electrons yielding radical anions which are subsequently protonated (via the presence of adventitious water) to give an initiating radical.

The rate of cure will be highly dependent upon the yield of low energy electrons. Thus the presence of easily ionisable groups is highly adventitious. It will have been noted that the ionisation process produces two oppositely charged species.

$$M \rightarrow M^{+\cdot} + e$$

These two species must separate and the low energy electron be efficiently scavenged by species that give initiating radicals. Clearly the higher the concentration of acrylate groups the more efficient will be the scavenging. Aromatic groups frequently ionise readily but the recombination process is often highly efficient (Equation 14).

Equation 14:   Ionisation of aromatic hydrocarbons

$$ArH \xrightarrow{\text{e b}} ArH \overset{\bullet}{+} + \; e \longrightarrow (ArH)^*$$

$(ArH)^*$ = an excited state - either singlet of triplet

This recombination process can be rendered less efficient by using compounds which undergo dissociative electron capture (Equation 15).

Equation 15:   Dissociative electron capture

$$ArHal \xrightarrow{\text{e b}} ArHal \overset{\cdot}{+} + e \longrightarrow (ArHal)^*$$

$$\longrightarrow Ar\cdot + Hal^- + e$$

$$(ArHal)^* = \text{An excited state}$$

The presence of haloaromatics in e.b. curable formulations has been shown to be of positive benefit.

Acrylate formulations containing a high loading of pigments can often be successfully cured by e.b. radiation. The pigments do affect the passage of electrons through the coating since they, by virtue of their mass, will react with the radiation. Many other pigments, e.g. azo dyes and phthalocyanines, may slow the cure rate by scavenging the low energy electrons. Many inorganic pigments will scavenge the low energy electrons due to the presence of defect sites e.g. as can be found in some samples of titanium oxide.

(iii)   Utilisation of Cationic Curing Systems

Cationic curing systems depend upon the radiation releasing as an acid - either Lewis or Bronsted. It is for this reason that <u>cationic photoinitiators</u> are added to the formulation. We have seen these compounds can be reductively fragmented either by electrons or radicals. Slow electrons can reduce species like onium salts and ferrocenium salts. The radicals generated by ionisation of the medium are the source of the protons (Figure 130).

$$-CH_2O- \xrightarrow{\text{e.b.}} \left[CH_2O\right]^{\overset{\cdot}{+}} + e$$

$$\left[CH_2O\right]^{\overset{\cdot}{+}} \longrightarrow -\overset{\cdot}{C}HO- + H^+$$

$$-\overset{\cdot}{C}HO- + ArI^+PF_6^- \longrightarrow -\overset{+}{C}HO- + ArI + Ar\cdot + PF_6^-$$

$$e + ArI^+PF_6^- \longrightarrow ArI + Ar\cdot + PF_6^-$$

Figure 130: Liberation of acid from cationic photoinitiators under
e.b. radiation

Epoxide groups do ionise upon e.b. radiation but the process does not lead to cationic cure (Figure 131).[187]

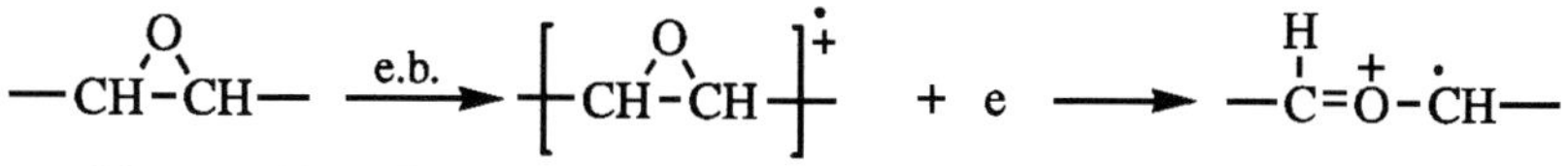

$$-\overset{O}{\underset{CH-CH-}{\diagdown}} \quad \xrightarrow{e.b.} \quad \left[\overset{O}{\underset{CH-CH}{\diagdown}} \right]^{\overset{\bullet}{+}} \quad + \quad e \quad \longrightarrow \quad -\overset{H}{\underset{C=\overset{+}{O}-\overset{\bullet}{C}H-}{|}}$$

Figure 131: Fragmentation of epoxides upon e.b. radiation

Vinyl ethers no doubt ionise readily but this does not lead directly to species that can initiate cationic cure.

It will have been noted that reductive decomposition of onium salts give free radicals and consequently e.b. curing of a mixture of epoxides and acrylates can lead to cure via both the functional groups. This was clearly demonstrated with the epoxy acrylate shown in Figure 100 using i.r. spectroscopy.[142]

Whilst in principle pigmented cationic coating formulations may be cured by e.b., the pigment may interfere by reacting with the acid released by the radiation.

CHAPTER V

PRODUCTION OF SURFACE COATINGS USING FREE RADICAL REACTIONS

CHAPTER V

PRODUCTION OF SURFACE COATINGS USING FREE RADICAL REACTIONS

(i)   Oxygen Inhibition[22, 188]

Oxygen inhibition not only reduces the rate of cure but also affects the properties of the coating by reducing kinetic chain length (and hence molecular weight) and by introducing oxygenated species into the coating.

The presence of oxygen in a coating formulation can lead to quenching the active excited state of the photoinitiator, scavenging the radicals generated by the initiator and scavenging of the growing macro radicals.

Type I photoinitiators usually have very short triplet lifetimes and hence do not suffer extensively from oxygen inhibition. This is not the case with Type II systems which involve a bimolecular reaction between the triplet initiator and the synergist. Oxygen will also compete with the amine synergist for the triplet ketone. Given that the concentration of oxygen in the coating will be 10^{-3} to 10^{-2}M, the synergist concentration needs to be at least ten times this value to ensure triplet-synergist interaction is effective. Thus use of 5% w/w of N-methyldiethanolamine as synergist is equivalent to approximately 0.5M which is substantially higher than the oxygen concentration.

Type I photoinitiators yield two radicals upon cleavage, both of which may be scavenged by oxygen as is found with acylphosphine oxides. The performance of this class of initiator is dramatically affected by the presence of oxygen and it was shown that both radicals are effectively scavenged by oxygen (Figure 132).[189]

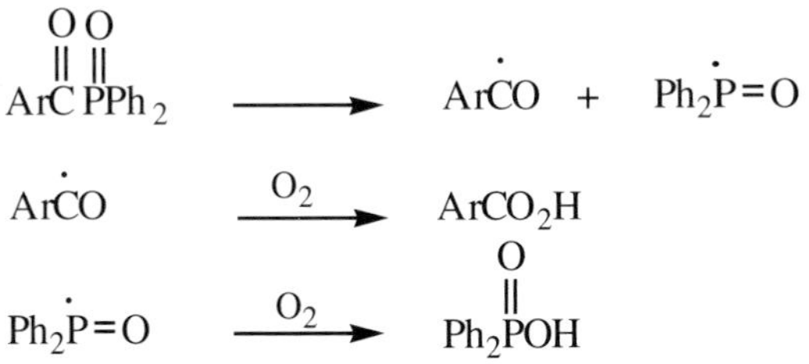

$$\underset{ArC\overset{\displaystyle O}{\overset{\|}{}}\overset{\displaystyle O}{\overset{\|}{}}PPh_2}{} \longrightarrow Ar\overset{\bullet}{C}O + Ph_2\overset{\bullet}{P}{=}O$$

$$Ar\overset{\bullet}{C}O \xrightarrow{O_2} ArCO_2H$$

$$Ph_2\overset{\bullet}{P}{=}O \xrightarrow{O_2} Ph_2\overset{\displaystyle O}{\overset{\|}{P}}OH$$

Figure 132: Reaction of oxygen with radicals generated by cleaving an acylphosphine oxide

As an example of how oxygen inhibition affects Type II initiator systems consideration of the benzophenone - N-methyldiethanolamine is instructive (Figure 133).

1. $Ph_2CO_{S_0} \xrightarrow{h\nu} Ph_2CO_{S_1} \xrightarrow{I.S.C.} Ph_2CO_{T_1}$

2. $Ph_2CO_{T_1} + {}^3O_2 \longrightarrow Ph_2CO_{S_0} + {}^3O_2$ Oxygen quenching of triplet ketone

3. $Ph_2CO_{T_1} + CH_3N(CH_2CH_2OH)_2 \longrightarrow Ph_2\overset{\bullet}{C}OH + \overset{\bullet}{C}H_2N(CH_2CH_2OH)_2$

4. $Ph_2CO_{T_1} + CH_3N(CH_2CH_2OH)_2 \longrightarrow Ph_2\overset{\bullet}{C}OH + HOCH_2\overset{\bullet}{C}HN(CH_3)CH_2CH_2OH$

5. $Ph_2\overset{\bullet}{C}OH + {}^3O_2 \longrightarrow Ph_2CO + H\overset{\bullet}{O}_2$

6. $\overset{\bullet}{C}H_2N(CH_2CH_2OH)_2 + {}^3O_2 \longrightarrow \bullet OOCH_2N(CH_2CH_2OH)_2$

7. $HOCH_2\overset{\bullet}{C}HN(CH_3)CH_2CH_2OH + {}^3O_2 \longrightarrow \underset{\underset{OO\bullet}{|}}{HOCH_2CHN(CH_3)CH_2CH_2OH}$

8. $\bullet OOCH_2N(CH_2CH_2OH)_2 + CH_3N(CH_2CH_2OH)_2 \longrightarrow \begin{array}{c} \overset{\bullet}{C}H_2N(CH_2CH_2OH)_2 \\ + \\ HOOCH_2N(CH_2CH_2OH)_2 \end{array}$

9. $\overset{\bullet}{C}H_2N(CH_2CH_2OH)_2 + $ Acrylate $\longrightarrow$ Polymer

10. $HOCH_2\overset{\bullet}{C}HN(CH_3)CH_2CH_2OH + $ Acrylate $\longrightarrow$ Polymer

Figure 133: Reaction of triplet benzophenone with N-methyldiethanolamine with an acrylate in presence of oxygen

Equation 1 of the Figure describes the population of triplet benzophenone and equation 2 shows how the triplet state is deactivated by oxygen via the energy transfer which leads to the production of singlet oxygen. This highly reactive species can also react with the amine to generate a reactive α-aminoalkyl radical (Figure 134) and this reaction contributes to the effectiveness of tertiary amines in overcoming oxygen inhibition.

$$^1O_2 \; + \; CH_3N(CH_2CH_2OH)_2 \longrightarrow H\dot{O}_2 \; + \; \dot{C}H_2N(CH_2CH_2OH)_2$$

$$H\dot{O}_2 \; + \; CH_3N(CH_2CH_2OH)_2 \longrightarrow H_2O_2 \; + \; \dot{C}H_2N(CH_2CH_2OH)_2$$

Figure 134: Reaction of singlet oxygen with a tertiary amine

Equations 3 and 4 of the Figure show how the triplet ketone reacts with the tertiary amine. In principle, two types of aminoalkyl radical may be generated and the evidence to date suggests that attack on the methyl group predominates.[190] In both reactions 3 and 4 the benzophenone ketyl radical is generated and this reacts with oxygen, as shown in equation 5, to generate a hydroperoxy radical which can in turn react withe amine (Figure 134) which in turn generates another α-aminoalkyl radical. The α-aminoalkyl radicals generated in reactions 3 and 4, react with oxygen to give peroxy radicals (equations 6 and 7) which in turn react with the amine generating α-aminoalkyl radicals.

Usually the aromatic amines that are used as synergists contain N,N-dimethylamino groups e.g. ethyl 4-N,N-dimethylaminobenzoate. With these amines hydroperoxide formation occurs in a similar way to that exhibited by N-methyldiethanolamine (Figure 135). When N,N-dimethylaniline is used the intermediate α-aminoalkyl radical gives rise to demethylation. Whether this occurs or not with esters of the type shown in Figure 134 has not been demonstrated.

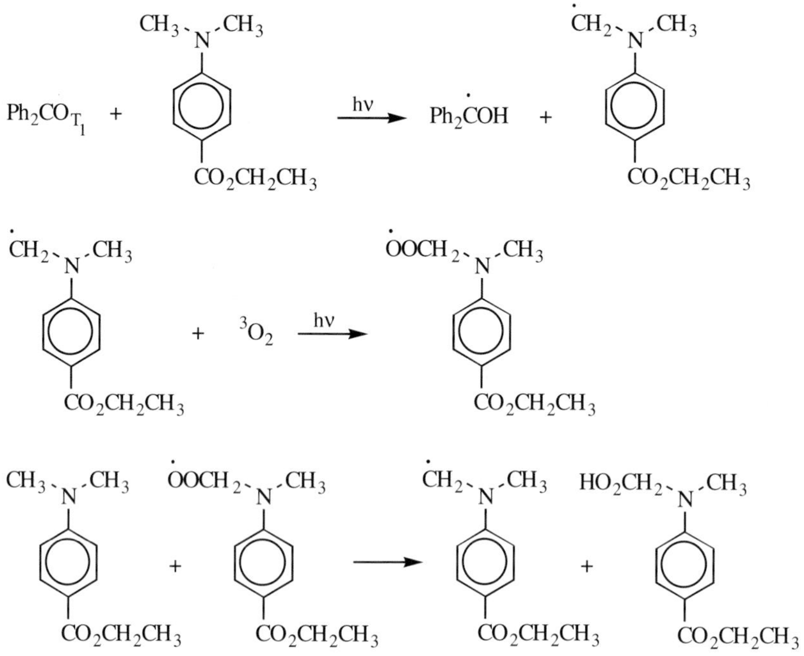

Figure 135: Use of an aromatic amine to reduce oxygen inhibition

Two features are common to the processes involving aliphatic and aromatic amines. Firstly, the amines are consumed in a chain reaction and it is this reaction which reduces the concentration of oxygen in the film. For the amines to reduce oxygen inhibition effectively, the depletion of oxygen must occur more rapidly than the ingress of oxygen into the coating. Thus high light intensities aid the process. Furthermore, if cure is very slow, the amine may well be consumed to a considerable extent before a reasonable degree of cure is achieved. A second feature that it is common to both aromatic and aliphatic amines is that α-hydroxyperoxyamines are produced curing. It is entirely possible that these species will undergo further reaction to yield coloured products that will provide sites for further photoreactions if the coatings are exposed to daylight. Since the efficiency of an amine as a synergist and its ability to reduce oxygen inhibition is related to the reactivity of its α-C-H bonds, so is its potential for stimulating photoyellowing when the cured films are weathered.[96] A polymerisation system that is less to oxygen is that of the vinyl ether-maleate ester system that was discussed earlier (Section II(i)(d)).

A radical mediated photoinduced polymerisation process that does not suffer from oxygen inhibition is the thiol-ene reaction (Section II(i)(c)) since in this case the reaction of the hydroperoxyl radicals with the thiol generates initiating radicals.

(ii) Factors Affecting the Degree of Cure in Acrylate and Methacrylate Systems

Most curing systems involve the photoinduced transformation of a liquid into a solid. One might expect therefore that as cure progresses the viscosity of the mixture will increase until a gel is produced and this in turn will undergo curing until vitrification takes place. The curing of a monoacrylate leads to a linear polymer and often the product is a soft solid or a liquid. Although as cure proceeds of these materials, there will be a rise in viscosity, the system remains sufficiently fluid so as to allow a high percentage utilisation of the acrylate double bonds (often approaching 100%). If the polymerisation is initiated by a benzoyl or substituted benzoyl radical, secondary crosslinking reactions may also occur which means that monoacrylates can give rise to lightly crosslinked coatings (Figure 136).

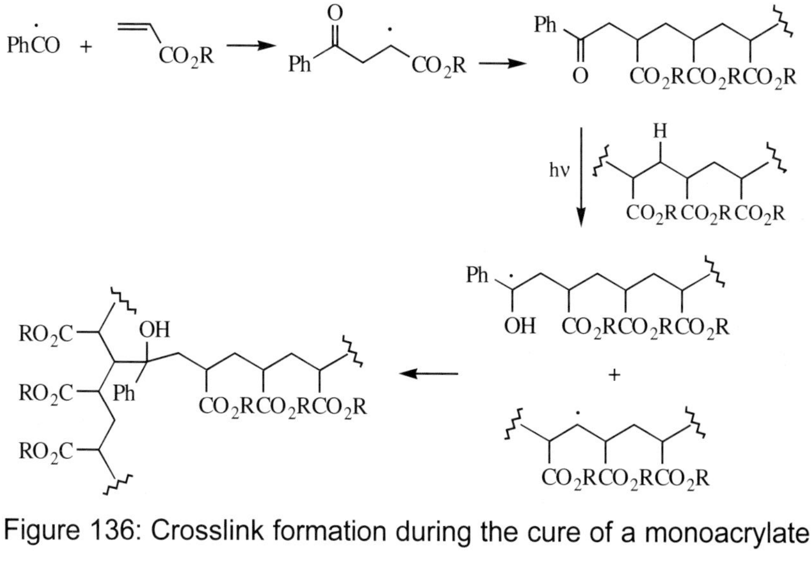

Figure 136: Crosslink formation during the cure of a monoacrylate

When a diacrylate is used crosslinks are formed and hence the onset of gelation and vitrification occurs at a much earlier stage than with monoacrylates. This early occurrence of vitrification leads to the "freezing out" of some double bonds and as a consequence, the cured coatings contain unreacted acrylate groups. Such groups are consumed on prolonged irradiation of the coating via "radical transfer" through the coating (Figure 137).[27]

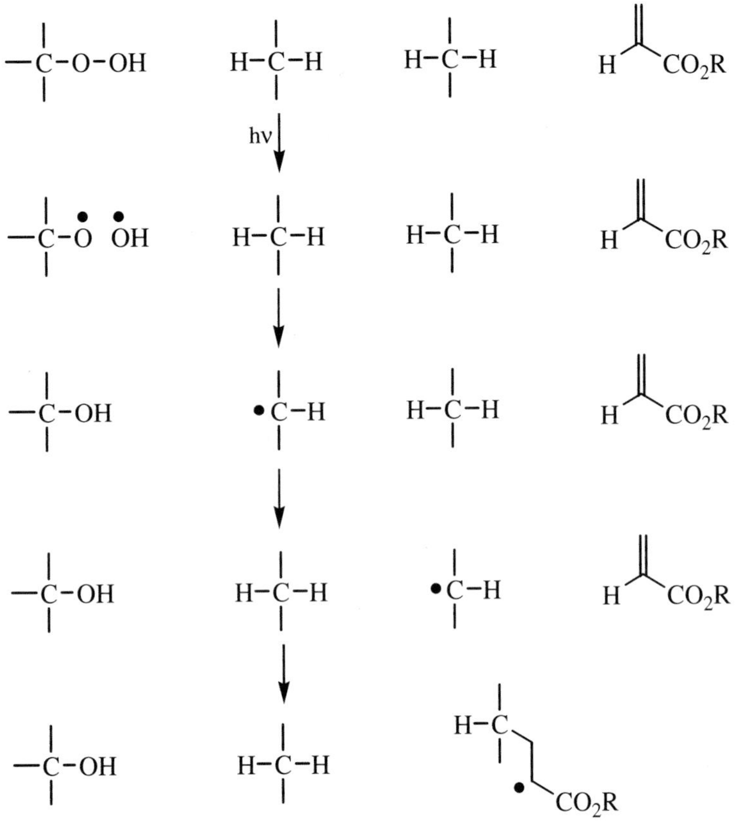

$$-\overset{|}{\underset{|}{C}}-O-OH \qquad H-\overset{|}{\underset{|}{C}}-H \qquad H-\overset{|}{\underset{|}{C}}-H \qquad H\overset{\diagup\diagdown}{\underset{CO_2R}{\diagup\diagdown}}$$

$$\Big\downarrow h\nu$$

$$-\overset{|}{\underset{|}{C}}-\overset{\bullet}{O}\;\;\overset{\bullet}{OH} \qquad H-\overset{|}{\underset{|}{C}}-H \qquad H-\overset{|}{\underset{|}{C}}-H \qquad H\overset{\diagup\diagdown}{\underset{CO_2R}{\diagup\diagdown}}$$

$$\Big\downarrow$$

$$-\overset{|}{\underset{|}{C}}-OH \qquad \bullet\overset{|}{\underset{|}{C}}-H \qquad H-\overset{|}{\underset{|}{C}}-H \qquad H\overset{\diagup\diagdown}{\underset{CO_2R}{\diagup\diagdown}}$$

$$\Big\downarrow$$

$$-\overset{|}{\underset{|}{C}}-OH \qquad H-\overset{|}{\underset{|}{C}}-H \qquad \bullet\overset{|}{\underset{|}{C}}-H \qquad H\overset{\diagup\diagdown}{\underset{CO_2R}{\diagup\diagdown}}$$

$$\Big\downarrow$$

$$-\overset{|}{\underset{|}{C}}-OH \qquad H-\overset{|}{\underset{|}{C}}-H \qquad\qquad \begin{matrix} H-\overset{|}{\underset{|}{C}} \\ \bullet\diagdown_{CO_2R}\end{matrix}$$

Further reaction with acrylate groups, CH bonds of oxygen

Figure 137: Utilisation of acrylate groups in a vitrified coating of a diacrylate

When considering the curing of a diacrylate the question arises as to whether the acrylate groups in the diacrylate are more reactive than the pendant acrylate groups (A) generated in the curing process (Figure 138).

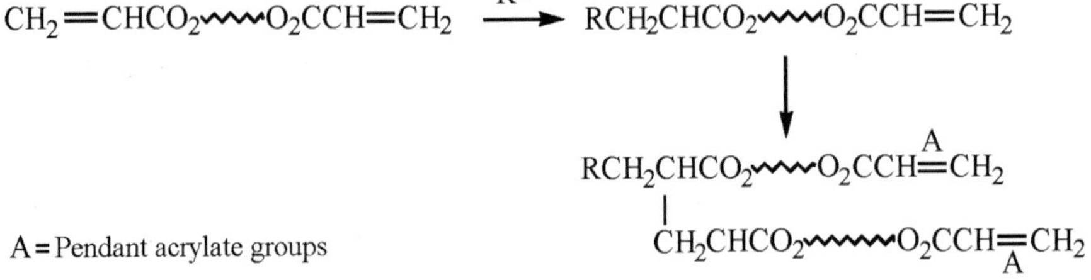

$$CH_2{=}CHCO_2\text{\small\wedge\wedge\wedge}O_2CCH{=}CH_2 \xrightarrow{\;R\bullet\;} RCH_2\overset{\bullet}{C}HCO_2\text{\small\wedge\wedge\wedge}O_2CCH{=}CH_2$$

$$\Big\downarrow$$

$$RCH_2CHCO_2\text{\small\wedge\wedge\wedge}O_2CC\overset{A}{H{=}}CH_2$$
$$\underset{CH_2CHCO_2\text{\small\wedge\wedge\wedge\wedge}O_2CC\underset{A}{H{=}}CH_2}{|}$$

A = Pendant acrylate groups

Figure 138: Polymerisation of a diacrylate

Careful studies have shown that the pendant groups are more reactive.[191] A modelling study using the percolation theory[192] shows that the growth of the polymer occurs in discrete areas rather than the polymer growing randomly throughout the matrix. This development of discrete areas of polymerisation can lead to areas of unreacted material and to phase separation. A further ramification is that reaction of the pendant groups gives rise to cyclic structures at the expense of crosslink formation and hence the crosslink density in the cured coating is reduced. This problem may be overcome by using diacrylates that possess a rigid interconnecting framework.

The curing of tri- and higher functionality leads to an even higher density of crosslinks and even more rapid onset of gelation and vitrification. This can reduce the extent of utilisation of acrylate double bonds by 40-50% (Figure 139) [193].

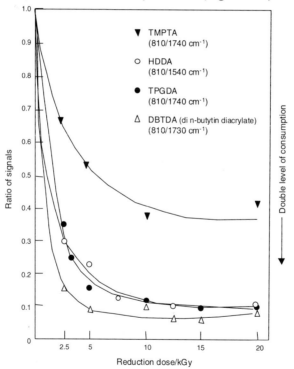

Figure 139: Consumption of double bonds as a function of dose in e.b. curing of mono- and polyfuctional acrylates

The onset of gelation can be retarded by increasing the temperature at which curing occurs (Figure 140) [194]. It is in these circumstances that the heat of reaction and the heat generated by the lamps becomes valuable.

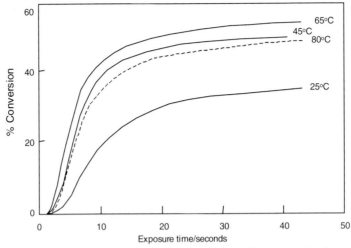

Figure 140: Effect of temperature upon the extent of cure

The glass transition temperature (Tg) of cured films is dependent upon the temperature at which cure occurs and this is an important fact to be borne in mind when attempting to maximise the mechanical performance of coatings or composites.

(iii)   Choice of Amine Synergist[22, 195]

Both aliphatic and aromatic amines are used as synergists for the reducing the effect of oxygen inhibition. Two factors need to be considered when deciding which type of synergist to use. The u.v. absorption properties of the aliphatic and aromatic amines are very different (Figure 141).

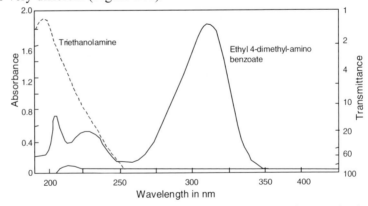

Figure 141: U.v. absorption spectra of triethanolamine and ethyl
4-N,N-dimethylaminobenzoate

If simple benzophenone derivatives are to be used the aromatic amine screens some of the light which could be usefully used by the aromatic ketone. Use of the alkanolamine does not present this problem and hence for benzophenone the aliphatic rather than the aromatic amine is a better choice. Recent work has shown that poly(ethylene glycol) and poly(propylene glycol) esters of N,N-dimethylaminobenzoic acid can be used in place of ethyl N,N-dimethylaminobenzoate with less attendant screening. If thioxanthones are being used, their strong absorption in the 330-400nm region means that an aromatic amine can be used without detriment to the cure rate. Another important factor is the solubility of the amine in water since in some processes, e.g. in lithographic printing, the coating comes into contact with water. The aromatic amines, unless specifically modified, are hydrophobic whereas triethanolamine is quite water-soluble and consequently aromatic amines are preferred for this application. The least hydrophilic of the commonly used aliphatic amines is N,N-dimethylethanolamine.

Nearly all the amine synergists have a relatively low molecular weight and therefore can migrate in the cured coatings. In order to reduce this tendency, polymerisable amines e.g. 2-dimethylaminoethyl acrylate have been made commercially available. An alternative strategy is to introduce a few amine groups into a multifunctional acrylate via the Michael addition reaction (Figure 142).[196]

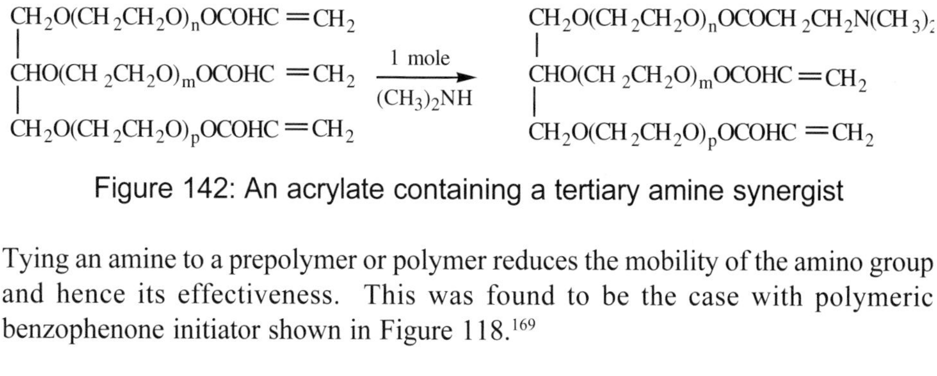

$$CH_2O(CH_2CH_2O)_nOCOHC=CH_2$$
$$|$$
$$CHO(CH_2CH_2O)_mOCOHC=CH_2 \xrightarrow[\text{(CH}_3)_2\text{NH}]{\text{1 mole}}$$
$$|$$
$$CH_2O(CH_2CH_2O)_pOCOHC=CH_2$$

$$CH_2O(CH_2CH_2O)_nOCOCH_2CH_2N(CH_3)_2$$
$$|$$
$$CHO(CH_2CH_2O)_mOCOHC=CH_2$$
$$|$$
$$CH_2O(CH_2CH_2O)_pOCOHC=CH_2$$

Figure 142: An acrylate containing a tertiary amine synergist

Tying an amine to a prepolymer or polymer reduces the mobility of the amino group and hence its effectiveness. This was found to be the case with polymeric benzophenone initiator shown in Figure 118.[169]

In another study it was shown that the use of a mixture of polymeric aromatic ketone initiator and a polymeric amine synergist was far less efficient than a mixture of their monomeric counterparts thus emphasising the importance of mobility.[167]

An alternative and very useful approach is to link an amine synergist to a relativly low molecular weight polymer that contains reactive C-H bonds which will facilitate crosslinking.

Esterification of 4-N,N-dimethylaminobenzoic acid with a poly(ethylene glycol) monomethyl ether (average molecular weight 350 to 550) gives a liquid synergist of high reactivity which is effectively immobilised in the coating[155]. The immobilisation is in part due to the crosslinking reactions which take place in the polyether chain.

A very recent approach of great promise is to use dendritic amines[197] (Figure 143).

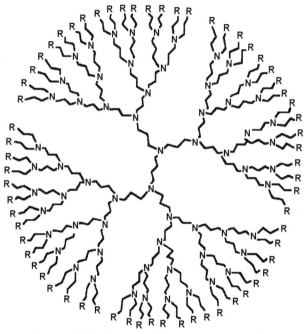

Figure 143: A dendritic amine synergist

As the generation of the dendrimer increases so the molecular weight increase but as with other dendrimers this is not accompanied by a large increase in viscosity. It is also interesting to find that 2-cyanoethylamines behave as synergists. These components are so readily prepared from a primary amine and acrylonitrile.

(iv)   Choice of Reactive Diluent for Acrylate and Methacrylate Based Systems[9]

Reactive diluents serve at least two purposes. The prime purpose is to reduce the viscosity of the prepolymers so that the mixture has an acceptable working viscosity. A second useful feature is that by using multifunctional diluents, the overall reactivity of the system can be increased. This is particularly valuable with prepolymers that may only contain acrylates at the termini of high molecular weight linear chains. Reactive diluents may also be used for other purposes. If a monoacrylate is used which possesses a long alkyl chain (e.g. isodecyl acrylate), the long chain will act as a plasticiser thereby increasing the flexibility of the coating.

Monoacrylates possessing bicyclic substituents such as bornyl or dicyclopentadiene derivatives impart hardness despite the fact that they are monosubstituted. Heavy chlorine substitution in the side chain aids adhesion to polymers such as PVC. Fluorinated acrylates[198] can be used to impart scratch resistance and resistance to soiling and graffiti. Use of diluents that contain groups which can give rise to water solubility or compatibility (e.g. CO_2H, OH, ammonium ions) of the curable coating are valuable in the production of waterborne coatings.

Table 2: Mono (meth)acrylates

Name	Uses/properties - Supplier
n-Butyl acrylate	Low viscosity and b.p./low reactivity
Iso-decyl acrylate	Increases flexibility of films/low reactivity
Lauryl acrylate	Increases flexibility of films/low reactivity
Stearyl acrylate	Increases flexibility of films/low reactivity/ increases water resistance
Iso-bornyl acrylate	Increases hardness without crosslinking/high reactivity - Henkel
Formyl acetal of trimethylolpropane monoacrylate	Increases hardness without crosslinking/high reactivity - Servo
Furfuryl acrylate	
Tetrahydrofurfuryl acrylate - caprolactone modified	Low odour & irritancy/high reactivity/increases flexibility
Terahydrofurfuryl acrylate	
Trifluoroethyl acrylate	Introduces surface active groups/improves slip - San Esters

Heptafluorodecyl acrylate	Introduces surface active groups/improves slip - San Esters
Ethoxyethyl methacrylate	Good diluent, low shrinkage
2-Phenoxyethyl acrylate	Forms tacky coatings-adhesives - Henkel
Phenol ethoxylate monoacrylate	Low odour & irritancy/increases flexibility - Henkel
Nonyl phenol ethoxylate monoacrylate	Low odour/medium viscosity/ increases flexibility/improves pigment wetting - Henkel
Nonyl phenol propoxylate monoacrylate	Low odour/medium viscosity/ increases flexibility/improves pigment wetting - Henkel
Phenyl glycidyl ether acrylate	Good adhesion/increases flexibility - Nippon Kayaku
2-Hydroxyethyl acrylate	Improve adhesion/water compatibility/ intermediate in synthesis
4-Hydroxybutyl acrylate	Improve adhesion/water compatibility/ intermediate in synthesis
6-Hydroxyhexyl acrylate	Produces a functionalised polymer and promotes adhesion - San Esters Corporation
2-Hydroxypropyl acrylate	Improve adhesion/water compatibility/ intermediate in synthesis
2-Ethoxyethoxyethyl acrylate	Reactive monoacrylate - San Esters Corporation
Polyethylene glycol monoacrylate	Increases flexibility/introduces reactive group/ aids water compatiblity - ISP
Polypropylene glycol monoacrylate	Increases flexibility/introduces reactive group - ISP
Methoxyhexan-6-ol acrylate	Fast cure,low viscosity,low shrinkage
Tripropyleneglycol monomethyl ether monoacrylate	Fast cure,low viscosity,low shrinkage
Ethoxylated neopentyl glycol monomethyl ether monoacrylate	Fast cure,low viscosity,low shrinkage
Acrylic acid	Introducing acidic groups/intermediate in synthesis

2-Hydroxyethyl phthalate monomethacrylate	Introduces acidic group/water compatible systems - ISP
2-Hydroxyethyl maleate monomethacrylate	Introduces acidic group,improves adhesion, with vinyl ethers - Hampford Research
Phosphate of 2-hydroxyethyl acrylate	Promotes adhesion - Nippon Kayaku
Phosphate of caprolactone modified 2-hydroxyethyl methacrylate	Promotes adhesion, low odour and skin irritancy - Nippon Kayaku
Bis(2-hydroxyethyl methacrylate)phosphate	Promotes adhesion - Hampford Research
Ammonium sulfatoethyl methacrylate	Water compatible systems - ISP
Dimethylaminoethyl acrylate	Polymerisable synergist,adhesion promoter, useful for dual cure with epoxides - CPS Chem.Company
Terabutylaminoethyl methacrylate	Adhesion promoter, antistatic formulations - CPS Chem.Company
2-Methacryloyloxyphenylurethane	- Hampford Research
Glycidyl acrylate	Introduces reactive epoxide group
Allyl methacrylate	Introduces crosslinking group,precursor for methacrylated siloxanes
2-Isocyanotoethyl methacrylate	Introduces group useful for crosslinking in a thermal reaction

In many cases the acrylate or methacrylate equivalents of the compounds shown are available

Table 3: Some Difunctional (meth)acrylates

Name	Uses/properties
Ethylene glycol dimethacrylate	Reactive, abrasion resistance - CPS Chem. Company
1,3-Butylene glycol dimethacrylate	- CPS Chem. Company

Butane-1,4-diol diacrylate	High reactivity, high crosslink density
Hexane-1,6-diol diacrylate	High reactivity, high crosslink density
Fatty acid diol diacrylate	Introduces flexibility - Servo Delden
Triethylene glycol dimethacrylate	High reactivity, high crosslink density
Tetraethylene glycol diacrylate	Aids water compatibility and adhesion
Dipropyleneglycol diacrylate	Low viscosity, low volatility, high cure speed
Tripropylene glycol diacrylate	High reactivity, good solvent
Neopentylglycol diacrylate	
Polyethylene glycol diacrylates	Available in various mol. weights, softens films, aids flexibility
Polypropylene glycol diacrylate	Available in various mol. weights, softens films, aids flexibility
Ethoxylated hexane-1,6-diol diacrylate	High reactivity, low irritancy
Ethoxylated neopentylglycol diacrylate	
Ethoxylated trimethylolpropane methoxy diacrylate	
Propoxylated trimethylolpropane methoxydiacrlate	
Hydroxypivalaldehyde/ trimethylolpropane diacrylate	Hard films, high cure speed, low skin irritation - Nippon Kayaku
Tricyclodecane dimethanol diacrylate	Good heat and chemical resistance, hard films - Nippon Kayaku
Epoxyacrylate of hexane-1,6-diol diacrylate	High cure speed, moderate flexibility - Nippon Kayaku
Diacrylate of ethylene oxide modified bisphenol A	Low odour and skin irritation, high cure speed - Nippon Kayaku
Diacrylate of caprolactone modifiedneopentylglycol hydroxypivalate ester	Low odour and skin irritation, high cure speed, low shrinkage - Nippon Kayaku

The acrylate and methacrylate equivalents of the compounds shown can usually be obtained

Table 4: Some tri and higher functionality (meth)acrylates

Name	Uses/properties
Trimethylol propane triacrylate	High reactivity, good miscibility with prepolymers
Propoxylated trimethylolpropane triacrylate	
Ethoxlated trimethylolpropane triacrylate	
Glycerol triacrylate	
Propoxylated glycerol triacrylate	
Pentaerythritol triacrylate	High viscosity due to hydroxyl group
Ethoxylated pentaerythritol triacrylate	Low skin irritation,low odour and volatility
Pentaerythritol tetraacrylate	High reactivity,high crosslink density
Ethoxylated pentaerythritol tetraacrylate	Low skin irritation,low odour and volatility - Servo Delden
Ditrimethylolpropane teraacrylate	High reactivity,high crosslink density
Dipentaerythritol penta acrylate	High reactivity,high crosslink density
Dipentaerythritol hexa acrylate	High reactivity,high crosslink density
Hexa acrylate of caprolactone modified pentaerythritol	Low skin irritation,low odour and volatility, high reactivity

A range of reactive diluents is listed according to degree of functionality in Tables 2,3 and 4. Usually the methacrylate equivalents are available.

A very important aspect of the diluents is their toxicity. Because most of the compounds are of relatively low molecular weight, they have relatively high vapour pressures. This facilitates ingesting by inhalation. Also their low molecular weight aids their transport through the skin. Acrylates, and to a lesser extent methacrylates, can induce an allergic response and some individuals can become sensitised to them.[199] Most of the diluents are classed as irritants and such is the irritancy of some of the compounds that their use is banned for the production of certain goods. Thus the excellent diluent hexane-1,6-diol diacrylate HDDA in inks and coatings is not allowed in the UK. To overcome this problem many of the diluents have had their molecular weights increased by introducing ethoxy and propoxy groups so as to reduce the concentration of acrylate groups per mole of diluent (Figure 144).[200]

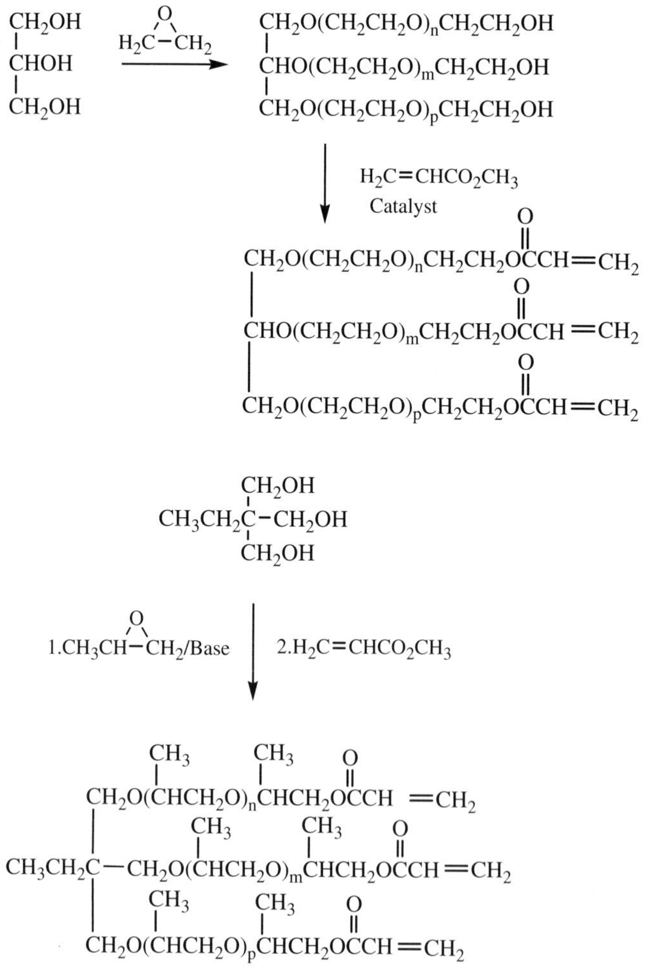

Figure 144: An ethoxylated and a propoxylated reactive diluent

These groups do introduce reactive C-H bonds that are susceptible to radical attack and which can give rise crosslinking and reduce sensitivity to oxygen inhibition. The poly(ethyleneoxy) group introduces water compatibility thereby making them useful in water-based formulations[201]. Another very useful diluent is N-vinyl pyrrolidone since it displays high reactivity, good solubilising power. When used in formulations that are applied to plastic substrates it softens the surface thereby enabling the formulation to penetrate and consequently the cured films exhibit good adhesion. Unfortunately it may have some undesirable toxicological properties and consequently formulators are now more reluctant to use it. An alternative compound is N-vinylcaprolactam and this is enjoying some popularity[202] although for some applications the hydrolytic instability of the lactam ring is giving rise for concern. A material that is attracting some attention is N-vinylformamide and this material forms an alternating copolymer with maleate esters and maleimides.

(v)   Choice of Prepolymer[9, 185]

To a large extent it is the prepolymer which controls the final properties of the film. For this reason it is important to consider the function of film when choosing which prepolymer or prepolymers should be used (see Section V(vi)).

The major classes of prepolymers are;

(a) unsaturated polyesters
(b) epoxy acrylates
(c) urethane acrylates
(d) polyester acrylates
(e) polyether acrylates
(f) acrylic acrylates/saturated resins
(g) silicone acrylates
(h) acrylated poly(butadienes)
(i) melamine acrylates
(j) dendritic acrylates

For many of the classes of compounds mentioned they may either be purely aliphatic or made up of aliphatic and aromatic residues. The extent of the aromatic content and the nature of the substituted pattern strongly influences the properties of the cured film.

Unsaturated polyesters are based on maleic, fumaric and phthalic acids. For preparing compounds based on maleic and fumaric acid the usual feedstock is maleic anhydride (Figure 145).

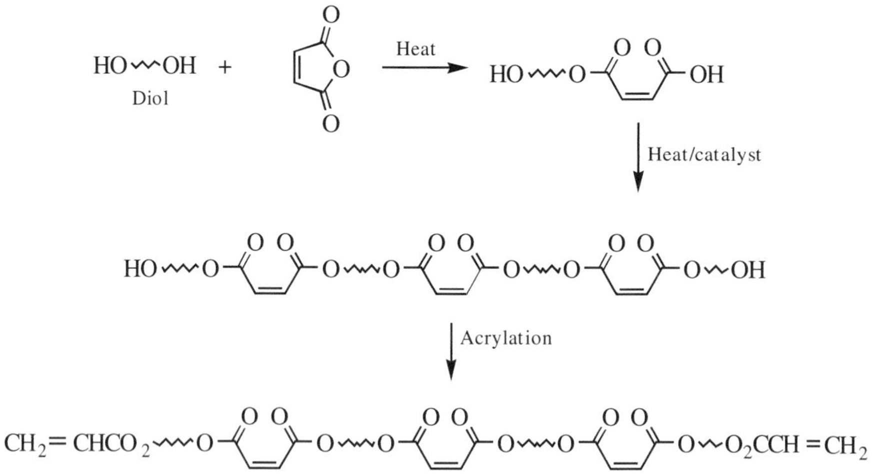

Figure 145: Preparation of an acrylated unsaturated polyester

The properties of these polyesters are influenced by nature of the diol employed. Thus in principle pure long straight or branched chain aliphatic diols may be used, or alternatively, diols containing cyclic structures e.g. cyclohexane-1,4-dimethanol (1,4-di(hydroxymethyl)cyclohexane). Diols containing aromatic structures may also be used. Sometimes, to obtain the desired end properties, mixtures of these diols are employed.

It is also possible to introduce aromatic residues by polymerising a mixture of diol plus an unsaturated acid (maleic or fumaric) and phthalic acid thereby enabling coatings having properties intermediate between the pure aromatic and unsaturated polyesters to be obtained. If unsaturated esters are present, water compatibility can be introduced by reacting with suitable amines via the Michael addition reaction.

The term epoxy acrylate refers to materials prepared by the opening of epoxide groups by acrylic acid. This is usually done by means of a catalyst e.g. tertiary amine, quaternary ammonium salts or a chromium catalyst. Some low cost epoxy acrylates are prepared by epoxidising unsaturated naturally occurring acids and esters followed by opening of the epoxide (oxirane) ring with acrylic acid (Figure 146).

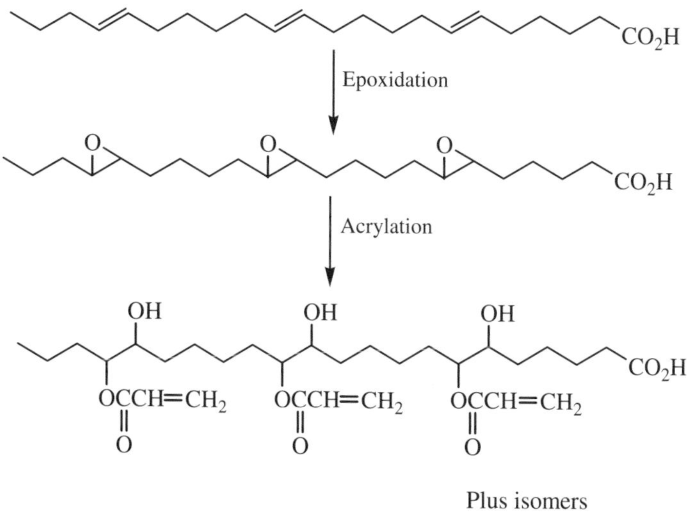

Plus isomers

Figure 146: Preparation of an epoxy acrylate from an unsaturated acid

Acrylated epoxidised oils which fall into this class can be used to improve the lithographic properties of inks and of the wetting of pigments. Usually these compounds exhibit slow curing and are frequently used in conjunction with other prepolymers.

The aromatic epoxy acrylates are frequently prepared from glycidyl ethers derived from bisphenol A or bisphenol F (Figure 147).

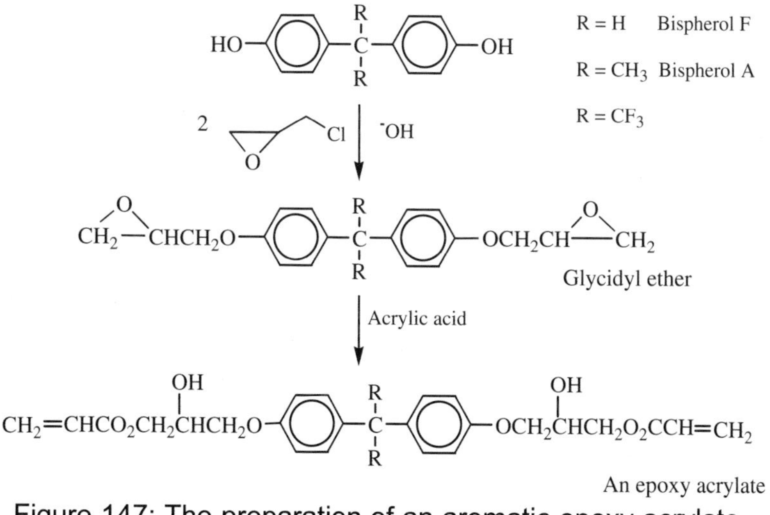

R = H   Bispherol F

R = CH$_3$ Bispherol A

R = CF$_3$

Glycidyl ether

An epoxy acrylate

Figure 147: The preparation of an aromatic epoxy acrylate

The structures of an epoxy acrylate are easy to elaborate. For example, bisphenol A glycidyl ether may be reacted with an epoxide (e.g. propylene oxide) so as to obtain a linear polymer containing polyether groups in addition to the aromatic groups and then end capped with hydroxyl groups which facilitate the introduction of acrylate groups (Figure 147). Water compatibility can be conferred by reacting aromatic epoxy's with formaldehyde and an amine (Mannich reaction).

Other phenolic materials which have been used include novolak resins (Figure 148). These by virtue of their free phenolic groups, can be glycidated and then acrylated.

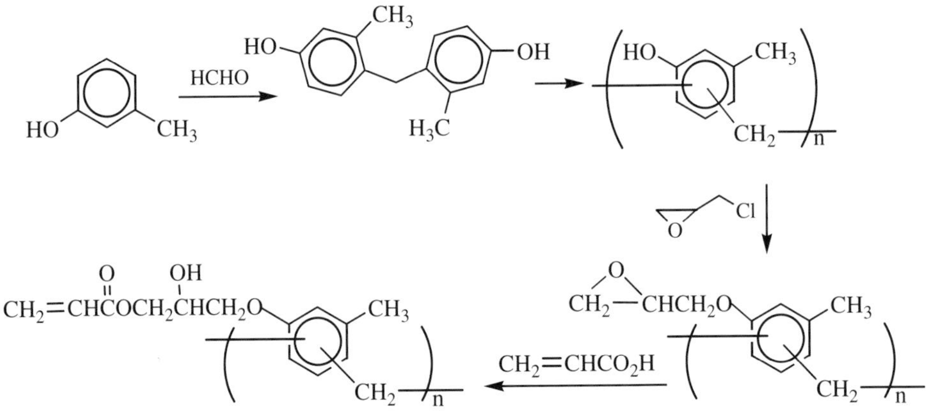

Figure 148: Preparation of an acrylated novolak

Acrylated novolaks give extremely hard coatings which exhibit yellowing in sunlight. They find extensive use in the manufacture of printed circuit boards. The opening of an epoxide group by an acrylic acid produces a secondary hydroxyl group. It is because of the hydroxyl group that epoxy acrylates are highly viscous due to intermolecular hydrogen bonding. If these hydroxy groups are acylated (including acrylation) or silylated, the viscosity of the resin can be reduced to the level that it can be used without recourse to a reactive diluent. The epoxy acrylates exhibit good reactivity and this has been attributed to the C-H bond of the alcohol group facilitating crosslinking (Figure 149).[203]

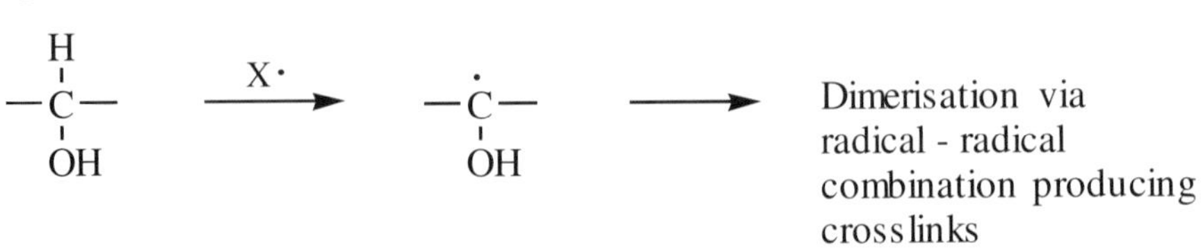

Figure 149: Crosslinking proposed as occurring in epoxy acrylates

Acrylated urethanes may be either aliphatic or aromatic. The urethane link is normally created via reaction of an alcohol with an isocyanate under the influence of a tin catalyst. Some of the commonly used isocyanates are shown in Figure 150.

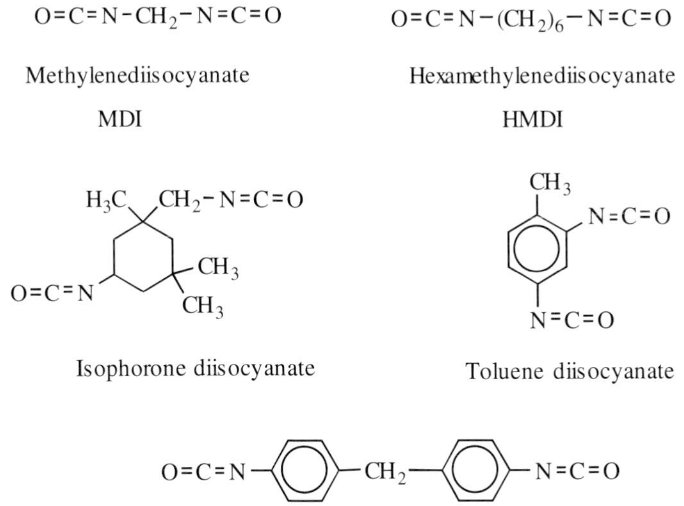

$$O=C=N-CH_2-N=C=O \qquad\qquad O=C=N-(CH_2)_6-N=C=O$$

Methylenediisocyanate   Hexamethylenediisocyanate

MDI   HMDI

Isophorone diisocyanate   Toluene diisocyanate

$$O=C=N-\bigcirc-CH_2-\bigcirc-N=C=O$$

Figure 150: Some diisocyanates commonly used in the preparation of polyurethanes

The diisocyanates are usually condensed with diols to yield hydroxyl group end-capped linear polymers which are suitable for acrylation. By using triols and tetraols instead of diols, crosslinked materials may be obtained. An alternative way of introducing acrylates is to condense mixtures of the diols, diisocyanates and 2-hydroxyethyl or 2-hydroxypropyl acrylate (e.g. Figure 151).[10]

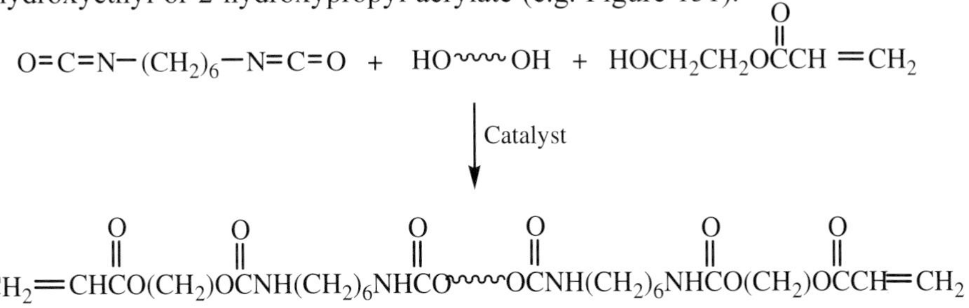

$$O=C=N-(CH_2)_6-N=C=O \ + \ HO\backsim\backsim OH \ + \ HOCH_2CH_2O\overset{\overset{\displaystyle O}{\|}}{C}CH=CH_2$$

↓ Catalyst

$$CH_2=CHC\overset{\overset{\displaystyle O}{\|}}{O}(CH_2)O\overset{\overset{\displaystyle O}{\|}}{C}NH(CH_2)_6NH\overset{\overset{\displaystyle O}{\|}}{C}O\backsim\backsim O\overset{\overset{\displaystyle O}{\|}}{C}NH(CH_2)_6NH\overset{\overset{\displaystyle O}{\|}}{C}O(CH_2)O\overset{\overset{\displaystyle O}{\|}}{C}CH=CH_2$$

Figure 151: An example of formation of an aliphatic urethane diacrylate

The aliphatic polurethanes give tough flexible films whereas aromatic polyurethanes give tough and hard films. Often the properties of polyurethanes can be tailor made to suit a particular purpose. Thus by introducing polyester units into an aromatic polyurethane, flexibility is conferred upon the cured films. Polyurethanes suitable for use in water-based formulations are made by reacting the isocyanates with polyols containing a water solubilising group e.g. carboxylic acid, sulfonic acid, quaternary ammonium groups. A frequently used diol for this purpose is 2-di(hydroxymethyl)-propionic acid.

Polyester acrylated resins may be obtained by esterifying diols with a di-acid (e.g. adipic) and end-capping the polymer by esterification with an acrylic acid (Figure 152).

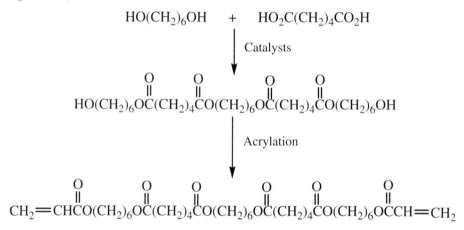

Figure 152: Preparation of an acrylated polyester

Aromatic polyester acrylates may be prepared by using an aromatic di-acid (e.g. phthalic acid) in place of the aliphatic di-acid.

Another way of preparing aliphatic polyesters is to use lactones such as caprolactone as the starting material (Figure 153).

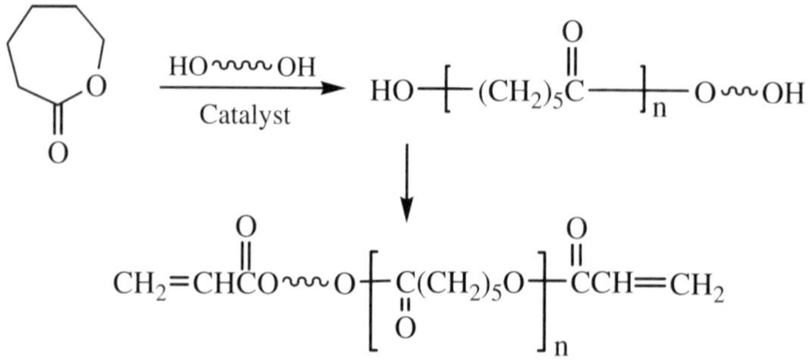

Figure 153: Preparation of a caprolactone glycol diacrylate

Polyether acrylates are usually based on poly(ethylene glycols),PEG's and poly(propylene glycols), PPG's. These diols are acrylated via transesterification with methyl acrylate. Polymerisation of these materials gives soft films. Addition of PEG diacrylates to u.v. curing formations usually leads to a decrease in the hardness of the film and aids adhesion to surfaces which contain hydroxyl groups.

Acrylic acrylates and vinyl prepolymers are prepared by polymerising or copolymerising the appropriate monomers. Functional groups can be introduced by copolymerising with vinyl monomers containing pendant acid, anhydride, hydroxyl or glycidyl groups. These prepolymers are normally dissolved in an acrylate diluent. Polymerisation of such formulations leads to an acrylated crosslinked polymer based on the diluent with an acrylic acrylate or vinyl prepolymers either being grafted into the network or, if they contain free double bonds, polymerised into the system.

Silicone acrylates find use as slip agents (e.g. to stop films sticking together) and in the coating of optical fibres. If a dichlorosilane or a mixture of dichlorosilanes is hydrolysed in presence of a hydroxyalkyl acrylate a silicone acrylate may be prepared (Figure 154).

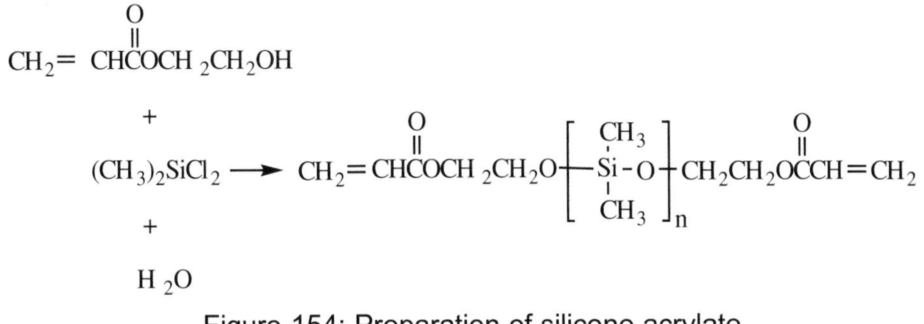

$$CH_2= CHCOCH_2CH_2OH$$

$$+$$

$$(CH_3)_2SiCl_2 \longrightarrow CH_2=CHCOCH_2CH_2O\left[Si(CH_3)(CH_3)-O\right]_n CH_2CH_2OCCH=CH_2$$

$$+$$

$$H_2O$$

Figure 154: Preparation of silicone acrylate

Side chain acrylate groups may be introduced via the hydrosilylation reaction (e.g. Figure 155).[204]

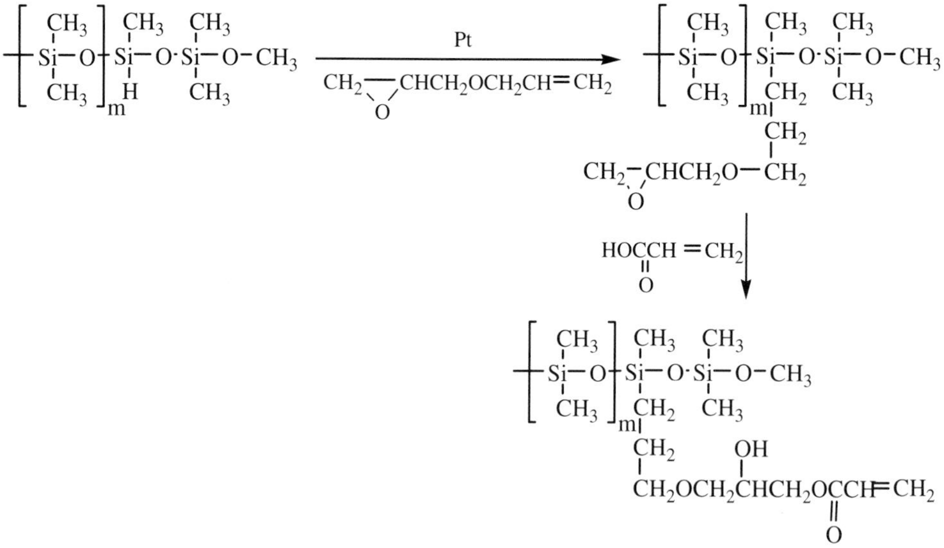

Figure 155: A polysiloxane containing pendant acrylate groups

Melamine acrylates are very versatile materials in more ways than one. The synthesis of these materials is very adaptable (Figure 156) enabling 1 to 6 acrylate groups to be introduced onto the melamine backbone.

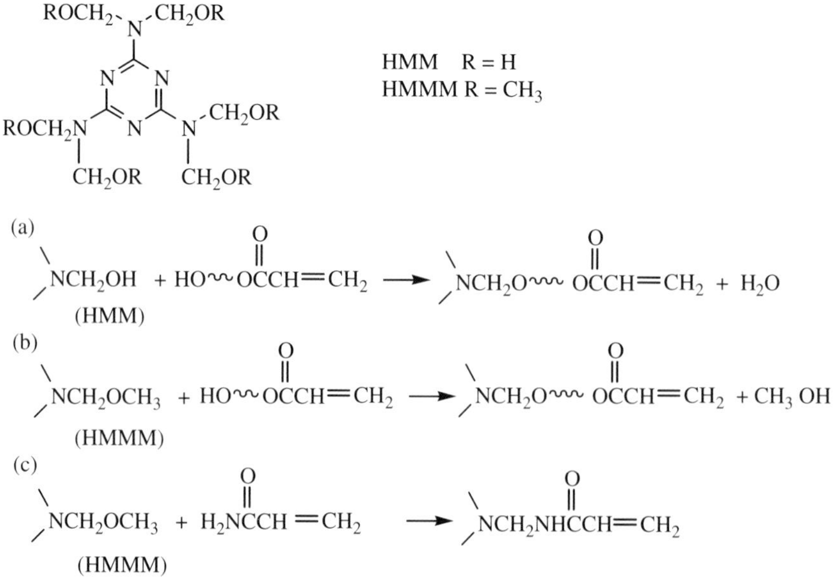

Figure 156: Synthesis of melamine acrylates

Their synthesis by trans-etherification has been well described[205] and the cure properties and those of the coatings produced have also been investigated[206] The compounds cure rapidly (both u.v. and e.b. radiation) to give hard strong coatings with these properties being modulated by the type and amount of reactive diluent added.   If initiators containing hydroxyl groups are reacted with hexakis(methoxymethyl)melamine in addition to a hydroxy acrylate, a resin is obtained which contains its own initiator and which on cure gives film which do not contain migratable initiator residues[207] Another valuable feature of melamines is that if some methoxymethyl groups remain in the acrylated material, the film produced via polymerising the acrylate groups can be further crosslinked by the application of heat[208]

Acrylated dendrimers are now attracting attention and one class that has an aromatic core has been described in detail[209] A methacrylated dendrimer is shown in Figure 157.

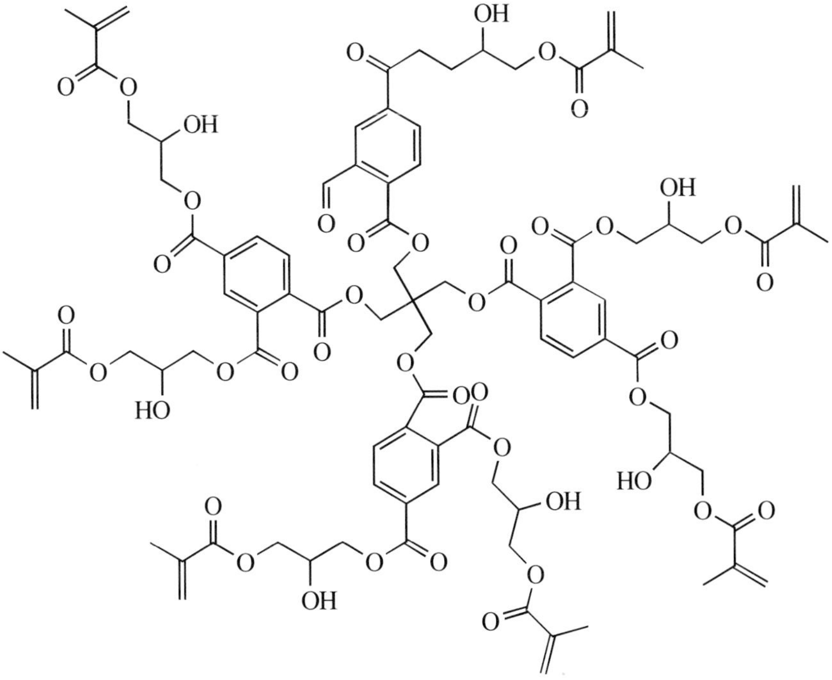

Figure 157: Methacrylated dendrimer

The viscosity (~ 50 pascals) of this material is low for its molecular weight and this is further reduced when the secondary hydroxyl groups are acylated. If the acylating agent introduces methacrylate groups it can be seen that a maximum of 18 methacrylate groups can be introduced intpo the molecule. Needless to say these materials cure at a very high rate to give hard coatings which contain a number of unreacted methacrylate groups. Since the films are highly crosslinked and it is not surprising that that they possess high Tg's and consequently their use in composites is being recommended. Addition of an aliphatic diluent increases the number of double bonds utilised on cure but also decreases the tensile strength of the films. Phase separation may also occur on cure. It is clear that with the basic building blocks of pentaerythritol and benzene-1,2,4-tricarboxylic acid that a wide range of materials can be prepared such as those of higher generation and using different acylating groups to modulate the hydrophobicity/hydrophilicity of the material. Other u.v. curable dendrimer/ hyperbranched polymerisable systems have been described and these include an allyl ether-maleate dendritic polyester[210] Another system which is wholly aliphatic is based on 2,2-bis(hydroxymethyl)propionic acid[211] and once again the properties of the materials were tuned by using a variety of acylating agents such as stearyl and poly(ε-caprolactone)[212] The simple aliphatic esters have the advantage of being biodegradable. Commercialised materials are hyperbranched polymers i.e. they are materials built up in the same way as dendrimers but they are not totally integral and therefore do not have a polydispersivity of one. Many other dendritic systems are known[213] and it will not be long before further radiation curable materials will be available. Undoubtedly the many admirable properties such as low viscosity in relation to molecular weight, their high reactivity, their miscibility with other radiation curable materials and the properties of the cured coatings will all hasten these developments.

(vi)   Matching the Choice of Materials to the Desired End Properties[185]

Some of the properties which are required of radiation cured films include the following:

- Resistance to chemical attack by solvents, acids, alkali, moisture.

- Optical properties such as gloss, mattness, discolouration in daylight.

- Mechanical properties such as hardness, flexibility, adhesion, abrasion resistance, strength, durability.

Factors which influence many of these properties are degree of cure and the extent of crosslinking. As the crosslink density is increased, so the hardness of the film will increase. However, the use of polyfunctional acrylates to increase crosslink density means that gelation sets in at an earlier stage during cure and consequently, the hard "cured" film may contain a high percentage (up to 40%)of uncured acrylate groups. With such systems the extent of cure can be increased by raising the temperature at which cure takes place e.g. curing of hexanediol diacrylate at 40°C led to 70% conversion of the acrylate groups whereas cure at 100°C led to 96% conversion.[25, 214]

The crosslink density will also have an effect upon the resistance of the coating groups to acids or bases and the ingress of moisture. At higher crosslink densities the ability of chemical species to enter the coating will be reduced. Similarly small molecular species contained in the coating (e.g. photoinitiator residues) also experience reduced mobilities. Inhibition, or retardation, of such migration will also help the films to retain their gloss.

Aliphatic saturated and unsaturated polyesters and epoxy acrylates based on natural oils tend to produce soft, flexible films of weak to moderate strength. Introduction of aromatic groups can increase the hardness of the films. Aromatic epoxy acrylates usually give hard inflexible films possessing a high tensile strength and good adhesion to the substrate. Films based on novolak epoxy acrylates are particularly tough but they discolour rapidly on exposure to sunlight. Acrylic acrylates give relatively soft films exhibiting good chemical resistance, high flexibility but low tensile strength. The polyurethane acrylates yield films covering a wide range of properties. Aliphatic urethanes yield highly flexible strong films whereas aromatic urethanes give strong hard films. By introducing polyester chains into acrylated aromatic urethanes materials are produced which on cure have properties intermediate between aliphatic and aromatic polyurethanes. Usually films produced from polymers containing aromatic groups tend to photoyellow (e.g. urethanes) (Figure 158) more than their purely aliphatic counterparts. Aliphatic polyurethanes give rise to the least photoyellowing of all the resins described and are being used for outdoor applications.

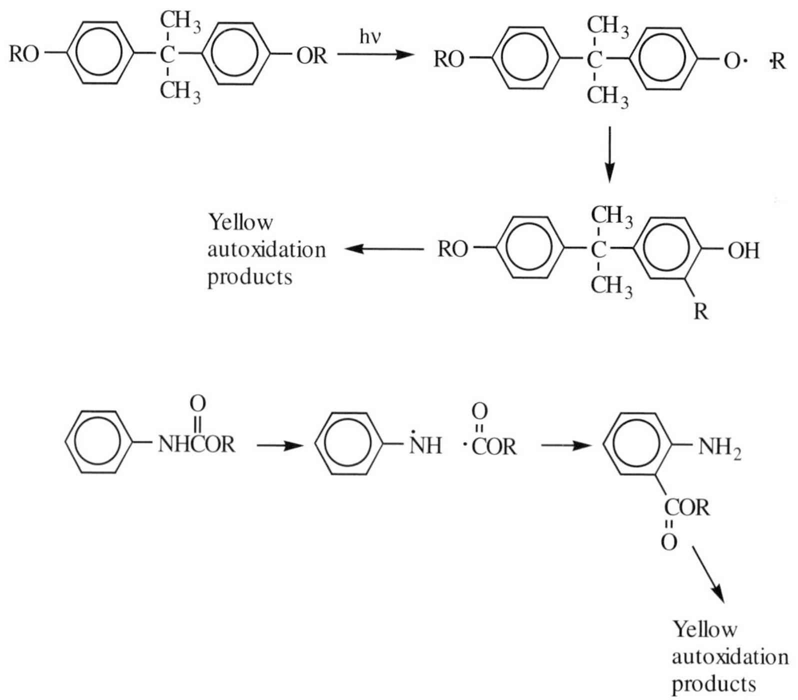

Figure 158: Processes leading to photoyellowing of a polyurethane and materials based on bisphenol A.

A very important property of any surface coating is the adhesion of the coating to the substrate. It is necessary for the surface energy of the formulation to match that of the surface to be coated if good wetting is to be achieved. Good wetting facilitates the formation of an evenly spread film. However, the cure of acrylates leads to the shrinkage with the degree of shrinkage increasing as the percentage of acrylates in the formulation increases. Before cure the distance between the molecules is determined by dipole-dipole interactions and dispersive forces. When polymerisation takes place, carbon-carbon bonds are formed with the consequence that molecules are brought closer together and hence shrinkage occurs, e.g. for methyl methacrylate 23% shrinkage occurs.[215] The shrinkage is often slower than the polymerisation process.[23] Thus for a diacrylate, gelation occurs at a very low conversion of the double bonds and as a consequence most of the polymerisation occurs in the gelled phase. In order to convert the free volume generated by chemical reaction into overall shrinkage the whole gel has to move in a co-operative way and this takes time - far slower than the diffusional motion of free monomer molecules. Because of this effect, acrylate groups will have a greater mobility than expected during the period before shrinkage catches up and as a consequence, higher degrees of cure can be obtained by increasing the light intensity. Thus, to obtain the higher maximum performance of films, it is better to cure at higher temperatures and high light intensities so as to utilise as many of the acrylate groups as possible.

If shrinkage occurs on cure, and particularly if it is rapid, the degree of adhesion between the film and the substrate is likely to be poor. Thermal annealing can help to remedy the situation since it allows the film to come into thermodynamic equilibrium with the substrate. The percentage shrinkage which occurs on the on the curing of the some acrylates is given in Table 2. The following generalisations can be made concerning the relationship between shrinkage and structure:

- Methacrylates give a lower degree of shrinkage than homologous acrylates.

- Multifunctional acrylates give higher shrinkage than monoacrylates.

- Ethoxylated and propoxylated acrylates give lower shrinkage than the parent acrylates.

- Methoxy acrylates give lower shrinkage than the parent acrylates.

Table 5: Percentage shrinkage observed on curing some acrylates

Monomer	Shrinkage%
Trimethylolpropane triacrylate (TMPTA)	26[a]
Ethoxylated trimethylolpropane triacrylate (TMP(EO)TA)	24[a] 17[b]
Propoxylated trimethylolpropane triacrylate (TMP(PO)TA)	15[a] 12[b]
Ethoxylated trimethylolpropane methoxy diacrylate (TMP(EO)MEDA)	19[a]
1,6-Hexanediol diacrylate (HDDA)	14[a]
1,6-Hexanediol methoxymonoacrylate (HDOMEMA)	8[a]
Tetraethyleneglycol diacrylate (TEGDA)	14[a]
Tetraethyleneglycol dimethacrylate (TEGMA)	9[c]
Isobornyl acrylate (IBA)	8[c]

a.)   F S Stowe, R Lieberman, Surface Coatings, Australia, 1986, 23 (August) p8

b.)   P May, Polymer Paint Colour J, 1993, 183 (4323) 55-512

c.)   S P Pappas, Ed. "UV Curing Science and Technology", Technology Marketing Corporation, Norwalk Conn USA, (1980), 1 and (1985) 2

Usually epoxy acrylates give films exhibiting good adhesion and this is probably due to the hydroxyl groups present in the film, bonding to polar groups on the surface of the substrate. Similarly the polar N-H bonds in polyurethanes aid adhesion.

Some substrates such as polyolefins e.g. polyethene, polypropylene and poly(vinyl chloride) are notoriously difficult to coat. The surfaces of these materials do no possess the polar groups necessary to aid bonding.[216] A commonly used practice which facilitates coating these substrates involves ageing the surface of the substrate by flaming, or application of a corona discharge or exposure to short wavelength u.v. light. These processes introduce polar groups into the surface layer.

Adhesion to metal substrates such as steel can cause problems. To alleviate this problem adhesion promoters are incorporated into the formulations. Some acrylates which contain groups aimed at promoting adhesion (e.g. phosphate, siloxane $[Si(OMe)_3]$) are available.

Another important property of the cured film is its Tg (glass transition temperature), i.e. the temperature at which the polymer molecules exhibit some molecular motion). Thus if a polymer is to remain hard over the temperature range 10-80°C, its Tg must be >80°C. The maximum Tg of any radiation cured film can be no higher than the temperature at which cure took place. Clearly the chemical nature of the molecular backbone of the prepolymer will determine the maximum T g obtainable, but it is possible that this may never be achieved unless cure is attained above this temperature, thereby polymerising all the acrylate groups in the system.[217]

Some new monoacrylates which exhibit fast cure, low viscosity, low shrinkage and good solvating properties include: 1,6-hexanediol methoxy monoacrylate (HDOMEMA), tripropyleneglycol methoxy monoacrylate (TPGMEMA), and ethoxylated neopentyl methoxy monoacrylate (NPG(EO)MEMA).

An extremely useful monofunctional polymerisable species often used in conjunction with acrylates is N-vinylpyrrolidone (NVP). This compound is miscible with a wide range of prepolymers over a wide working range. Furthermore, it often aids the adhesion of cured films to surfaces such as polymers (polyolefins, polyester, PVC). N-Vinylcaprolactam has similar properties.

(vii)   U.v. Curing of Pigmented Systems

(a)   Physical Properties

The curing of pigmented systems presented a major challenge to the industry. Incorporation of pigments into u.v. curable formulations perforce generates problems associated with light absorption since the pigments reduce the amount of light available to the photoinitiator by absorption and scattering. For some pigments it is possible that they will act as quenchers of excited states (e.g. azo dyes) thereby decreasing the efficiency of initiation. There is also the possibility that the presence of pigments may decrease the shelf life formulations due to their having a free radical content (e.g. carbon black). Sometimes, groups present in a pigment (e.g. nitro groups) may decrease the efficiency of polymerisation by acting as a radical scavenger.

To achieve cure of a pigmented u.v. curable formulation it is essential for the photoinitiator to be able to absorb the u.v. radiation efficiently. Clearly the u.v. absorption properties are of great importantance and they need to be compatible with those of the pigment so that they make the most of the light that is not absorbed by the pigment. It might be expected that the effectiveness of light absorption by the initiator at a particular wavelength in a mixture which contains several components that absorb at this wavelength could be determined by applying the Beer-Lambert law.

i.e.

$$I_A = I_O \left(1 - 10^{-d(\varepsilon, c, + \varepsilon_2 c_2 ... \varepsilon_n c_n)}\right)$$

Where: I_a is the intensity of the absorbed light

I_0 is the intensity of the incident light

d is the optical pathlength

ε is the molar extinction coefficient of compound n at wavelength

C_n concentration of compound

Strict application of this equation would lead one to the conclusion that curing of most pigmented systems would be very difficult. However, pigments also possess light scattering properties and hence it is possible for light to be transmitted further into a film than one might expect. This is shown schematically in Figure 159.

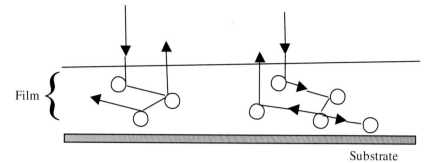

Figure 159: Schematic drawing of light penetration of a pigmented film

The light scattering properties of the pigment are clearly of great importance. This degree of scattering is influenced by:

(i)   The difference in refractive index between the pigment and the vehicle (i.e. formulation minus the pigment).

(ii)   The particle size of the pigment.

(ii)   The concentration of the pigment.

(iv)   The wavelength of the incident light (N.B refractive indexes are wavelength dependent).

Quantifying the amount of light that reaches the bottom of a pigmented film for a given light intensity is very difficult. Some important features which need to be borne in mind when using pigmented films include:

(a)   Scattering increases reflectance at the air-coating interface thereby reducing the fraction of light which reaches the bottom of the coating.

(b)   Since scattering increases the light path, the amount of light available to initiator molecules at the base of the coating will be less (application of the Beer-Lambert law). This effect leads to more light absorption by initiators present at the surface the film.

(c)   The degree of scattering is wavelength dependent and hence the extent of attenuation of the light is wavelength dependent.

Most formulations that contain pigments also contain a cocktail of initiators. Some initiators are included to aid surface cure e.g. benzophenone, whereas others are selected so that they can utilise light in various parts of the spectrum that either are not or are only partially absorbed by the pigment. Bleachable photoinitiators are particularly valuable for curing pigmented systems particularly if the film thickness is fairly high. The ability of the diluent and the resin to wet the pigment is most important if stable dispersions are to be obtained. As yet no one has enunciated the rules governing wetting but polyethers and derivatised natural oils e.g. acrylated soya bean oil, appear to be attractive candidates.

(b)   Choice of Photoinitiator

The curing of thick films[218, 219] (e.g. as used in wood coating) presents special problems. If the film is not to suffer from under-cure, relatively low concentrations of initiator have to be used so as to enable light to penetrate the film in order to activate photoinitiator molecules at the base of the film. If the concentration of initiator is lowered, the rate of cure is also decreased and this has a marked effect upon the surface cure. At low initiation rates oxygen inhibition becomes very important. To overcome these problems it is common practice to use a mixture of photoinitiators. If a photoinitiator is selected that is a weak absorber at >300nm but is a strong absorber at <300nm e.g. benzophenone, 2,2-dimethoxy-2-phenylacetophenone, the light below 300nm will be absorbed at and just below the surface with little penetration into the depth of the film. Use of a photoinitiator that absorbs light >300nm at an appropriate concentration will initiate cure throughout the bulk of the film (see Figure 160). If the surface cure is sufficiently rapid, the film will become "sealed" thereby decreasing the rate of ingress of oxygen thereby facilitating the through cure which will occur over a longer timescale. For a mixture of photoinitiators to give good results it is necessary to choose their concentrations carefully and also to choose the correct light source. It is important that the light source produces relatively intense radiation at <300nm and >300nm if both types of initiators are to function properly. The absorption of light by the photoinitiator responsible for the through cure will be strongly affected by the absorption and scattering properties of the pigment. It is important that the radiation source emits light of high intensity at those wavelengths were the initiator absorbs and light absorption by the pigment is minimal. Usually these requirements can be met by the use of a doped medium pressure mercury lamps or the use of an electrodeless lamp containing the appropriate gas mixture. An interesting alternative is to use two lamps in tandem. Fluorescent lamps emitting in the 370-470nm range can be used in the first stage to effect through uniform cure with a high pressure mercury lamp being used in the second stage to effect surface cure.[218]

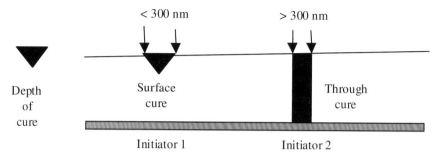

Figure 160: Curing of a thick pigmented film using a mixture of photoinitiators having different light absorption properties

For a u.v. curing system based on a free radical polymerisation process, the formulator has a good choice of photoinitiators. There are many Type I initiators which have a relatively weak absorption at >300nm and can therefore be used to effect surface cure. Of the Type II systems benzophenone is the most popular. It has been found that in many cases the addition of an amine synergist is unnecessary when benzophenone is used in conjunction with a Type I photoinitiator. This rather surprising result has been attributed to the benzophenone sensitising (via the triplet state) the homolysis of hydroperoxides thereby generating hydroxyl and alkoxyl radicals. Given that many reactive diluents used in the formulations contain ether groups eg $-CH_2O-$ and $-CH(CH_3)O-$ initiating radicals may be generated by attack of triplet benzophenone upon the C-H bonds adjacent to oxygen.

Thioxanthones (e.g. isopropyl thioxanthone) are well established as being useful for curing white pigmented films. A compound that has recently come to the market is 1-chloro-4-propoxythioxanthone (CPTX) and this exhibits absorption maxima at 387, 314 and 254nm. The thioxanthones have to be used with an amine synergist and this poses problems since the amines promote yellowing of the cured films when they are subsequently exposed to daylight.[96] A further problem encountered when thioxanthones are used for curing white lacquers is that the cured films contain thioxanthones which also impart a yellow appearance of the film. The availability of α-aminoacetophenone Type I photoinitiators which exhibit absorption at >300nm has played an important part in the development of radiation cured coatings (Figure 161). 2-Methyl-2-morpholino-1-(4-methylthiophenyl) propan-1-one and 2-benzyl-2-dimethylamino-1-(4-morpholinophenyl)butan-1-one are particularly useful in this respect but it should be pointed out that the use of the latter compound leads to yellowing of cured white films on exposure to sunlight. Films cured using acetophenone carrying a 4-methylthiophenyl substituent possess a distinctive unpleasant odour due to the production of 4-methylthiobenzaldehyde. Acylphosphine oxides, although more expensive than the α-aminoacetophenones are used for curing pigmented films. These and the related bisacylphosphine oxides exhibit absorption peaks between 300 and 400nm and are particularly useful for achieving through cure. A further valuable feature of these compounds is that they are bleachable ie following α-scission, the chromophore giving rise to the absorption band between 300 and 400nm is destroyed. This effect aids through cure. A further important feature is that the use of these compounds in white lacquers does not lead to yellowing of the cured films on subsequent exposure to sunlight.

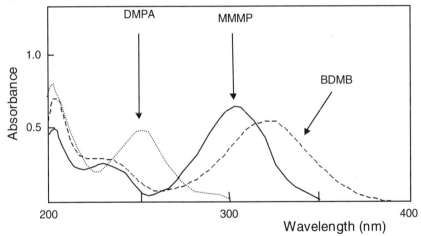

Figure 161: Absorption spectra of 2,2-dimethoxy-2-phenylacetophenone (DMPA), 2-methyl-2-morpholino-1-(4-methylthiophenyl)propan-1-one (MMP) and 2-benzyl-2-dimethylamino-1-(4-morpholinophenyl)butan-1-one (BDMB)

The choice of initiators discussed relates to the curing of acrylates and methacrylates. However, a very popular curing system for wood coatings contains unsaturated polyesters dissolved in styrene. For reasons presented earlier (II(i)(b)) Type II initiator systems based on aromatic ketones cannot be used with this system. Since acyl and bisacylphosphine oxides have very short triplet lifetimes and consequently they can be used to great effect with formulations based upon styrene and an unsaturated polyester.

Far less work has been done on the curing of pigmented cationic systems. The two factors which have contributed to this state of affairs are, the small range of available cationic photoinitiators (with very few showing an acceptable level of absorption between 300 and 400nm) and the inhibitory effect upon cure that many pigments exhibit.[220]

Currently, line speeds for curing pigmented systems cationically do not match those of the free radical systems.

(c)   Pigment Properties

A pigment is introduced into the formulation so that it will impart the desired colour to the cured film. In some cases more than one pigment has to be used if the desired colour is to be achieved. The amount of pigment in a formulation that is required is determined by its colour strength. Clearly less and less pigment is required as the colour strength is increased.

The most popular white pigment is the rutile form of titanium dioxide. This crystalline modification is far more photostable than the anatase form. The absorption spectra of these and other white pigments is shown in Figure 162.[94]

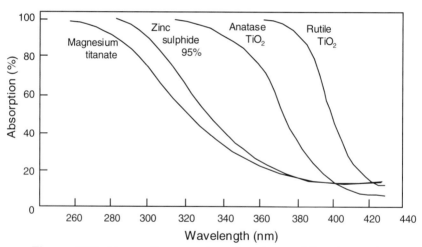

Figure 162: Absorption spectra of various white pigments

The absorption spectrum of rutile given in Figure 162 shows that very few of the available photoinitiators will absorb significant amounts of light when used with this pigment. Acylphosphine and bisacylphosphine oxides are the most successful materials.

To attain maximum cure speed it is necessary to use doped lamps so as to maximise the light absorption by the initiator. Manufacturers of rutile control the particle size so as to maximise the scattering of green light. Scattering of u.v. light does still occur.

Coloured pigments not only absorb in the visible but also in the u.v. Their spectra usually exhibit spectral windows i.e. wavelength regions where light absorption is minimal. Yellow and red pigments show a relatively low absorption in the 300 to 400nm range which means that formulations containing these pigments can be cured using α-aminoacetophenones, acyl and bisacylphosphine oxides and thioxanthones (when acrylates and methacrylates are the polymerisable species). Blue pigments absorb much more strongly than yellow and red pigments in the 300-400nm and consequently it is more difficult to cure these systems. Usually a mixture of photoinitiators is employed. Some results are shown in Figure 163.

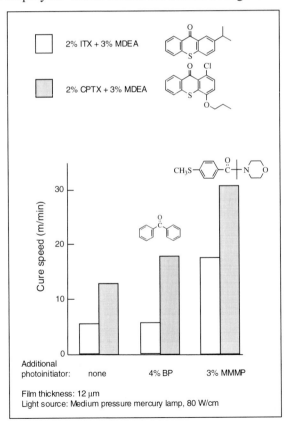

Figure 163: Curing of a blue screen ink by thioxanthones in the presence of N-methyldiethanolamine and other photoinitiator systems

CHAPTER VI

PRODUCTION OF SURFACE COATINGS USING CATIONIC CURING SYSTEMS[221]

CHAPTER VI

PRODUCTION OF SURFACE COATINGS USING CATIONIC CURING SYSTEMS[221]

(i)   Systems Based on the Ring Opening of Epoxides

Although the introduction of radiation curable systems based on the acid catalysed ring opening of epoxides to the market occurred some two decades ago, it has been slow to gain widespread acceptance. Undoubtedly, the cationic cure of epoxides has some advantages over the free radical cure of acrylates and methacrylates. Two important advantages are that cure does not suffer from oxygen inhibition and minimal shrinkage occurs on cure. The latter, together with the fact that hydroxyl groups are generated upon cure[133, 141, 142] often leads to the cured coatings exhibiting good adhesion to substrates such as metals. Another bonus is that in general, the monomers and prepolymers exhibit less skin irritancy than their acrylate counterparts.

In view of these benefits, why has the application of the cationic curing of epoxides been slow to take off? In the early days it was remarkably difficult to obtain pure samples of the commercially used initiators thereby inhibiting development work by formulators. The range of epoxides suitable for radiation curing is slowly increasing. Another important fact is the paucity of cationic photoinitiators that are available. Undoubtedly sulphonium salts and to some extent iodonium salts have found a market. However, they are not without drawbacks which include poor solubility in common monomers and very poor absorption properties at >300nm. The poor light absorption properties of these compounds and that many pigments possess basic surfaces has meant that there are few cationically cured pigmented systems described. A number of alternatives to the initiators based on iodonium and sulphonium salts have been explored e.g.the iron arene complexes, but they have had little impact upon the marketplace.

Whilst the cationic systems, including vinyl ethers, do not suffer from oxygen inhibition, they are affected by moisture. Surprisingly large amounts of water can be tolerated in the curing formulation but high humidity can wreak havoc with the speed of cure.[134] It is believed that when the humidity is high, the initiating species e.g. hydrogen fluoride and phosphorus pentafluoride migrate from the coating into the atmosphere thereby retarding cure. Water present in the formulation facilitates chain transfer.

Initiators based on sulphonium salts are frequently used. Unfortunately, photolytic breakdown of these compounds leads to the production of aryl sulphides. These compounds impart an unpleasant smell to the coating. Presumably, this problem could be overcome by the use polymeric photoinitiators in which the sulphide groups is part of the polymer chain.

(a)   Epoxy Reactive Diluents

Some of the commercially available diluents are shown in Table 6. It will be seen that all have di or a higher functionality and this favours the formation of crosslinked films. On the whole, the cycloaliphatic epoxides are more reactive than the glycidyl derivatives and this is attributed to the opening up of cycloaliphatic epoxides releasing more ring strain. The aliphatic epoxides have a low viscosity and are readily miscible with prepolymers.

There is a number of naturally occurring oils, castor, soya, palm etc, that are esters of unsaturated fatty acids. These materials can be epoxidised and the products are excellent diluents having a good reactivity[223]

(b)   Epoxy Prepolymers

A class of aromatic epoxy prepolymers is the epoxy novolaks, which are produced by reacting novolak resins with epichlorohydrin (e.g. Figure 164).

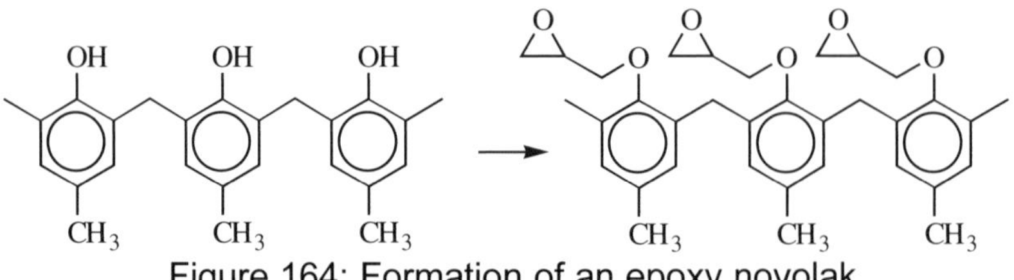

Figure 164: Formation of an epoxy novolak

Epoxy poly(butadienes) are also available.[224]

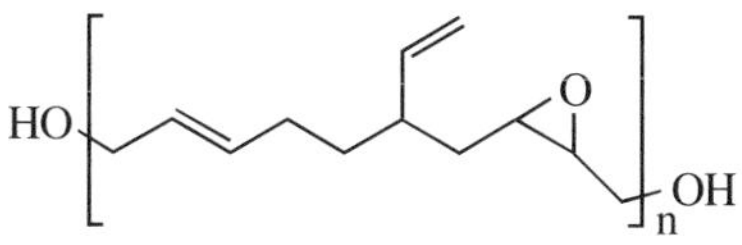

Figure 165: An epoxidised poly(butadiene)

Epoxidised poly(butadiene) does not dissolve too readily in the normal epoxy diluents but it is readily miscible with some vinyl ethers. Use of these vehicles gives formulations which cure rapidly[225].

Some alicyclic tetra-epoxides are available which can be modidified by reaction with dibasic acids etc. to give prepolymers which can be cured via the remaining epoxide groups[226]

Of particular interest to those concerned with formulating adhesives are the epoxidised poly(isoprene)poly(ethylene/butylene) copolymers carrying a terminal primary hydroxyl group[227]. These compounds which contain up to nine epoxide groups undergo rapid cure.

Much effort has been put into producing epoxy siloxanes (eg Figure 166).[228]

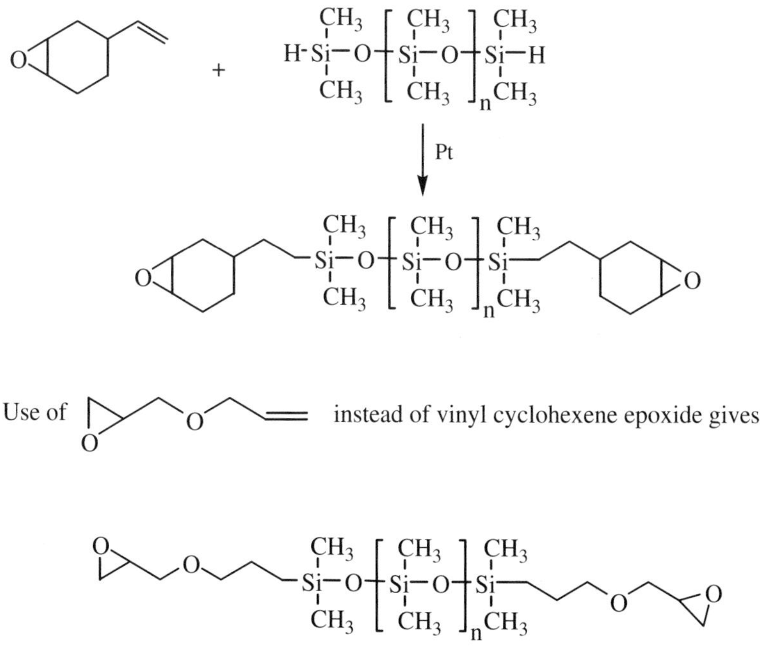

Use of [structure] instead of vinyl cyclohexene epoxide gives

Figure 166: Synthesis of epoxy silanes

(c)   Crosslinking of Epoxy Systems

Whilst it is relatively easy to obtain multifunctional epoxides, the range of prepolymers is somewhat limited. However, highly crosslinked systems can be obtained by the addition of polyols, polyphenolics.[229] The mechanism of the reaction (Figure 167) emphasises that cationic curing involves living polymers and that acid remains in the coating after cure.

N.B. this has now been included in the discussion of cationic cure.

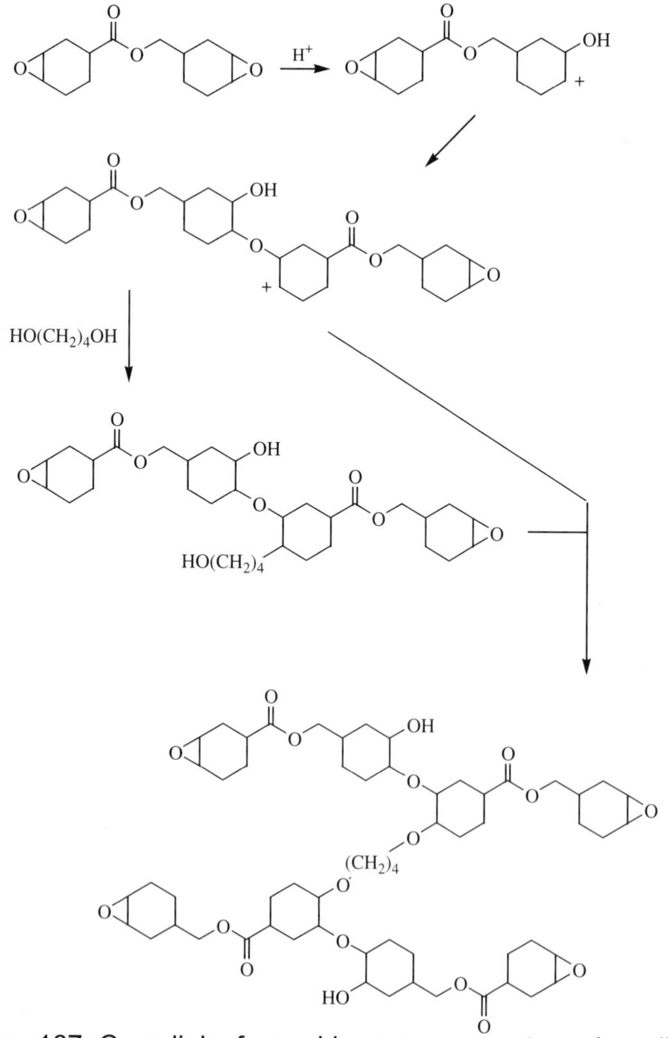

Figure 167: Crosslinks formed in an epoxy system via a diol

Table 6: Some Epoxy Diluents

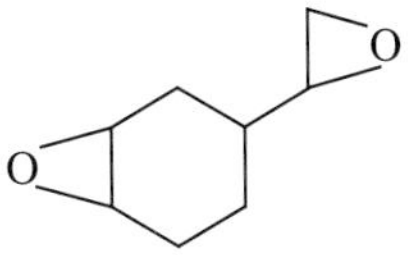

Limonene diepoxide - a rather volatile material

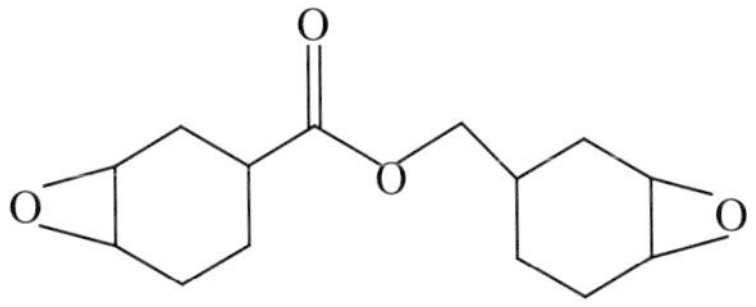

3,4-Epoxycyclohexylmethyl-3,4-epoxycyclohexane carboxylate

The standard "work-horse" of most epoxy formulations

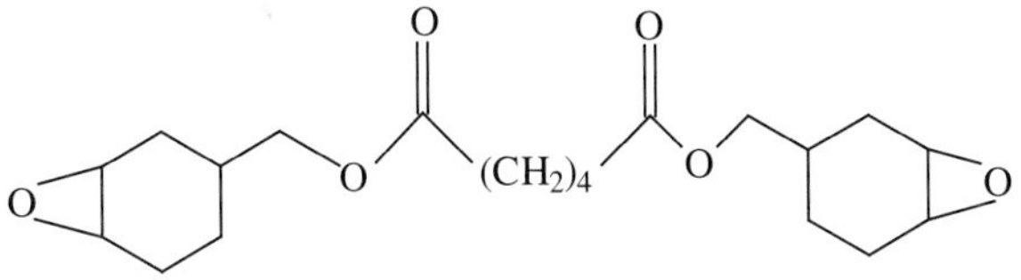
O
O
O
O
$(CH_2)_4$
O
O
O

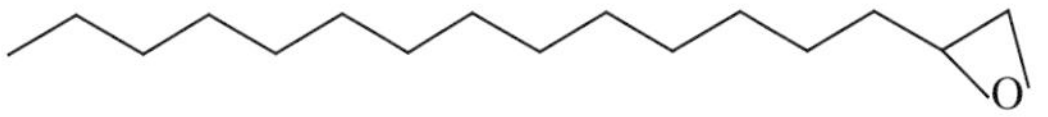

1,2-Epoxyhexadecane

Epoxidised Soy bean, castor and palm oils
(triglycerides containing epoxidised unsaturated acid residues)

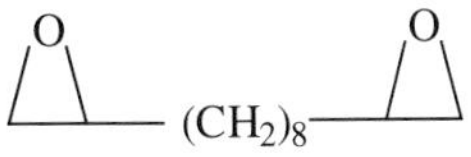
O
O
$(CH_2)_8$

Glycidyl ethers

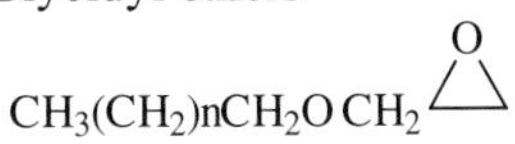
O
$CH_3(CH_2)nCH_2O\ CH_2$

n = 6, 8

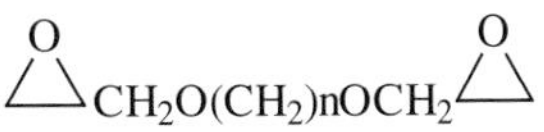
O
O
$CH_2O(CH_2)nOCH_2$

n = 4 - 10

(ii)   Oxetanes (trimethylene oxides)

This is an area which is very much in its infancy with patents describing their preparation, their curing properties and how they may be used with benefit in association with epoxides, appearing at frequent intervals[230]. The oxetane ring is less strained than the oxirane ring (106.7 KJ/mol. compared with 114.1 KJ/mol but it is more basic (pK$_a$ -2.02 compared with -3.7)[231]. The basic building block (2-ethyl-2-hydroxymethyloxetane) for most of the described oxetanes is derived from 1,1,1-trimethylolpropane and one of the routes is shown in the Figure 168.

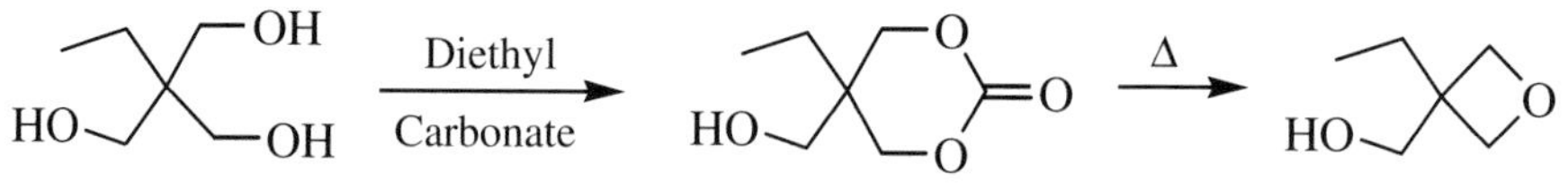

Figure 168: Synthesis of 2-ethyl-2-hydroxymethyloxetane

The presence of a neopentyl primary hydroxyl group in the oxetane enables a range of mono and multifunctional oxetanes to be prepared.[232]

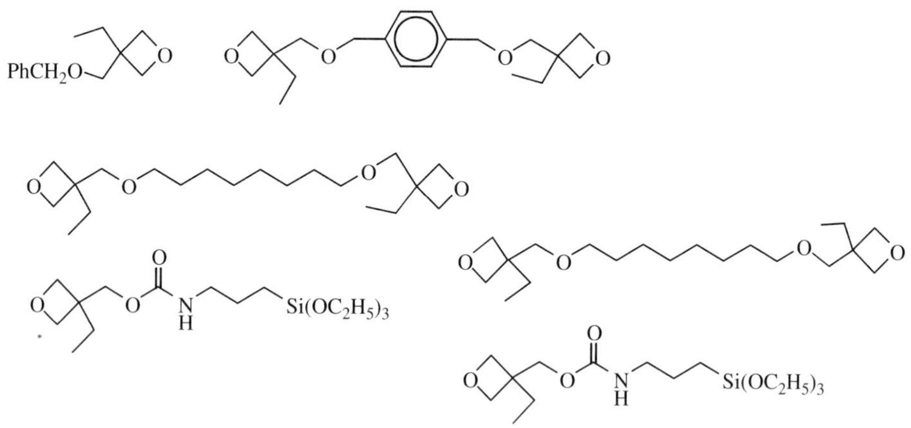

Figure 169: Some oxetanes based on 1,1,1-trimethylolpropane

Oxetanes containing an epoxide group have also been prepared and being bifunctional can be used to form crosslinked structures[233]

Oxetanes undergo acid-catalysed ring opening (Figure 170) and the acids generated from iodonium and sulfonium salts have been found to be effective. Esterification of the primary hydroxyl group reduces the reactivity of the oxetane. Crosslinking can be introduced into the polymers by adding polyols to the curing formulation.

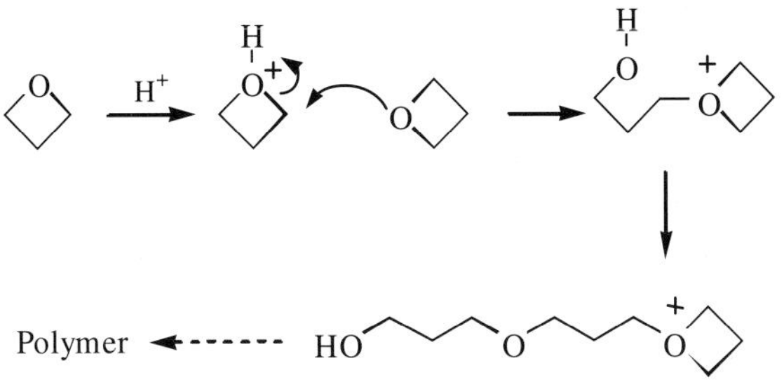

Figure 170: The acid catalysed Ring Opening of an Oxetane

(iii) Vinyl Ether Systems[234]

Vinyl ethers undergo acid catalysed polymerisation to give polymers having a C-C backbone with pendant ether groups. The reaction involves carbocations as intermediates and consequently, the propagating chain can be terminated by reaction with nucleophiles e.g. water or amines (Figure 40).

Reaction with water produces a hemiacetal which is unstable and breaks down liberating acetaldehyde and terminating the growing polymer chain with a primary hydroxyl group.[235] Reaction of the growing polymer chain with either a vinyl ether or water via a chain transfer process produces another initiating species i.e. CH_3CH^+OR and H^+ respectively. Chain transfer may not necessarily slow down the polymerisation process and conceivably it may have a beneficial effect when gelation begins to set in since the reactive low molecular weight species generated (CH_3CH^+OR) has a greater mobility than the growing polymer chain.

Species such as amines are very effective chain terminators (Equation 16).

Equation 16

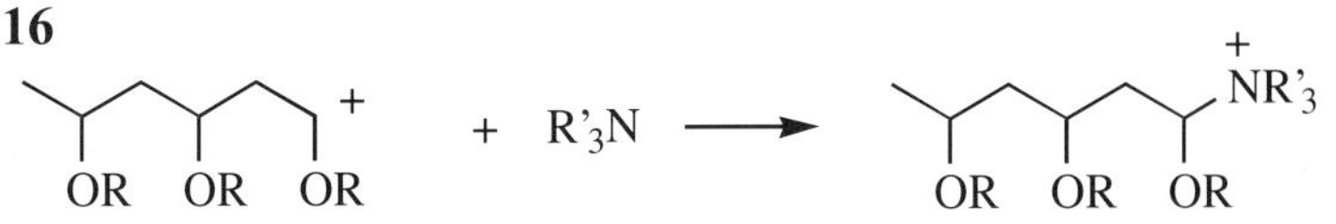

It is probably the presence of such materials in radiation curing formulations, that accounts for the curing not producing a living polymer. To produce a living polymer by the acid catalysed cure of vinyl ethers requires the reaction to be carried out under carefully controlled conditions using high purity reagents.

A particularly attractive feature of the vinyl ether polymerisation process is the high reactivity of the ethers. Differential photocalorimetry (DPC) (also known as photodifferential scanning calorimetry - photo DSC) has been used to measure the relative rates of polymerising a divinyl ether (triethyleneglycol divinyl ether), a triacrylate (trimethylolpropane triacrylate) and an epoxide (3,4-epoxycyclohexymethyl-3',4'-epoxycyclohexane carboxylate) (Figure 171).[236] The results are shown in Figure 171.

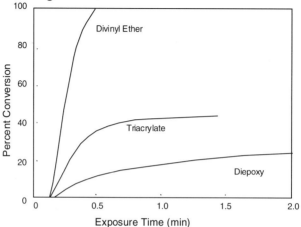

Figure 171: Relative rates of polymerisation of a divinylether and a diepoxide as measured by photo DSC

From this figure it can be seen that the divinyl ether is highly reactive and unlike the epoxide system, does not need a thermal bump if extensive cure is to be observed. The low Tg of the polymer obtained from the vinyl ether is also an important factor which contributes to the high degree of conversion.

As with epoxides, the photoinitiators commonly used for the polymerising of vinyl ethers are iodonium and sulphonium salts. Not surprisingly the reactions do not suffer from oxygen inhibition but are strongly affected by nucleophilic impurities.

(a)   Routes to Vinyl Ethers[234]

Divinyl ethers of diols are readily prepared by reaction of the diols with ethyne (acetylene) (Equation 17).[237]

Equation 17

$$HO\text{\textasciitilde\textasciitilde\textasciitilde}OH \ + \ 2\ HC{\equiv}CH \ \xrightarrow[180^\circ C]{5\%\ KOH} \ CH_2{=}CHO\text{\textasciitilde\textasciitilde\textasciitilde}O\ CH{=}CH_2$$

Commonly encountered divinyl ethers prepared via this route include are shown in Table 7.

Table 7: Some vinyl ether and propenyl ether diluents

Structure	Name
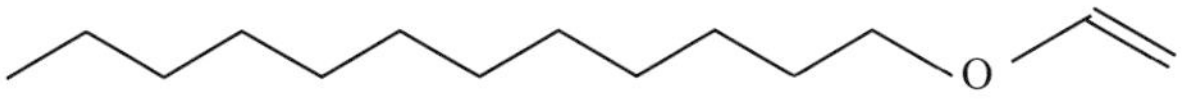 (structure)	Dodecyl vinyl ether
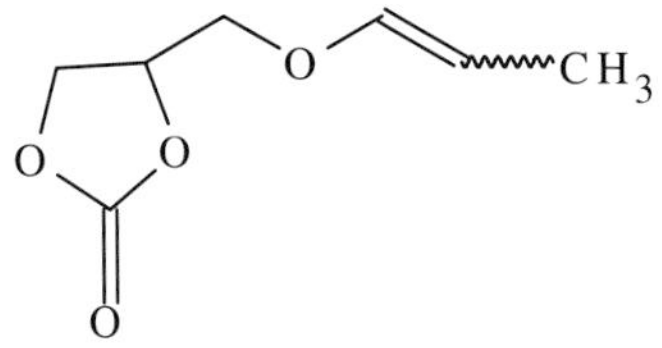 (structure) CH_3	Propenyl ether of propylene carbonate
 (structure) OH	4-Hydroxybutyl vinyl Ether (HBuVE)
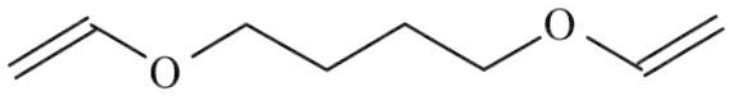 (structure)	Butane-1,4-diol divinyl ether (BuVE)
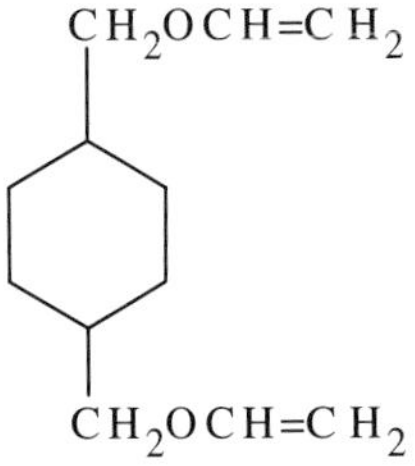 $CH_2OCH{=}CH_2$ (structure) $CH_2OCH{=}CH_2$	1,4-Cyclohexane dimethanol divinyl ether (ChxDVE)
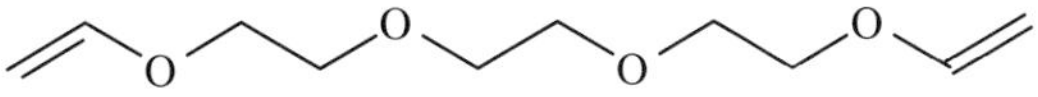 (structure)	Triethylene glycol divinyl ether (TEGDVE)
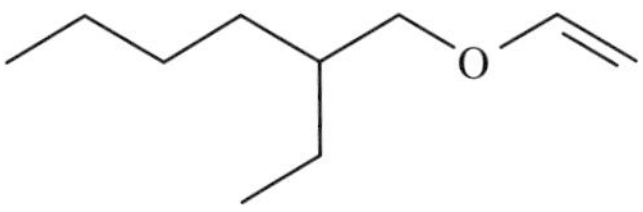 (structure)	2-Ethylhexyl vinyl ether
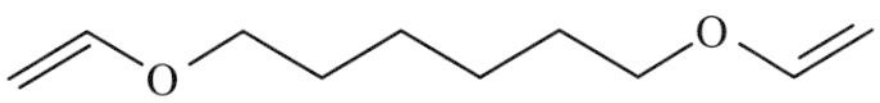 (structure)	Hexane-1,6-diol divinyl ether
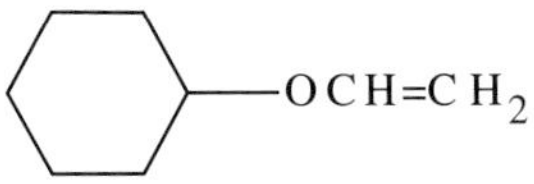 (structure) $OCH{=}CH_2$	Cyclohexyl vinyl ether (ChxVE)

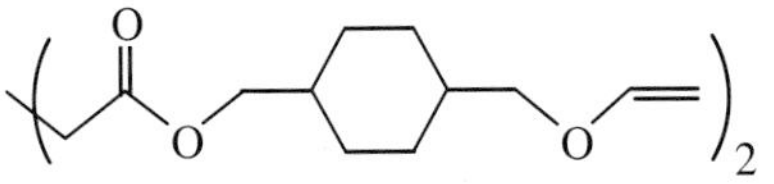

Vectomer 4010 (V 4010)

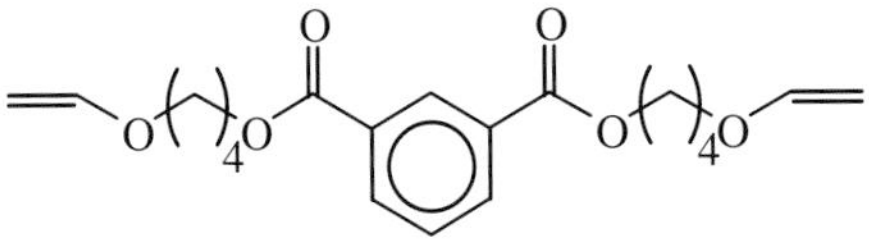

Vectomer 4020 (V 4020)

Stopping the reaction of the diol with ethyne before conversion has occurred facilitates the preparation of hydroxyvinyl ethers.

The availability of a free hydroxyl group makes the preparation of oligomers feasible.

Routes to vinyl ethers not employing ethyne directly or not at all as intermediate include:

The cracking of acetals (Equation 18)

$$CH_3CHO + ROH \xrightarrow{H^+} CH_3CH(OR)_2 \xrightarrow{250 - 400\,^{\circ}C} CH_2{=}CHOR$$

The use of 2-chlorovinyl ether (Equation 19)

$$ClCH_2CH_2OCH_2CH_2Cl \xrightarrow{HO^-} ClCH_2CH_2OCH{=}CH_2 \xrightarrow{ROH} ROCH_2CH_2OCH{=}CH_2$$

Catalytic transvinylation (Equation 20)[238]

$$CH_2{=}CHOCH_2CH_3 \xrightarrow[Hg^{2+}]{ROH} CH_2{=}CHOR + HOCH_2CH_3$$

Such routes afford a wide scope to the synthetic chemist thereby enabling a large range of compounds to be prepared.

(b) Vinyl Ether Prepolymers and Reactive Diluents

Vinyl ether esters may be prepared by reaction of an activated multifunctional carboxylic acid with a hydroxyvinyl ether (Equation 21).

Equation 21

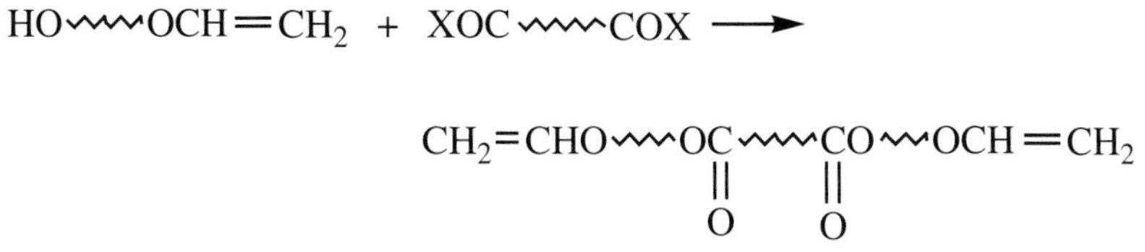

$$HO\text{\small\textasciitilde\textasciitilde\textasciitilde}OCH{=}CH_2 \ + \ XOC\text{\small\textasciitilde\textasciitilde\textasciitilde}COX \longrightarrow$$

$$CH_2{=}CHO\text{\small\textasciitilde\textasciitilde\textasciitilde}OC\underset{O}{\overset{||}{}}\text{\small\textasciitilde\textasciitilde\textasciitilde}CO\underset{O}{\overset{||}{}}\text{\small\textasciitilde\textasciitilde\textasciitilde}OCH{=}CH_2$$

Thus a diacid chloride (X=Cl) may be used. Such a reaction liberates acid and it is necessary to neutralise the acid rapidly and effectively if hydrolysis or polymerisation of the vinyl ether is to be avoided. If an amine is used to neutralise the acid, all the amine has to be removed from the product since its presence will decrease the efficiency of the polymerisation via chain termination. An attractive route to the product is via transesterification (Equation 22).[239]

Equation 22

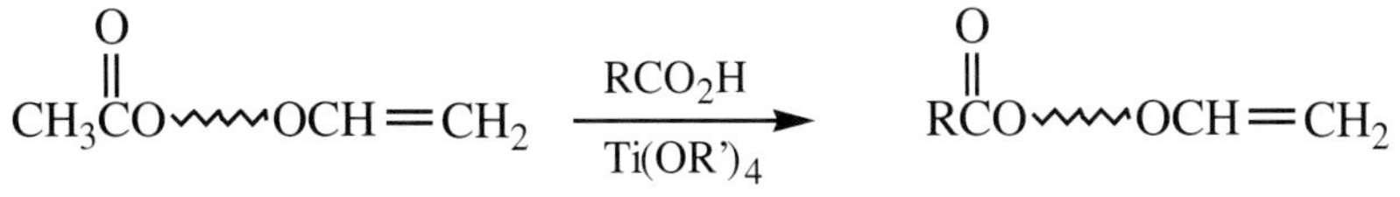

$$CH_3\overset{\overset{O}{||}}{C}O\text{\small\textasciitilde\textasciitilde\textasciitilde}OCH{=}CH_2 \quad \xrightarrow[\text{Ti(OR')}_4]{\text{RCO}_2\text{H}} \quad R\overset{\overset{O}{||}}{C}O\text{\small\textasciitilde\textasciitilde\textasciitilde}OCH{=}CH_2$$

Use of simple dibasic acids e.g. succinic acid and a range of hydroxy-terminated vinyl ethers gives products whose properties vary from being low viscosity liquids to solids (Figure 172).

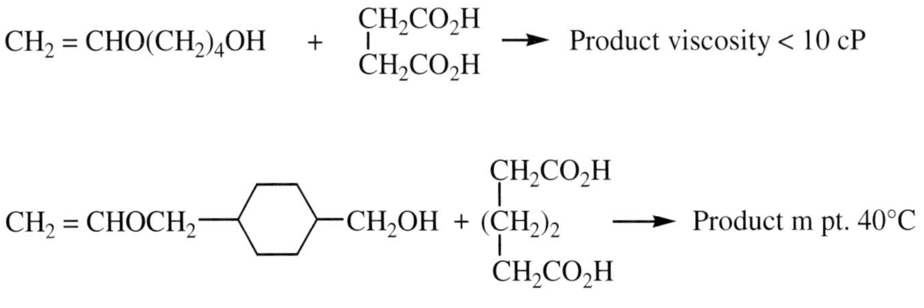

$$CH_2 = CHO(CH_2)_4OH \quad + \quad \begin{array}{l} CH_2CO_2H \\ | \\ CH_2CO_2H \end{array} \longrightarrow \text{Product viscosity} < 10 \text{ cP}$$

$$CH_2 = CHOCH_2\text{—}\hexagon\text{—}CH_2OH + (CH_2)_2 \begin{array}{l} CH_2CO_2H \\ | \\ \\ | \\ CH_2CO_2H \end{array} \longrightarrow \text{Product m pt. } 40°C$$

Figure 172: Some vinyl ether terminated esters

Vinyl ether terminated aromatic esters can also be prepared via the transesterification route (Figure 173).

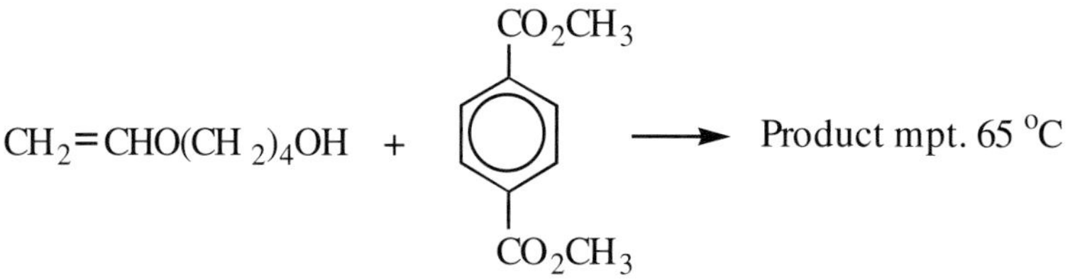

$$CH_2=CHO(CH_2)_4OH \quad + \quad \text{(aromatic ring with } CO_2CH_3 \text{ groups)} \quad \longrightarrow \quad \text{Product mpt. } 65\ ^{\circ}C$$

Figure 173: Vinyl ether terminated aromatic ester

Urethanes can be readily prepared by reaction of isocyanates with hydroxyvinyl ethers (Figure 174).

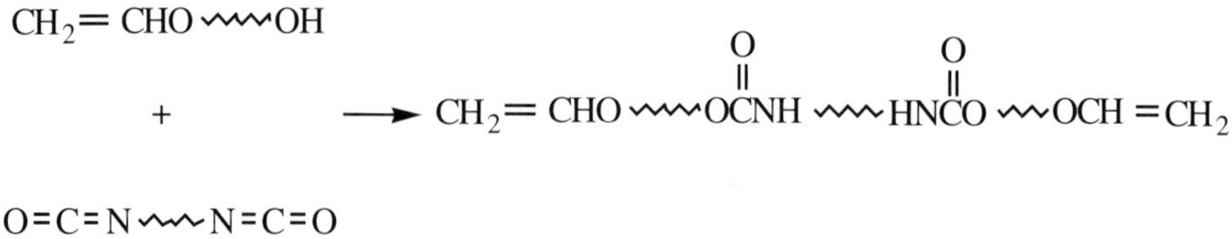

$CH_2=CHO\text{\wwwww}OH$

$+$

$O=C=N\text{\wwwww}N=C=O$

$\longrightarrow CH_2=CHO\text{\wwwww}OCNH\text{\wwwww}HNCO\text{\wwwww}OCH=CH_2$

Figure 174: Vinyl ether terminated urethane

Vinyl ether terminated urethanes have been prepared from toluene diisocyanate (TDI), diphenylmethylene diisocyanate (MDI) and isophorone diisocyanate (IPDI). This chemistry can be readily adapted to the synthesis of vinyl ether end-capped polyurethanes (Figure 175).

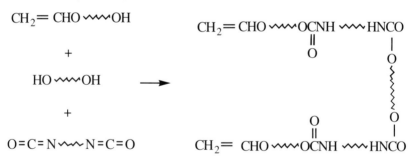

Figure 175: A vinyl ether terminated oligomeric urethane

2-Chloroethyl vinyl ether has been used to prepare vinyl ether terminated aromatic ethers (Figure 176).

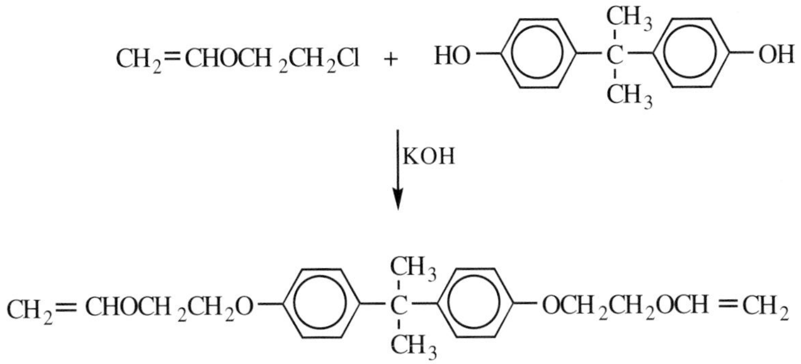

$$CH_2 = CHOCH_2CH_2Cl \quad + \quad HO \text{---} \bigcirc \overset{CH_3}{\underset{CH_3}{\text{---}C\text{---}}} \bigcirc \text{---} OH$$

$$\downarrow KOH$$

$$CH_2 = CHOCH_2CH_2O \text{---} \bigcirc \overset{CH_3}{\underset{CH_3}{\text{---}C\text{---}}} \bigcirc \text{---} OCH_2CH_2OCH = CH_2$$

Figure 176: Vinyl ether terminated aromatic ether

Such a route offers the opportunity of functionalising novolak resins.

Of particular interest to the adhesives industry is the preparation of vinyl ether siloxanes. These may be prepared via the hydrosilylation of allyl vinyl ether (Figure 177).[240]

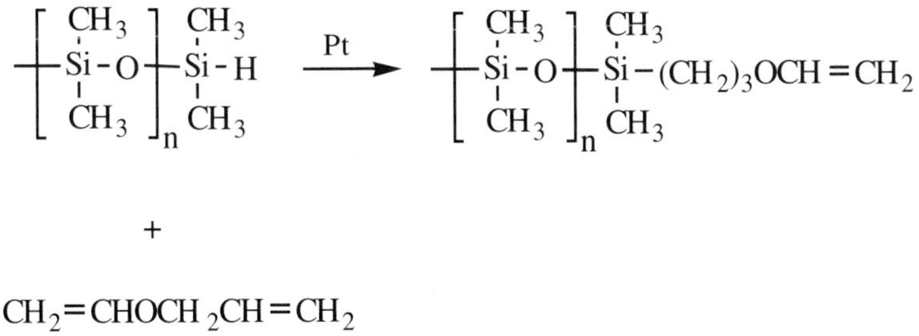

$$\left[\begin{matrix} CH_3 \\ | \\ Si-O \\ | \\ CH_3 \end{matrix} \right]_n \begin{matrix} CH_3 \\ | \\ Si-H \\ | \\ CH_3 \end{matrix} \quad \overset{Pt}{\longrightarrow} \quad \left[\begin{matrix} CH_3 \\ | \\ Si-O \\ | \\ CH_3 \end{matrix} \right]_n \begin{matrix} CH_3 \\ | \\ Si-(CH_2)_3OCH = CH_2 \\ | \\ CH_3 \end{matrix}$$

$$+$$

$$CH_2 = CHOCH_2CH = CH_2$$

Figure 177: A vinyl ether terminated siloxane

CHAPTER XII

ASSESSING THE QUALITY OF A COATING

CHAPTER VII

VII   ASSESSING THE QUALITY OF A COATING

(i)   Factors Affecting the Quality of a Coating[241, 242, 243,244]

To define the quality of a coating requires one to know for what purpose the coating has been produced. Thus the protective coating on a compact disc will be expected to meet criteria which would be inappropriate for a clear varnish overcoat applied to the cover jacket of a book. For this reason the term "functionally-cured" is sometimes used to indicate the point at which the desired performance characteristics of the coating have been attained. This is very different to the term fully cured which implies all the reactive groups e.g. acrylates have been consumed in the radiation curing process. To assess whether a coating is functionally-cured requires the use of empirical tests whereas to determine the extent of functional group conversion requires the making of precise measurements. Before looking at the test methods in detail it is worth pointing out that a coating will "fail" if the cure process has not taken place in the appropriate way and furthermore, the coating will not possess the right properties unless the choice of molecular backbone in the prepolymer has been made correctly. For a coating to stand a chance of being classified as satisfactory it is essential that sufficient of the functional groups have been utilised and the molecular weight of the polymer and degree of crosslinking are appropriate i.e. the chemistry has to take place satisfactorily to obtain a good coating.

(ii)   Empirical Test Methods

(a)   The "Thumb-Twist" Test[242, 243]

In this simple test the coating is touched with a finger to determine if (a) there is tackiness, or (b) whether the film produced slips off the substrate when the finger is pushed along the coating. If the surface of a film produced by radical polymerisation is tacky, then in all probability the surface has not cured properly due to oxygen inhibition. This situation may be remedied by use of either a more efficient photoinitiator system, which incorporates a sacrificial photoinitiator (a low cost Type I initiator) whose radicals will be used primarily to scavenge oxygen, or by adding an appropriate tertiary amine to reduce the oxygen inhibition. Occasionally surface tackiness can be caused by the use of too much photoinitiator (e.g. benzophenone) with the result that some of the initiator migrates to the surface of the film where it exhibits a plasticising effect. The occurrence of surface tackiness with cationically cured films can sometimes be due to the curing being carried out under conditions of high humidity.

If a film cures at and near the surface but not at the bottom, the film will exhibit no adhesion to the substrate. Such an effect usually arises because the lower regions of the film have received insufficient light. Under these circumstances it is necessary to review the initiator package being used and to take proper account of the light absorbing properties of the resin and of the pigment if a pigment is present. The use of strongly absorbing photoinitiators with thick films can give rise to poor through cure. Often an effective remedy is to use a bleachable photoinitiator.

If the coating appears hard to the to the finger, it may then be examined by the thumb twist test. The thumb is planted firmly on the coating and then twisted back and forth several times. If a good hard coating has been obtained this treatment will have no effect on the coating whereas if it is soft due to incomplete cure it will scuff. A "mechanical version of the thumb twist" is available. The number of thumb twists required to mark a coating is a good indicator as to how crosslinking has occurred. It should, however, be borne in mind that the rigidity of the coating will also reflect the nature of the molecular backbone of the prepolymer e.g. a polyether backbone will give a softer coating than aromatic ester backbone.

(b)   Solvent Rub Test[242, 243]

In this test a cloth soaked in solvent (usually methyl ethyl ketone or acetone) is rubbed backwards and forwards across the coating until the coating is finally rubbed away to reveal the substrate. This test may be carried out by hand or mechanically. The number of double rubs (one in each direction) gives an idea as to the amount of crosslinking that has occurred. In a study of the u.v. and e.b. curing of films of HDDA, it was found that the e.b. cured coating showed much greater solvent resistance than u.v. cured coatings for which a similar number of acrylate groups had been polymerised. These experiments showed that e.b. radiation induces crosslinking (via the backbone as well as via the acrylate groups) at a much earlier stage than u.v. radiation (where crosslinking occurs via the acrylate group and the terminal benzoyl groups introduced in the polymerisation process).

(c)   The Permanganate Stain Test[243]

In this test a small amount of potassium permanganate solution (1% w/v in water) is applied to the coating to cover an area about ½" diameter. If there is some unreacted material in the coating, manganese dioxide is produced and this stains the coating. The permanganate solution is washed off the coating and the intensity of the brown stain measured. This gives an idea as to how much unreacted material is present in the coating. If the test is repeated on a similar sample, several hours after the first sample, the intensity of the brown stain will reveal if oxidisable materials have migrated to the surface during this period of time.

(d)   Hardness Measurements[241]

The rigidity of a crosslinked structure and the mechanical strength of the material are the main contributors to the hardness of the material. The degree of hardness exhibited by a material is very dependent upon the method used to assess the hardness. Some of the methods employed are:

(i)   Resistance of a material to indentation by a spherical or pointed indenter.

(ii)   Resistance to a material to scratching by another material e.g. by a sharp point drawn across the surface or by rubbing with an abrasive.

(iii)   Energy absorbed from an oscillating pendulum.

(iv)   Energy absorbed from a dropped object.

One of the simplest tests of this type is the pencil hardness test.[242] Lead pencils are classified to the hardness of the graphite lead ranging from 2B (very soft) to 9H (very hard). The coated surface to be tested is positioned under a device which holds the pencil in a vertical position and in such a way that the pencil is applying pressure to the coating. The coating is then pulled through the device. Lead pencils of increasing hardness are used successively until one is found which makes a visible mark on the test surface. The hardness of the pencil causing the mark is assigned to the hardness of the coating e.g. 2H. The test is quick and gives a rapid indication as to the hardness of the coating. Unfortunately the steps in the hardness between grades of pencils is not uniform. Nevertheless, this method is used extensively by the coatings industry.

The pendulum test is a far more sophisticated test than the pencil hardness test. For this method to be utilised the coating must be at least 30μm thick and applied to a flat surface. The coating and its substrate are used to support the fulcrum of a beam which carries weights at its extremities (Figure 178). The pendulum is set in motion and the time taken for te amplitude of the oscillation to reduce to a particular value is noted e.g. from 6° to 3°.

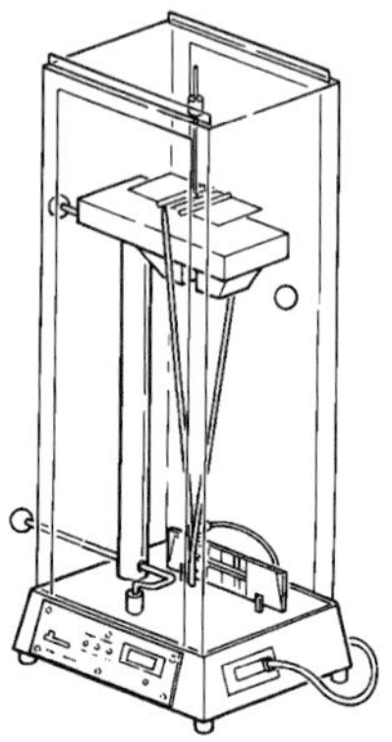

Figure 178: Pendulum hardness tester.

The hardness of the coating is calculated by using the equation

$$Hp = t / (2.303 (\log A_0 - \log A_t)$$

where Hp is the hardness (in units of seconds) and A_0 and A_t are the initial amplitude and amplitude after time t respectively.

The value Hp reflects the damping effect of the coating. If a very hard coating is used, little damping of the pendulum will be observed whereas the reverse is true for a very soft coating. It is found that Hp gives a good indication as to the extent of crosslinking and can be used to give an idea of the extent of cure. It should be noted that the value of Hp is highly dependent upon the type of substrate e.g. the same type of coating on glass and a composite board give very different results.

(e) Brittleness

This test involves folding a coated substrate through 180° and assessing the amount of debris along the crease. An arbitrary scale from 1 (no debris, i.e. flexible coating) to 5 (large amount of debris, very brittle) is used. Brittleness/flexibility of a coating reflects the extent of crosslinking and the molecular structure of the prepolymer and diluents.

(iii) Quantitative Test Methods

(a) Infra red Spectroscopy

This spectroscopic method is useful for determining the extent to which the functional group has been utilised in the curing process. To examine a coating attached to its substrate, e.g. paper, plastic or metal, requires the use of special sampling techniques. The successful introduction of high quality FTIR (Fourier Transform Infra Red) spectrometers at a reasonable cost has opened up the way for these more specialised sampling methods to be used routinely and with much greater precision.

Use of a photoacoustic spectroscopy detector has proven invaluable for examining coatings applied to paper and similar substrates. The photo acoustic effect was first described by Alexander Graham Bell as long ago as 1881.[245] The detection system consists of a hermetically sealed cell which has a window for admitting the i.r. radiation and one face is linked to a microphone (Figure 179).

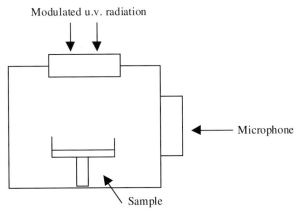

Figure 179: Photoacoustic cell

Absorption of i.r. radiation leads to excitation of particular bonds causing them to undergo vibration e.g. stretching, bending, rocking etc. The absorbed energy is degraded to heat and the periodic change of temperature at the surface of the sample leads to the production of acoustic waves which are detected by the microphone. It is possible in some cases, by varying the modulation frequency of the i.r. beam to depth profile the sample. Photoacoustic spectroscopy has been used with success to monitor the degree of cure on a paper substrate as a function of e.b. dose.[139, 193] Another frequently used sampling method is attenuated total reflectance (ATR) (often referred to as multiple internal reflectance spectroscopy - MIR).[139] A schematic drawing of the attachment is shown in Figure 180.

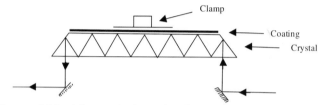

Figure 180: Attenuated total reflectance accessory

The coating is applied to the surface of the crystal and with the aid of a clamp, good contact between the coating and the crystal face can be obtained. This is essential if any quantitative work is to be done. The extent to which the i.r. beam enters the coating is determined by the type of crystal used (e.g. zinc selenide or germanium) and the angle of cut at the extremities of the crystal. Coatings applied to paper, glass etc. can be readily examined by this method. The method has also been used to determine the extent of surface and through cure of some acrylate formulations in which acylphosphine oxides were used as initiators.[246] A major advantage of the ATR accessory is that the analysing i.r. beam interrogates the sample surface many times and this is invaluable for obtaining a signal having a good signal to noise ratio. This is of major importance when very thin films e.g. $2\mu m$. are being examined.

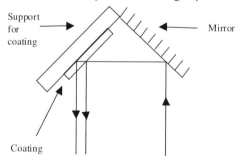

Figure 181: Reflectance attachment

The much simpler and far less costly attachment is the specular reflectance accessory (Figure 181). In this device the a beam of i.r. radiation impinges on the surface of the coating.[139] The incident radiation may be partially reflected by the surface and this gives the specular reflectance spectrum. If the support is a good reflector of i.r. radiation, some of the i.r. radiation may be transmitted by the coating to the surface of the support where it is reflected and emerges from the coating thereby giving a reflection-absorption spectrum. Thus spectra obtained with the reflection-attachment are often composite spectra and contain reflection-absorption and specular components. An example taken from the cationic curing of an epoxide is shown in Figure 182.

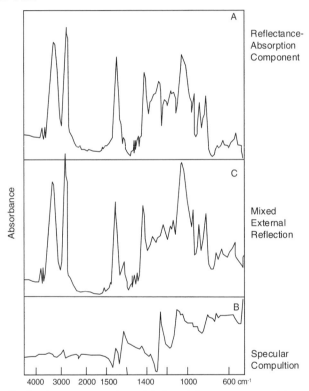

Figure 182: Reflectance spectra obtained from an epoxide coating

(b)   Raman and Confocal Raman Spectroscopy

A matter of great interest to anyone producing coatings is the extent of cure at different depths in the coating. Limited information is afforded by the attenuated total reflectance i.r. spectroscopy and by photoacoustic spectroscopy (both i.r. and u.v.). A relatively new technique which is well suited for depth profiling cured films is confocal Raman spectroscopy. Confocal microscopy (classical visible light and fluorescence microscopies) has been used by biologists for a number of years and the power of this type of microscopy which lies in its ability to allow the observer to see what is happening at specific depths in the sample has now been harnessed to the analytical facilities of Raman spectroscopy. Real Time Raman Spectroscopy has been used with success to monitor the cationic cure of vinyl ethers[247] The experimental arrangement is relatively simple (Figure 183).

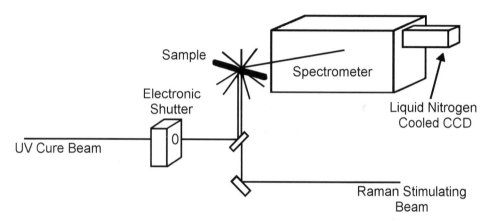

Figure 183: Experimental arrangement for monitoring cure in real time using Raman Spectroscopy

Cure could be monitored by following the decrease in intensity of the peaks associated with the double bond which are found at 1322, 1622 and 1636 cm^{-1} .

A schematic layout of a confocal Raman Spectrometer for examining specimens following cure is shown below. Such equipment allows a $1\mu m^3$ volume to be spectroscopically interrogated.at magnification of 100X. The capabilities of the technique have been demonstrated in several ways[248].

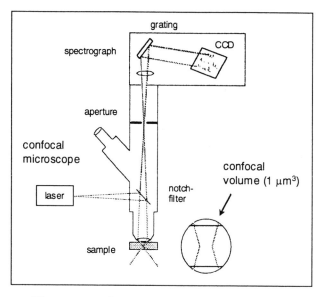

Figure 184: Confocal Raman Spectrometer

The Figure shown below shows Raman spectra of a cured polyether acrylate film and it can be seen that the spectra in the middle and bottom of the film possess weaker absorbancies due to acrylate groups than do the spectra associated with the surface and near the surface.

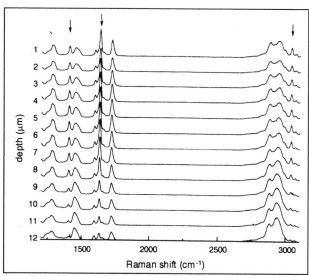

Figure 185: Depth profile of a cured polyether acrylate film

In similar fashion it was shown that including a tertiary amine into the system or applying a protective surface to the uncured polyether acrylate film led to a significant reduction in the number of uncured acrylates at the surface. The technique has also been used to show that when thick films (e.g. 500μm) (Figure186) are cured that undercure in the lower regions of the film can be detected and quantified and that the problem can be remedied by use of an appropriate photoinitiator. Such studies should be of great value in determining the reasons for adhesion failure of coatings.

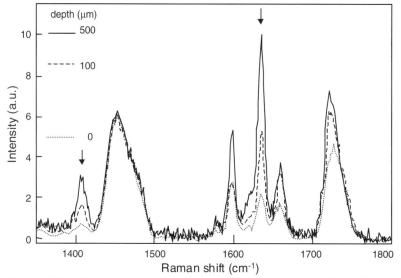

Figure 186: Raman spectra of a cured polyether acrylate films at varying depths

To study pigmented films requires the films to be microtomed so that the distribution of the groups of interest can be mapped laterally. In this way it was shown that 30μm thick film containing 10% titanium dioxide was fully cured on the bottom surface but the top of the film was not fully cured due to oxygen inhibition. Lateral mapping has also been used to map the distribution of u.v. absorbers and light stabilisers (HALS) in a cured film. Such additives can influence the curing process and in the case of u.v. absorbers they compete with the initiator for light thereby reducing the rate of cure. That this is the case has been demonstrated and again the results show how necessary it is to choose the right initiator. Mapping the whereabouts of the additives in the cured films is also important in assessing how successful such materials may be in preventing weathering of the films. It is clear that there are many more applications of this versatile technique[249].

(c)   Electron Spectroscopy for Chemical Analysis (ESCA)[241]

This is an extremely powerful tool for examining the atomic composition of surfaces. The surface of the sample is bombarded with a soft x-ray beam and this leads to <u>photoionisation</u> (i.e. loss of a core electron), <u>shake-up</u> (which is excitation of a valence electron from an occupied to an unoccupied electronic level simultaneously with photoionisation) and <u>shake-off</u> which is ionisation of a valence electron accompanying photo-ionisation. The energy associated with each of these processes is determined by the element with which the electron is associated and bonding associated with that element. Thus oxygen may be present both as an ether and a carbonyl group. The binding energy of the oxygen electrons is sufficiently different in these two groups for the two groups to be distinguished. Thus ESCA gives information concerning elemental composition (except hydrogen) and specific details concerning chemical structure. In addition the technique can also be used to depth profile coatings and to determine their surface homogeneity. ESCA has been used with some success to study weathering (i.e. photodegradation in natural and simulated sunlight) of radiation cured coatings. For acrylate coatings cured using a Type II photoinitiator system it could be shown that the amine component of the initiator system had migrated to the surface.

(d)   Sol-gel Analysis[241]

A sol may be defined as a material which is soluble in good solvents e.g. dichloromethane, tetrahydrofuran, acetonitrile and consists of linear or branched chains. A gel is considered to be a material which is insoluble in good solvents (although it may be swelled by such solvents) and is composed of crosslinked polymer chains. For a coating the gel content can be considered as that portion of the coating which remains after it has been extracted with a good solvent. Usually the extraction is carried out using a Soxhlet extractor. By weighing the sample before and after extraction the gel content can be ascertained. If the curing process has been successful a very high gel content should result. However, the usual radiation curable coatings will give rise to extractables composed of photoinitiator, photoinitiator degradation products, amine synergist, unpolymerised monomers and any non-polymerisable additives which make up the formulation (e.g. antioxidants, u.v.screens, slip agents). With the increasing legislation it is now becoming more important to identify and quantify the extractables since they be considered migratables within the coating. To reduce the amount of migratables attributable to photoinitiators, polymeric photoinitiators have been synthesised. In the case of a

Type II (benzophenone) polymeric photoinitiator, when used with an acrylate formulation and N,N-dimethylethanolamine as synergist it was found (using g.c.-mass spectrometry) that the cured coating contained extractables which were in the main unpolymerised acrylates and amine synergists (Figure 187).

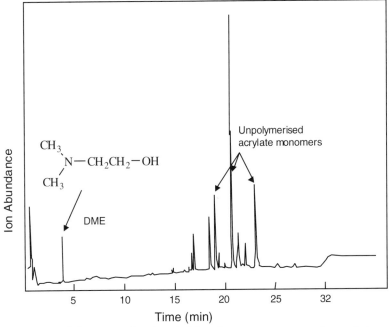

Figure 187: GC trace of extractables from a u.v. cured acrylate coating (mass spectrometer used as the detector

(e)   Dynamic Mechanical Thermal Analysis (DMTA)[241]

This analytical method allows the mechanical properties of a polymer sample to be recorded over a range of temperatures (-150^0 to 500^0C). Samples can analysed as free standing films, or as coatings on supports such as glass braid. For thin films as encountered with radiation cured coatings, formulations are often applied to a braid, cured, and then analysed. The samples are subjected to a sinusoidal mechanical stress to produce a sinusoidal strain of pre-selected amplitude. The samples possess both a Storage Modulus (E') and a Loss Modulus (E''). E' is a measure of the energy stored per cycle of strain and is associated with the in phase stress. E'' is associated with the energy lost in the cycle due to heat loss. The ratio E''/E' is equal to tan δ. It is easier to understand the term δ by reference to the Figure 188.

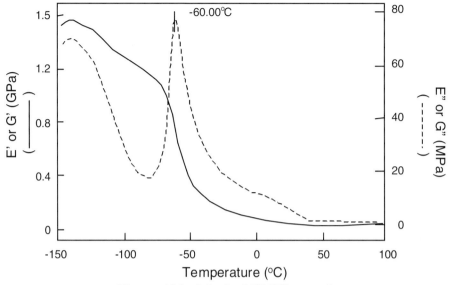

Figure 188: A typical DMTA report

Information on how a sample performs is usually presented as a plot of E' and tan δ versus temperature. A typical plot is shown in the Figure and relates to u.v. cured composite based on an epoxy acrylate containing 4 plies of stitched unidimensional glass fibre cloth.

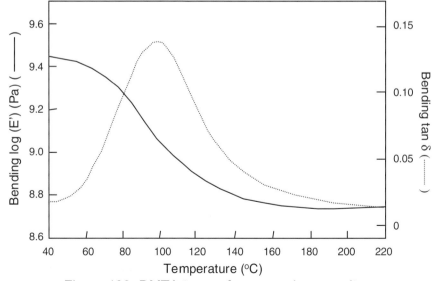

Figure 189: DMTA trace of u.v. cured composite

The reduction in E' with temperature marks the gradual change from the solid to the liquid state whereas the maximum in the tan δ plot is the Tg of the sample (~100°C). Other parameters such as crosslink density can be determined by DMTA. If it is wished to compare the properties of films produced from different formulations, a glass braid can be dipped into the formulation and the coated braid cured and then tested in the normal way[250] The results for a u.v. curable water-borne coating are shown in the Figure 190.

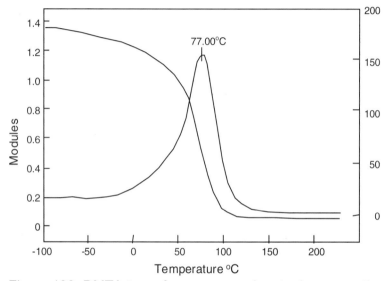

Figure 190: DMTA trace for a u.v. cured water-borne coating

Undoubtedly DMTA is one of the most powerful methods for characterising a coating in terms of its properties and for predicting the performance of a coating.

(f)   Differential Scanning Calorimetry

Calorimetry is used to determine the amount of heat given out or taken in by a process. Softening, melting, thermal degradation are endothermic processes whereas many polymerisation processes are exothermic. The temperatures which these processes occur are dependent upon the composition of the system. A differential calorimeter allows formulations to be heated over a range of temperatures so that the temperatures at which these different processes can be recorded. The equipment consists of two sample pans that can be heated with their temperatures being recorded by the use of thermocouples. Information from the thermocouples is fed into an electronic system, which controls the heating of the pans so that they are both maintained at the same temperature. One pan is used for the formulation and the other for a blank. If, as the pans are being heated, an endothermic process occurs more energy will have to be supplied to the sample pan if it is to be kept at the same temperature as the pan containing the blank. The amount of energy supplied is directly related to the number of calories required to bring about the endothermic process undergone by the sample. If the sample undergoes an exothermic process, heat will have to be supplied to the pan containing the blank and the energy required to do this is directly related to the amount of heat liberated by the sample.

An important parameter for any coating and indeed polymer is its glass transition temperature, Tg since this property will determine under what conditions the material may be used. In the case of radiation cured coatings it is also related to the degree of cure (number of polymerisable groups consumed). The glass transition temperature is that temperature at which there is enough thermal energy to allow conformational movement. For a linear polymer having a polydispersity of one (i.e. it has a unique molecular weight) the T_g will be a discrete value. When chains of different lengths are present in the polymer (i.e. the polymer has a polydispersity >1) each having their own discrete Tg values the endotherm as recorded by the calorimeter will be spread over a range of temperatures and as a consequence it is no longer observed as a sharp peak on the output but as a broad peak. If this peak becomes very broad it becomes difficult to observe. This situation is commonly found with crosslinked polymer systems since the length of the chains between chains is likely to vary enormously and hence there is a large range Tg's. For this reason DSC is not used to any great extent for determining Tg values of cured coatings but it is valuable in many cases for determining the extent to which unpolymerised groups are present in the coating. For coatings produced by polymerising acrylates, heating the coating leads to thermal polymerisation of residual acrylate groups and this registers as an exotherm with the amount of heat liberated being proportional to the number of groups thermally polymerised.

(g)   Glass Transition Temperature (Tg)[241]

The Tg of a coating reflects the molecular structure of the prepolymer and diluent, the extent of polymerisation and the degree of crosslinking. Given that in the curing process the liquid formulation is transformed into a sol and then into a gel, the temperature at which the curing is occurring is vitally important. As the temperature of cure is increased, so the onset of gelation will be delayed and hence a greater proportion of the polymerisable groups will be utilised. Thus the temperature at which cure occurred will be reflected in the Tg value and this value will never significantly above the cure temperature.

DMA (DMTA) can be used to determine Tg values of coatings but the method does have some limitations e.g. it could not be used to determine Tg values of thin coatings on a metal substrate. DSC also is rather limited in that it is very difficult to monitor the heat flow changes associated with Tg for crosslinked system. An alternative method which does cope with such samples is based on the fact that disperse dyes enter polymers at temperatures which are associated with their soften-ing i.e. their Tg.[251] If a fluorescent dye is used the entry of the dye into the polymer can be readily tracked by fluorescence microscopy. The equipment is shown in diagrammatic form in Figure 191.

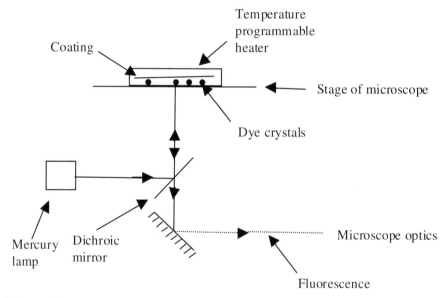

Figure 191: Fluorescence microscope and attachment for determining the Tg of thin layers of polymers

Using this equipment the influence of varying the ratio of reactive diluent to prepolymer and of varying the amount of amine synergist upon Tg values was obtained (Figure 192).

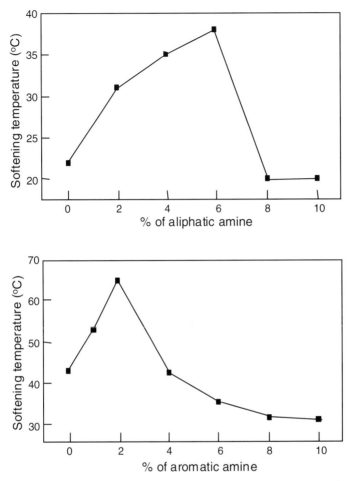

Figure 192: Effect of varying the amount of amine synergist upon
the Tg of a cured acrylate film

(h) Microwave Dielectrometry[241]

The dielectric properties of a coating are very different to those of the reactive
diluent and the prepolymer used to produce the coating. Their differences are
sufficiently large as to enable measurement of dielectric properties to be used for
determining monomer : polymer ratio in the coating e.g. to determine the amount of
residual monomer. This method has also been used for following the curing
process.

CHAPTER XIII

METHODS FOR ASSESSING THE EFFICIENCY OF PHOTOINITIATION AND POLYMERISATION

CHAPTER VIII

METHODS FOR ASSESSING THE EFFICIENCY OF PHOTOINITIATION AND POLYMERISATION

In addition to characterising cured coatings it is of great importance to those developing new materials for the radiation curing industry, to know how effectively the polymerisation process is occurring. If, for instance, one is developing new photoinitiators it is advantageous to use well defined systems which enable to progress of reaction to be readily monitored. There is also a place for relatively simple screening methods which help to identify the most promising materials.

(i)   U.v./Visible Spectroscopy

Given that one is initiating reactions by means of u.v./visible light it is absolutely essential to know the u.v./visible absorption properties of all the components of the formulation and the transmission properties of any glass that is situated between the coating and the lamp. Whilst it is true that most manufacturers of photoinitiators show absorption spectra on their publicity data, it is rare to find such information for reactive diluents and prepolymers.

Given that prepolymers and reactive diluents are used in the absence of solvent it is essential to record their spectra as thin films by diffuse reflectance or by transmission spectroscopy using very short pathlength cells (e.g.1mm). The use of prepolymers containing aromatic groups can very effectively cut out light below 340nm at depths grater than 1µm.

U.v./visible absorption spectroscopy can be used to monitor the course of reactions. For photoinitiated free radical polymerisation reactions it is sometimes possible to monitor destruction of the photoinitiator. This is particularly true of bleachable photoinitiators such as 2-benzyl-2-dimethylamino-1-(4-

morpholinophenyl)butan-1-one (A) and acylphosphine oxides. The photodestruction of (A) in a curing formulation has been monitored in real time. (Figure 193)[252]

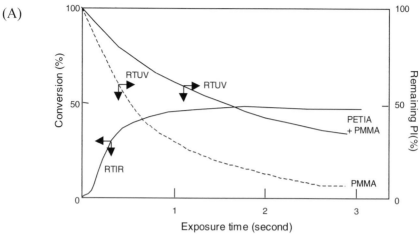

Figure 193: Use of real-time u.v. spectroscopy to follow the decomposition (A)

The α-cleavage of acylphosphine oxides destroys the chromophore which gives rise to the wavelength (λ_{max} 350nm) of these compounds. Consequently, if used in a clear lacquer formulation, the colour of the formulation changes from yellow to clear as the photoinitiator is destroyed.

$$
O\diagdown N\diagdown\!\!\!\!\bigcirc\!\!-\!\!\bigcirc\!\!-\!\!\underset{\underset{}{\overset{O}{\overset{||}{C}}}}{}\!\!-\!\!\underset{\underset{CH_2Ph}{|}}{\overset{\overset{CH_2CH_3}{|}}{C}}\!\!-\!\!N(CH_3)_2
$$

(A)

Many dyes, e.g. eosin, chlorophyll etc are photoreduced by tertiary amines and this leads to loss of their characteristic colour. This is particularly marked if curing is carried out under nitrogen. In the presence of air the reduced form of the dye (the leuco form) is oxidised by oxygen to regenerate the dye. Such changes can be conveniently monitored by u.v./visible absorption spectroscopy. A similar situation is encountered with 2,3-diphenylquinoxaline. Irradiation of this compound in the presence of a tertiary amine and under nitrogen leads to bleaching (Figure 194). When air is admitted, the quinoxaline is regenerated in high yield.

The regeneration process makes a very important contribution to the efficiency with which the quinoxaline initiates polymerisation.

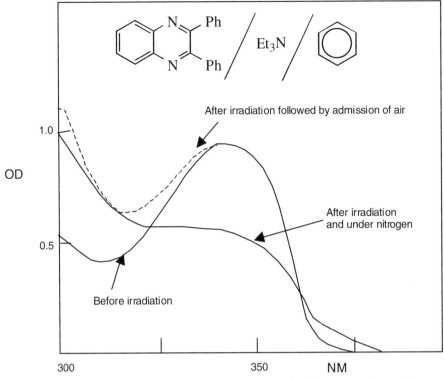

Figure 194: The photobleaching of 2,3-diphenylquinoxaline

RTIR spectroscopy (see Section VIII.iii) shows that when the quinoxaline tertiary amine system is used in the absence of oxygen it is very inefficient but when oxygen is present, polymerisation occurs efficiently.

Polymerisation processes which involve destruction of a chromophore can be followed by u.v./visible spectroscopy. The stilbazolium salts undergo a [2+2] cycloaddition process which destroys the conjugation between the two aromatic rings (Figure 47). As the cycloaddition reaction proceeds the absorption band at 360nm. decreases in intensity with concomitant increase in a new band at 270nm. Other cycloaddition reactions which can followed in this way include those associated with cinnamate (Figure 42) and chalcone groups (Figure 46).

U.v./visible diffuse reflectance spectroscopy finds extensive use in the determining the extent of yellowing that occurs on the curing of clear lacquers. A study has been made of the influence of that amine synergists have upon the colour of cured films and of the colour changes which ensue when these films are weathered in artificial sunlight.[72] A benzophenone-epoxy acrylate/TPGDA mix was used and various aminoalcohols used as synergist. When N-methyldiethanolamine is used the cured films initially undergo bleaching (first 20 hours of irradiation) and then the film begins to yellow. These effects can be readily seen from the diffuse reflectance spectra such as those shown in Figure 195.

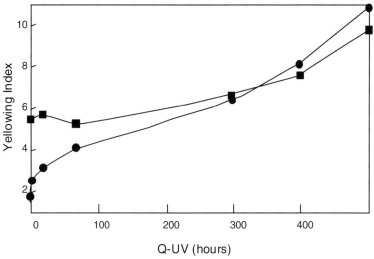

Figure 195: Photoyellowing which occurs upon irradiation of an epoxy acrylate film cured using benzophenone – triethanolamine mixture (n) and using benzophenone alone as initiator (l)

The extent of yellowing is often reported as a measurement of the Yellowness Index. These indices are determined by reflectance spectroscopy according to the standard test method ASTM-E313-73. Usually a colorimeter rather than a spectrometer is used for industrial testing. The yellowness indices are calculated using the equation below

$$YI = 100 \ (X\text{-}Z)/Y$$

where X,Y and Z are the tristimulus values associated with the reflectance at 650 (red), 450 (blue) and 550 (green) nm. There are other colorimetric methods which measure whiteness e.g. the Post Colour Number (PCN). This is obtained using a reflectometer operating at 457nm. and employing the equation.

$$PCN = 100 \ X \ [(K/S)_t - (K/S)_{t=0}]$$

Where:

$$K/S = (1 - R\infty)^2 / (2R\infty)$$

t_0 is the reflectivity of the standard sample and $R\infty$ is the reflectance of a sample through which no light is transmitted

(ii)   Fluorescence Spectroscopy

Occasionally photoactive chromophores fluoresce following excitation. A particular example is that of the stilbazolium salts (Figure 47). These compounds are acetalised onto poly(vinyl alcohols) and films of the polymer can be readily cast. The positively charged pendant groups tend to aggregate and this has a profound effect upon the fluorescence and photoactivity of the stilbazolium group. Aggregation leads to a new broad featureless fluorescence band (Figure 196).

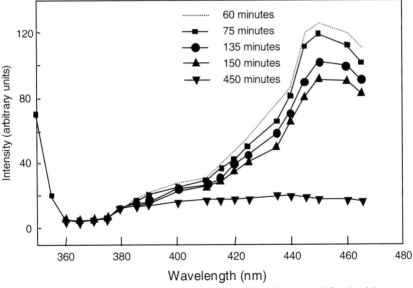

Figure 196: Fluorescence of a PVOH film modified with
a stilbazolium salt

When the films are irradiated this emission band decreases in intensity and this suggests that the cycloaddition process is favoured by aggregation.

Fluorescence probes have been used to monitor the photoinitiated polymerisation process. Examples are known of compounds where the fluorescent excited singlet state complexes with a ground state molecule thereby forming an excited dimer (excimer) whose fluorescence emission is red shifted from that due to the locally excited singlet state. A particularly well known example is that of pyrene.

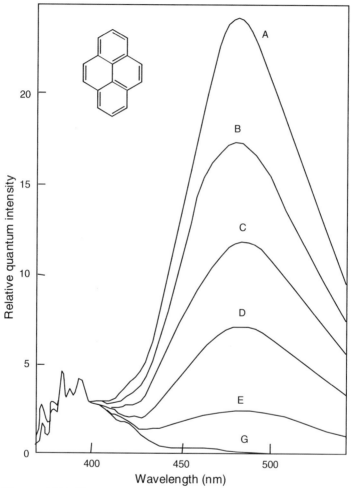

Figure 197: Fluorescence spectrum of a solution of pyrene

It will be noted that the excimer emission is broad and structureless as opposed to emission from the localised state which exhibits fine structure.[70] One of the parameters that has an effect upon the efficiency of formation of excimers is viscosity. Thus if pyrene is present at the appropriate concentration in a liquid radiation curable formulation, it will exhibit excimer formation but as the viscosity of the mixture increases upon curing the ratio of the intensity of the excimer emission to that from the localised state will change with the concentration from the latter increasing.[253] Excimer formation can be favoured by linking two molecules of the same type e.g. naphthalene or pyrene, via a flexible chain provided that the chain allows the two end groups to interact with each other, e.g. (B).

$$CH_2CH_2CH_2$$

(B)

Another type of probe is that which relies upon solvent viscosity affecting intramolecular motion. Compounds such as 4-N,N-dimethylaminobenzonitrile and 1-dimethylaminonaphthalene-5-sulphonyl-n-butylamide (1,5-DASB) form excited intramolecular charge transfer complexes (Figure 198).[254, 255]

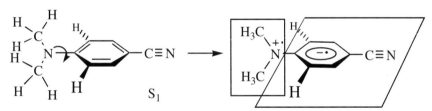

Figure 198: Conformational changes following excitation of 4-N,N-dimethylaminobenzonitrile

These complexes emit to the red of the localised excited singlet state and consequently the effect of increasing viscosity upon the twisting of the molecules is readily monitored by observing the change in intensity and spectral shift of the emission. In the case 1,5-DASB, increase in viscosity of the medium leads to a blue shift of the fluorescence band (Figure 199).

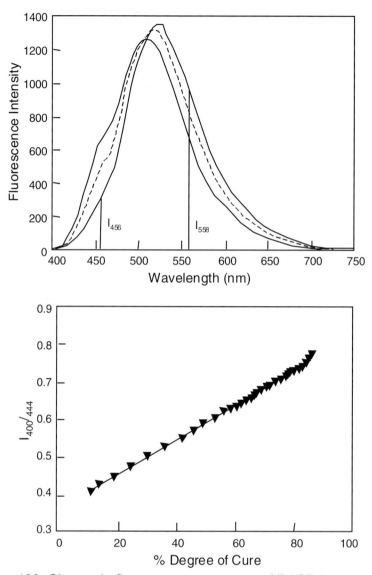

Figure 199: Change in fluorescence spectrum of DASB in an acrylate coating as a function of degree of cure

The extent of the shift to shorter wavelengths can be correlated with the amount of acrylate polymerised. An instrument (Figure 200) is now available for on-line monitoring of cure which relies upon these changes in fluorescence which occur as polymerisation proceeds.

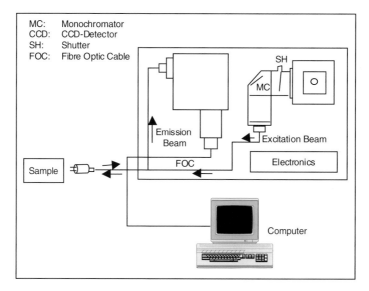

Figure 200: Diagram of a Radiation Cure Monitor

To use the technique it is necessary to dope the formulation to be cured with a suitable fluorescent species. In the case of acrylate and methacrylate formulations 1,5-DASB is suitable although the coumarin laser dye shown below has been used to good effect (Figure 201).

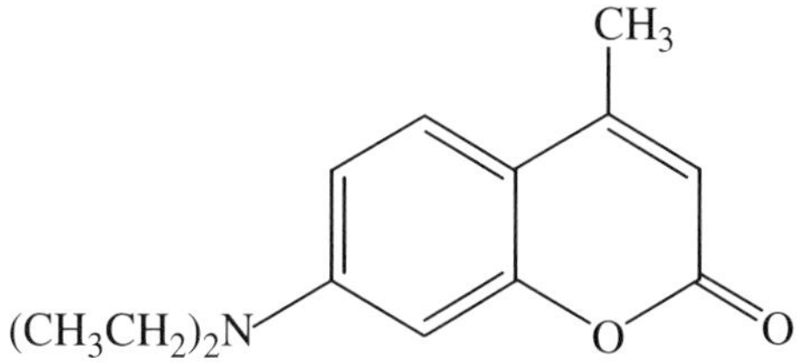

Figure 201: Coumarin laser dye used for on-line monitoring of cure

The fluorescent probe may be excited by the u.v. light being used to initiate polymerisation or from an external source and the cure monitor, which is in essence a spectrofluorometer, monitors the fluorescence intensity at two preselected wavelengths which when ratioed reflect the extent of the spectral shift and hence the degree of cure. This is illustrated in Figure 202. In (a), the raw data is displayed and in (b) the extent of cure as determined by the ratios of the emission intensity at 444 and 400nm is shown.

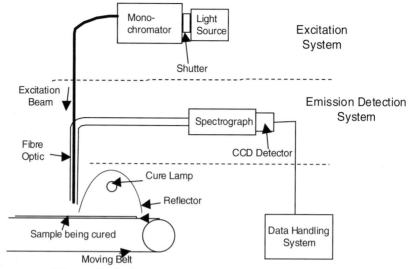

Figure 202: A commercial on-line monitor

It will be noted that the probes described so far are amines and consequently cannot be used to monitor the cure of cationic systems. Some suitable probes are the oligophenylenevinylenes such as the one shown in Figure 203.

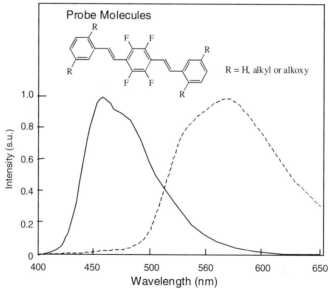

Figure 203: Structure of oligophenylenevinylene suitable for monitoringcationic cure plus fluorescence spectrum

The restriction in molecular motion caused by going from the solution to the solid phase manifests itself as a large blue shift as can be seen from the fluorescenc spectrum shown above. Such probes have been used for monitoring the cationic cure of an epoxy silicone[256].

The cure of pigmented radical and cationic systems have been monitored using this method but it is clear that some pigments may make it difficult to excite the probe or if they themselves are fluorescent, the fluorescence intensities as detected by the instrument will not reflect the degree of cure accurately.

(iii)   Infrared Spectroscopy[103, 241]

Infrared spectroscopy can be used to monitor the cure of acrylates, epoxides and vinyl ethers by following the rate of disappearance of absorption bands associated with these groups (810, 792 and 820cm^{-1} respectively) with time (Section VII.iii.(a)). The formulation to be cured may be applied to sodium chloride plates, metal etc. Following curing of the coating, i.r. spectra can be run. When sodium chloride plates are used, transmission spectra can be readily recorded. If the coating has been applied to a substrate that is not transparent to i.r. radiation, other sampling methods have to be used e.g. i.r. photoacoustic or attenuated total reflectance spectroscopy. In recent years a technique known as real time infrared spectroscopy has been introduced. The principle behind this method is that a sample, held in the i.r. spectrometer is irradiated with u.v. light and simultaneously, the decrease in absorption due to the group which is polymerising is monitored. A typical experimental layout is shown in Figure 204 and a typical plot obtained for curing an acrylate shown in Figure 205.

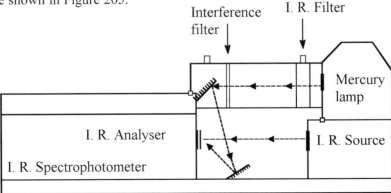

Figure 204: Outline of equipment used for carrying out RTIR spectroscopy

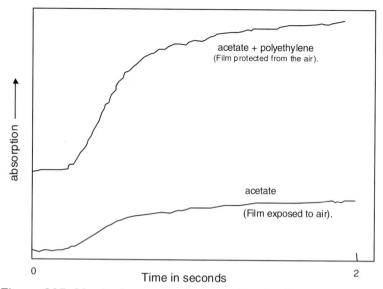

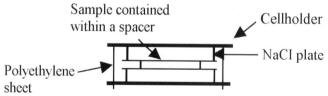

Figure 205: Monitoring cure of an acrylate by RTIR spectroscopy

If an FTIR rather than a dispersive ir spectrometer is used, spectra taken at relatively short intervals are recorded and from these spectra at the rate of decrease of a particular absorption band with time can be obtained. However, in this case the curve is produced by linking data points as opposed to the true curve produced by the dispersive instrument. Given that the sample is held in the vertical position, the formulation can run down the sodium chloride plate unless precautions are taken. If the sample is contained in a solution cell, there is always the danger that the solution will cure so well that the plates of the cell become permanently cemented together. In order to study multifunctional acrylates, which are most likely to give rise to this undesiribable effect, we apply the formulation to a polythene sheet that is equipped with a spacer of appropriate thickness. With the formulation inside the spacer, a second sheet of polythene is applied and then this sandwich interspersed between two sodium chloride plates (Figure 206).

Figure 206: Accessory to enable formulations which undergo crosslinking to be studied by RTIR

Polythene does not interfere too badly with observation of the i.r. absorbance bands associate with acrylates, epoxides and vinyl ethers.

To overcome the problems described above a new methodology has been introduced.[257] FTIR spectrometers can usually be interfaced with an i.r. microscope thereby enabling i.r. spectra of minute samples to be recorded. Such microscopes can be adapted so that u.v. light can be transmitted through the optics of the microscope so that it impinges upon the same area of the sample that is being interrogated by the i.r. beam. High sensitivity detectors (mercury cadmium telluride) are used with the microscope and this enables good quality spectra to be recorded after very few scans. The spectra can be stacked as u.v. irradiation proceeds and the results displayed as a set of spectra or a single band of interest selected and its change in absorption intensity with irradiation time displayed. Figure 207 shows the optical arrangements for simultaneous irradiation of the sample with u.v. and ir light and Figures 208 and 209 shows spectra obtained for curing of an acrylate and a vinyl ether respectively.

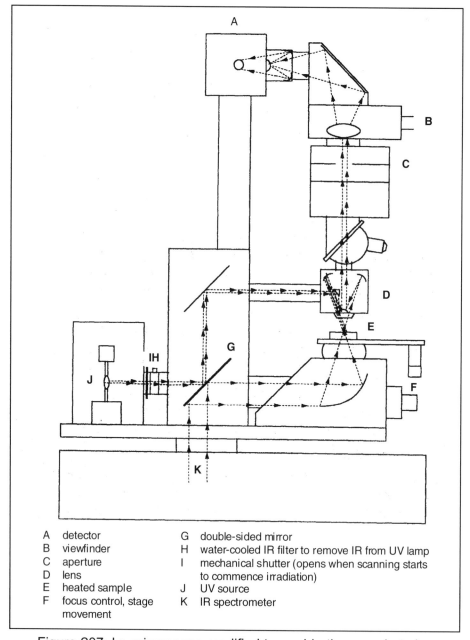

A   detector
B   viewfinder
C   aperture
D   lens
E   heated sample
F   focus control, stage
     movement

G   double-sided mirror
H   water-cooled IR filter to remove IR from UV lamp
I   mechanical shutter (opens when scanning starts
     to commence irradiation)
J   UV source
K   IR spectrometer

Figure 207: I.r. microscope modified to enable the sample to be irradiated with u.v. light

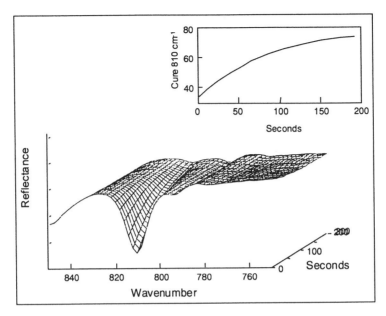

Figure 208: RTIR trace showing the cure of an acrylate

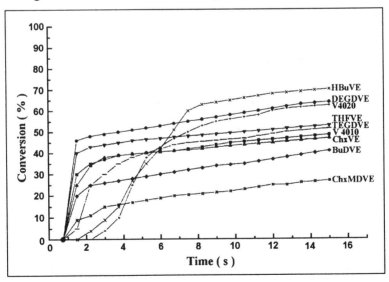

Figure 209: RTIR trace showing the cure of selected vinyl ethers

Use of the microscope enables samples in the horizontal position to be studied and this opens up a number of possibilities. In the attachment shown below provision is made to both heat the sample and to carry out cure under nitrogen or in air.

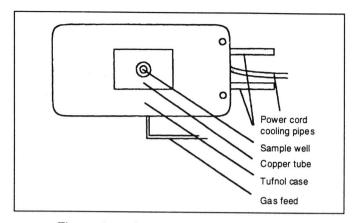

Figure 210: Attachment for microscope

The ability to study the influence of temperature upon the rate of cure was found to be particularly useful when investigating the cure of some acrylated liquid crystals where it was shown that the extent of cure was greatest when the crystals were aligned.

The facility to study the cure of samples at a number of different temperatures is very useful for investigating the cure of powder coatings[258] An accessory for an FTIR spectrometer which allows this is shown below.

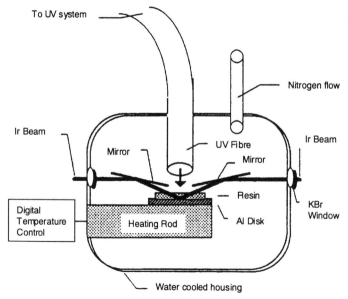

Figure 211: A large angle transflection (LARI) cell

The rate of cure of a powder coating at 110°C based on a maleate ester - vinyl ether system is shown below and the versatility of an FTIR spectrometer in allowing cure at two different wavelengths to be monitored simultaneously is underscored. The traces show that the fumarate and vinyl ether groups are being consumed concurrently which is consistent with the polymerisation process giving an alternating copolymer.

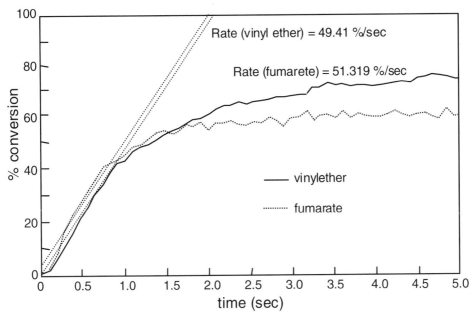

Figure 212: Cure of a powder coating based on a maleate-vinyl ether system

(iv)   Photodifferential Calorimetry (photo DSC, photo DPC)[259]

This method employs a differential scanning calorimeter operating in the isothermal mode (i.e. the sample is not heated or cooled) and the reaction is brought about the irradiation of the sample (Figure 213). In this way the rate of heat evolution and reaction rate can be recorded as a function of irradiation time.

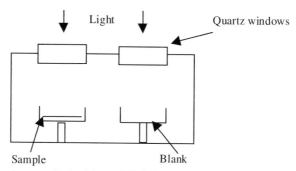

Figure 213: Modified sample holder of DSC apparatus to allow illumination of the sample and reference

Given that the heat evolved is proportional to the number of monomer moles reacted, the degree of monomer conversion (α) as a function of time can be calculated from the following equation

$$\alpha = ([M]_0 - [M]_t / [M]_t) \times 100 = (H_t/H_0) \times 100 \ (mol \ \%)$$

$[M]_0$ and $[M]_t$ are monomer concentrations before and after time (t) irradiation. H_0 is the heat of polymerisation associated with total conversion of monomer and H_t is the heat liberated after irradiation for time t. For such an equation to be of value it is necessary to know the amount of heat liberated upon full conversion. This may be calculated or alternatively determined experimentally. Thus if a simple monoacrylate is photopolymerised, with the heat liberated being determined and the degree of conversion of monomer measured by i.r. spectroscopy the amount of heat liberated for conversion of an acrylate bond can be calculated. A typical heat output with time is shown in Figure 214.

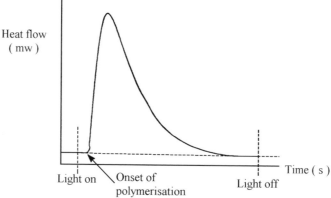

Figure 214: A typical photo-DSC trace

The total amount of heat evolved in the reaction is given by the area under the curve. Photo DSC has many uses e.g.

a)   The effect of using different light sources upon the reaction can be assessed.
b)   The effect of changing the excitation wavelength upon the reaction can be assessed.
c)   The effect of light intensity upon the reaction can be assessed.
d)   The effect of nitrogen inerting can be readily determined.
e)   The effect of temperature upon the reaction can be readily assessed.
f)   The effect of pigmentation upon the curing process can be readily seen.

Needless to say the method does have some limitations. The time constant (response time) of the instrument may be such that for fast reactions the heat output versus time graph may be distorted. There are difficulties associated with the sample pans used with the equipment. It is very difficult to get a uniform depth of sample due to the liquids creeping up the walls of the container. In addition the thickness to be cured (60μm) is often much greater than that of the coating for which the formulation is to be used. Nevertheless, despite the cited drawbacks, the technique is of real value. In a recent example a number of polymeric photoinitiators based on benzophenone synthesised and the relative efficiencies of these compounds at initiating polymerisation of a mixture of urethane acrylate and trimethylolpropane triacrylate were readily assessed (Figures 215 and 216).[260]

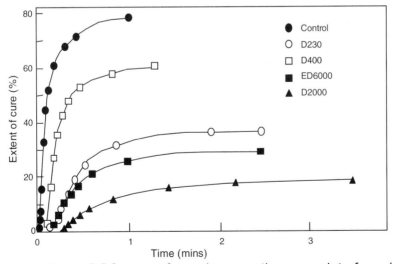

Figure 215: Photo DSC traces for curing a urethane acrylate formulation in air using polymeric benzophenone initiator systems

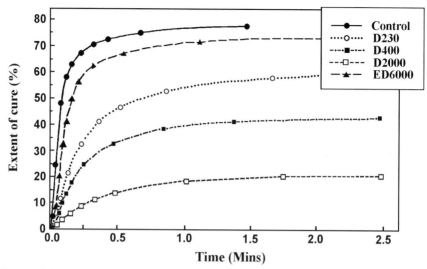

Figure 216: Photo DSC traces for curing a urethane acrylate formulation under nitrogen using benzophenone initiator system

The effect of nitrogen blanketing was particularly marked for the less efficient initiators. Examples have also been given of the curing of cationic systems such as epoxides to investigate the curing of a diepoxide initiated by an iron arene hexafluorophosphate. The trace of heat liberated versus time (Figure 217) indicates that a number of events are occurring.

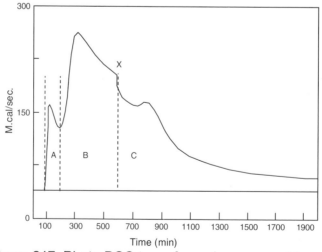

Figure 217: Photo DSC trace for curing an epoxide using a cationic photoinitiator

In region A of the curve it was proposed that the initiator was reacting with oxygen to give an iron(III) species which initiates polymerisation generating a layer of polymer on top of the liquid monomer. In region B, polymerisation is occurring in an oxygen depleted system which reduces the efficiency of the initiator. At point X, the light was turned off, but polymerisation continues (i.e. post cure) until vitrification sets in.

(v)   Gel Permeation Chromatography (gpc)[241]

GPC or size exclusion chromatography as it is sometimes called is an invaluable technique which relies upon molecular size for separation of the components of a mixture. If one makes the assumption that size (e.g. volume) equates to molecular weight, then the method can, if suitable standards are chosen, be used to determine molecular weight distribution. It is this application which makes the technique so valuable to polymer chemists.

If a cured coating is subjected to extraction, low molecular weight species e.g. unreacted photoinitiator, photoinitiator residues, amine synergist and oligomers are removed from the coating. HPLC analysed and HPLC/mass spectrometry, are ideal methods for identifying and quantifying the amount of non oligomeric products. GPC can be used to investigate the oligomeric products. The amount of low molecular weight (oligomeric materials) will be linked to such factors as photoinitiator concentration and light intensity and the occurrence of chain transfer processes.

GPC can only be used with solvent soluble materials and therefore restricts its use with crosslinked systems. Nevertheless, it is a highly valuable technique for investigating polymerisable systems. Thus if one wishes to assess the efficiency of a particular initiator system, the system is used to initiate polymerisation of a monoacrylate e.g. isodecyl acrylate. From the amount of polymer formed and the molecular weight distribution of the polymers and oligomers information concerning the initiation process can be deduced. An added advantage of using such a system is that the monoacrylate can be cured as a thin film using a typical radiation curing unit. GPC chromatographs are usually equipped with a refractive index and a variable wavelength detector. By means of the refractive index detector (RI) the relative amounts of polymer, oligomer and prepolymer can be determined. By judicious choice of the analysing wavelength, the end group (derived from the photoinitiator and in some cases the amine synergist) of the polymers and oligomers can be detected. Use of the results from the RI detector and the u.v. detector allows the amounts of end group present in the polymer and oligomer to be determined. By employing this methodology it was possible to show that a thioxanthone - ethyl 4-dimethylaminobenzoate initiator system for polymerisation of lauryl acrylate gave a polymer containing both a thioxanthone and amine groups.[81] In another example, a polymerisable thioxanthone (an acrylated thioxanthone) photoinitiator was used and by the use of the RI detector in conjunction with the u.v. detector it was possible to show that thioxanthone was incorporated into the polymer. This was most conclusively demonstrated when a u.v. monitoring system which employed a diode array detector was used (Figure 218).[187]

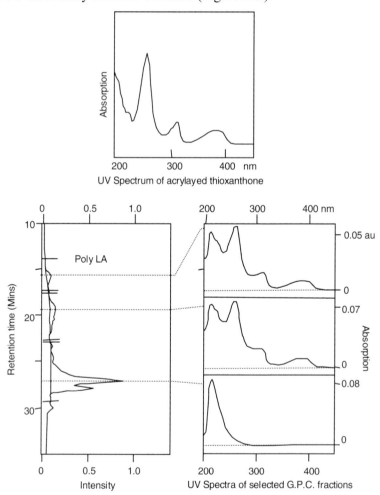

Figure 218: GPC trace and u.v. spectra of selected peaks, obtained from lauryl acrylate polymerised using an acrylated thioxanthones

CHAPTER IX

INVESTIGATING THE CHEMISTRY OF PHOTOINITIATORS

CHAPTER IX

INVESTIGATING THE CHEMISTRY OF PHOTOINITIATORS

Most users of photoinitiators rely on the information supplied by the manufacturer as to the type of reactions exhibited by the photoinitiator, its wavelength response and the by-products formed in the decomposition process. An in depth description of photophysical and photochemical processes is beyond the scope of this text and the reader is referred to some of the good books available for further reading[64,262]. Some of the methods available for studying the photochemistry of photoinitiators are outlined in subsequent sections.

(i)   Laser Flash Photolysis

The technique of flash photolysis was introduced by Norrish and Porter[263] and later, with the advent of lasers, laser flash photolysis was developed.[264] In its most frequently encountered form, the sample is photolysed by means of a short pulse of light (a few nanoseconds duration) and the transient products e.g. excited states (typically triplet states), radical ions and radicals are detected by u.v. spectroscopy. This method of detection requires the transient species to have a readily detectable absorption spectrum. When this is not the case, production of transients can be detected by optoacoustic spectroscopy.[265]

The Type I photoinitiator (C) in a variety of solvents was

$$\underset{\underset{CH_3}{|}}{Ph-\overset{\overset{O}{\|}}{C}-\overset{\overset{OH}{|}}{C}-CH_3} \qquad (C)$$

subjected to laser flash photolysis[69] and in this way the triplet yield (~ 0.25) was determined and evidence provided for the triplet state undergoing α-cleavage to give a benzoyl radical. When the hydroxyl group is replaced by an acetoxyl group, the triplets state is long lived indicating that α-cleavage is inefficient. Not surprisingly this compound is an inefficient photoinitiator.

Microsecond flash photolysis was used to established that amine synergists reduce triplet aromatic ketones to give ketyl derived from the ketone e.g. $Ph_2\dot{C}OH$

Later work, using nano- and femtosecond laser flash photolysis clearly established that the primary photochemical reaction is electron transfer from the amine to the triplet ketone (Figure 53).[266]

These examples illustrate how flash photolysis can be used to unravel the processes which lead to the generation of photoinitiating radicals.

(ii)   Electron Spin Resonance (E.S.R.)

This technique is used to demonstrate the presence of radicals in a system and to identify them. Two approaches are commonly used. In the first approach the initiator is irradiated in a cell located in the cavity of the e.s.r. spectrometer and therefore under favourable circumstances the radicals generated can be identified. When more than one type of radical is generated ENDOR spectroscopy can be used to advantage. Sometimes it is extremely difficult to obtain spectra of sufficient quality to identify the radicals. Under these circumstances spin trapping can often be used to advantage.[267] Compounds commonly used for such purposes are shown in Figure 219.

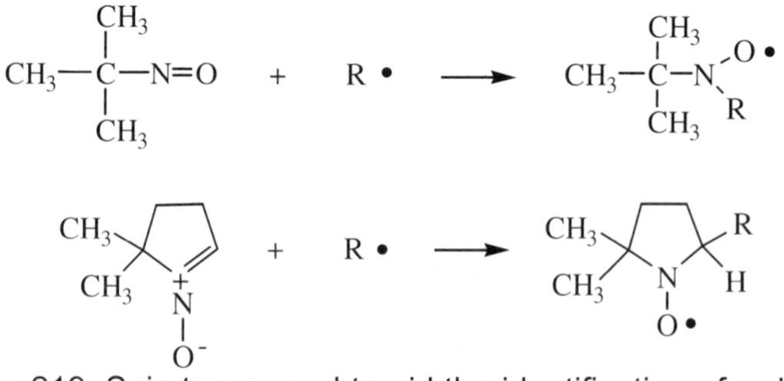

Figure 219: Spin traps used to aid the identification of radicals

Examples of the use of these techniques include the identification of ketyl radicals generated in the reaction of triplet ketones with tertiary amines and the trapping of aminoalkyl radicals generated on reaction of triplet thioxanthone with ethanolamines and triethylamine.[268] The radicals shown in Figure 220 were identified by these trapping reactions.

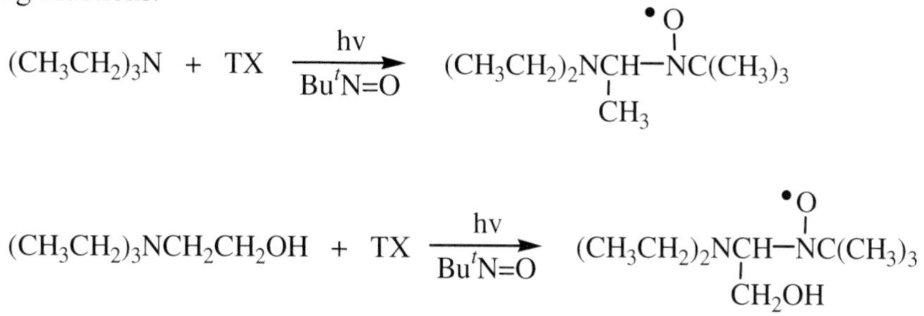

$$(CH_3CH_2)_3N \ + \ TX \ \xrightarrow[\text{Bu}^t\text{N=O}]{hv} \ (CH_3CH_2)_2NCH\overset{\displaystyle \overset{\bullet O}{\|}}{-}NC(CH_3)_3$$
$$\underset{CH_3}{|}$$

$$(CH_3CH_2)_3NCH_2CH_2OH \ + \ TX \ \xrightarrow[\text{Bu}^t\text{N=O}]{hv} \ (CH_3CH_2)_2NCH\overset{\displaystyle \overset{\bullet O}{\|}}{-}NC(CH_3)_3$$
$$\underset{CH_2OH}{|}$$

Figure 220: Trapping of α-aminoalkyl radicals with
2-methyl-2-nitrosopropane

In all cases cited so far the radicals have been generated in solution and are therefore free to tumble and to align themselves with the magnetic field thereby yielding highly resolved spectra which are essential for making unequivocal identification. There are many systems where radicals are generated in rigid matrices. Of relevance to radiation curing is the trapping of radicals in a polymerisation reaction after vitrification has set in.[269] For a polymerised 1,6-hexanediol diacrylate system the mid-chain radicals (D) (Figure 221) were identified. When 1,6-hexanediol dimethacrylate is polymerised the radicals present in the matrix are the end chain radicals (E).

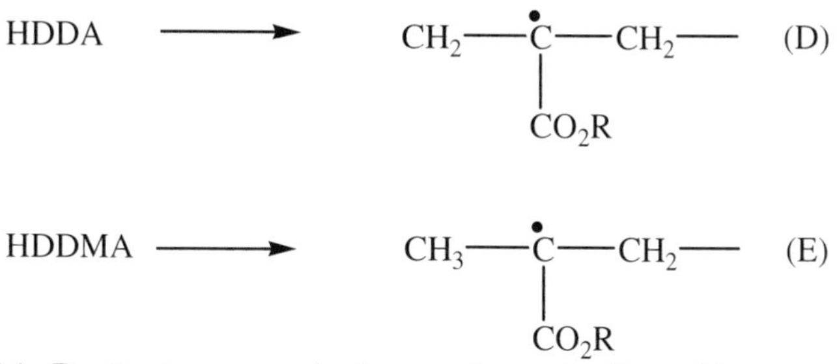

$$HDDA \ \longrightarrow \ CH_2\overset{\displaystyle \bullet}{-}\underset{\underset{CO_2R}{|}}{C}-CH_2- \quad (D)$$

$$HDDMA \ \longrightarrow \ CH_3\overset{\displaystyle \bullet}{-}\underset{\underset{CO_2R}{|}}{C}-CH_2- \quad (E)$$

Figure 221: Radicals generated on polymerisation of hexane-1,6-diol
diacrylate and dimethacrylate

The radicals are very long lived in the matrices in which they are present, provided oxygen is absent. Their reaction with oxygen leads to peroxyl radical production.

In all cases cited steady state steady state illumination has been used. It is possible, however, to use pulsed light sources and such experiments can lead to the discovery of much more information. This technique is known as time resolved <u>C</u>hemically

Induced Dynamic Electron Polarisation (CIDEP). CIDEP enables radicals to be identified and characterised and in addition determine whether they were generated from an excited singlet or triplet state. Using this technique the radicals produced upon irradiation of 2,4,6-trimethylbenzoyldiphenylphosphine oxide were characterised and the triplet state of the acylphosphine oxide shown to be their precursor.[91] Figure 222 shows the CIDEP spectrum and the occurrence of both absorption and emission lines observed. It is from the pattern of absorption and emission lines that the excited state responsible for radical production can be identified.

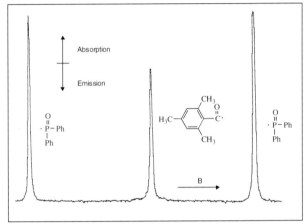

Figure 222: Radicals generated by photolysis of an acylphosphine oxide

(iii)   N.M.R. Spectroscopy[241]

Irradiation of mixtures contained within the cavity of an n.m.r. spectrometer (either ^{1}H or ^{13}C) can be invaluable in tracing product evolution. Thus if solutions of Type I photoinitiators in a non-polymerising medium are irradiated, the products derived by radical-radical combination and disproportionation can be identified. However, other effects can also be observed. In some cases the occurrence of cage reactions leads to signal intensities in the spectrum of the reaction products that deviate strongly from their chemical equilibrium values. This effect is known as chemically induced dynamic nuclear polarisation CIDNP (the n.m.r. equivalent of CIDEP). In CIDNP experiments both emission and enhanced absorption bonds are observed and it is from this information that using (Kaptein's rules) it may be deduced whether the products are derived from singlet or triplet radical pairs. The [1]H-FT-CIDNP spectra derived by investigating initiator (F) in deuterated benzene is shown in Figure 223.[74]

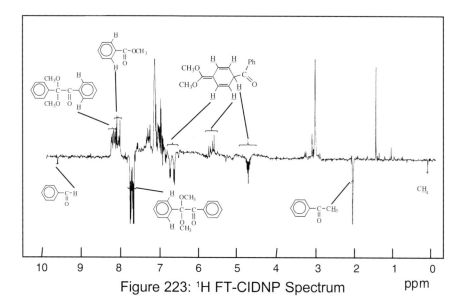

Figure 223: ^{1}H FT-CIDNP Spectrum

ppm

The spectrum shows, in addition to the resonance of the expected products i.e. benzaldehyde and acetophenone, the resonance due to the radical-radical combination products (G) (Figure 224).

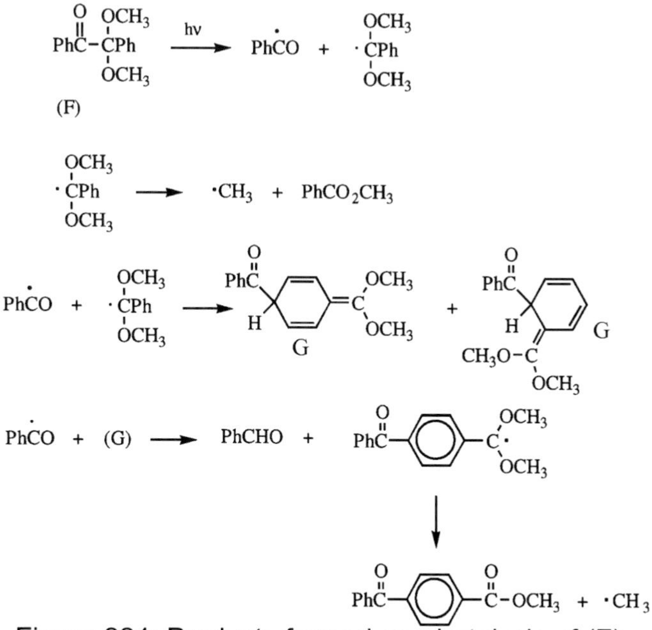

Figure 224: Products formed on photolysis of (F)

Time resolved CIDNP is used to separate radical-radical processes which occur via geminate radical pair processes (fast) and the much slower random phase processes which are diffusion controlled processes. A time resolved CIDNP spectrum (recorded 1μsec after the laser pulse) of the initiator H contained in degassed benzene is shown in Figure 225.[87]

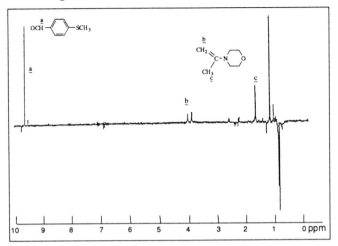

Figure 225: Time resolved ¹H n.m.r. CIDNP spectrum of an irradiated degassed sample of initiator (H) in the presence of 2-isopropylthioxanthone

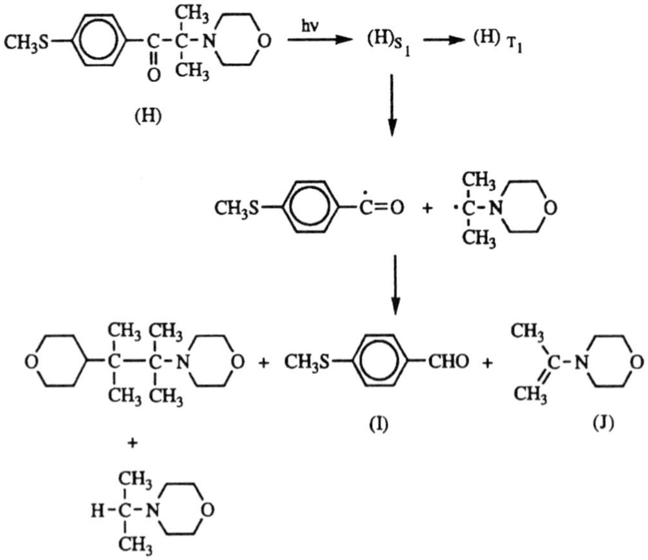

Figure 226: Products generated from the escaped radicals produced by irradiating H

These experiments demonstrated unequivocally that triplet thioxanthones can sensitise, via energy transfer, the α-cleavage of (H) (Figure 226). The strong signal seen at 9.64ppm (enhanced absorption) is due to the aldehyde proton of (I). Two signals due to the olefinic protons are observed at 3.98 and 3.86ppm. and are due to the methylene group present in (J). The methyl group of this compound is located at 1.68ppm. The strongly polarised signal at 0.87ppm. is due to the methyl groups of another product 2-(N-morpholino) propane.

(iv) Chemical Identification of Radicals Produced by Initiator Systems

Irradiation of Type I initiators generates two radicals. These radicals can be converted to stable compounds by radical trapping with nitroxyl radicals. The most frequently used of these traps is 2,2,6,6-tetramethylpiperidinoxyl (TMPO) (Figure 227).[8, 63]

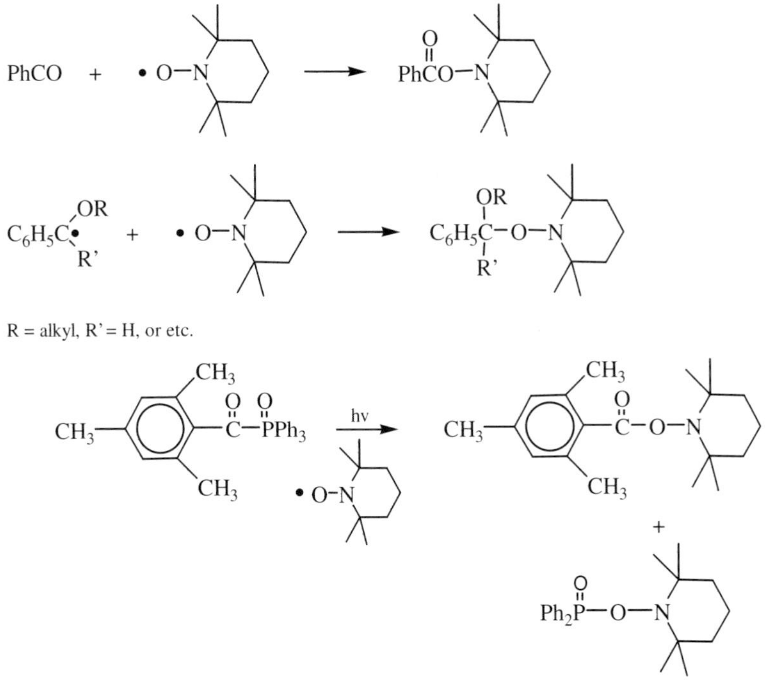

Figure 227: Trapping of photogenerated radicals with a nitroxyl radical

Structural elucidation of these products yields the structure of the trapped radical. Another highly successful way of trapping radicals is to use a non-polymerisable alkene[270]. 1,1-Diphenylethene and 1,1-di(4-methylphenyl)ethene have been used for this purpose (Figure 228).

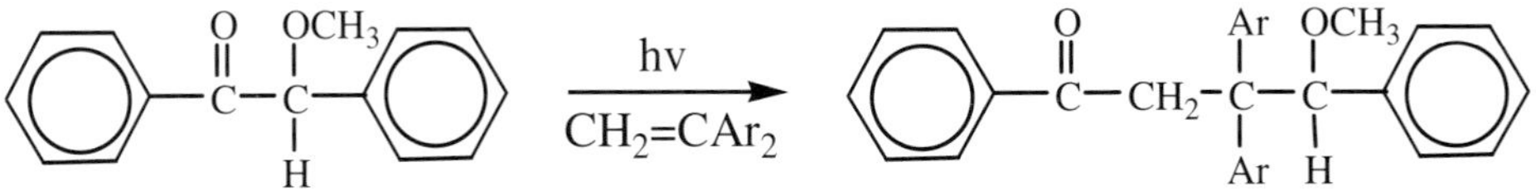

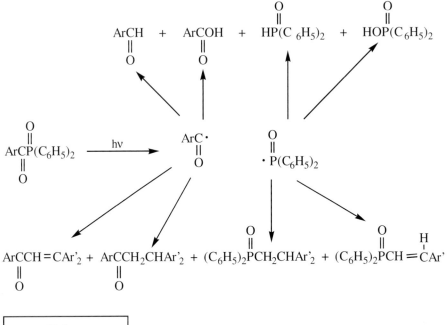

Figure 228: Trapping of photogenerated radicals with 1,1-diphenylethene

Decomposition of 2,4,6-trimethylbenzoyldiphenylphosphine oxide in the presence of 1,1-di(4-methylphenyl)ethene gave some interesting products. (Figure 229).

Figure 229: Use of a non-polymerisable alkene to trap the radicals generated by photolysis of an acylphosphine oxide

CHAPTER X

APPLICATIONS OF RADIATION CURING

CHAPTER X

APPLICATIONS OF RADIATION CURING

(i)   An Overview

Radiation curing (u.v./e.b.) is a rapidly expanding technology with annual growths of ~10% being achieved.[271] What has led to this growth? The three most important drivers have been: (i) the process is solvent free (other than water-based) i.e. it is a 100% solids system and generation of VOC'S (volatile organic compounds) is not an issue, (ii) the process is energy efficient and (iii) the process is economical on space. Much concern was voiced in the last two decades of the twentieth century about emission into the atmosphere of VOC's due to the active role they play in producing atmospheric pollution which give rise to health debilitating smogs. The level of concern was such that legislation was passed in most of the developed countries to either substantially reduce emissions or eliminate them altogether. For processes where solvents have to be used, solvent recovery or incineration is practised. Radiation curing is undoubtedly a clean technology and consequently it carries in addition the "green technology" label. The continued growth of the technology is in part due to it being an environmentally friendly process. Another great impetus to early growth was the perceived energy savings that would accrue if this technology was accepted. Undoubtedly, thermal curing and drying operations where speed is important is expensive which in part is due to inefficiency. Because chemical and equipment manufacturers could see expansion of the business a wider range of materials was developed and equipment to match. The industry today is still dominated by acrylate/methacrylate chemistry and consequently much effort has been put in to increasing the range of these products. Concern about the toxicity of "radcure" products and in particular acrylates led to the development of low toxicity materials. Many simple, highly valuable acrylates e.g. 1,6-hexanediol diacrylate obtained a bad reputation in the early days of "radcure" because they exhibited high irritancy. In many cases these highly undesirable effects could be traced to the presence of free acrylic acid in the product. Manufacturers now take extreme care to remove all traces of this material. Another way of reducing the irritancy of acrylates was to advance the alcohol precursor using either ethylene or propylene oxide followed by acrylation of the product (Figure 146). This process reduced the acrylate content of the molecule and consequently when these compounds are used on the same weight for weight basis as the unmodified acrylates the content of acrylic groups in the formulation is lower. This of course lowers the reactivity of the formulation but it is to some extent offset by the polyether groups aiding cure by virtue of their containing reactive C-H bonds adjacent to oxygen.

Undoubtedly much progress has been made to reduce the irritancy of acrylates but this is one of their properties that will never be completely eliminated and is therefore driving a search to find safer alternatives. Currently it would seem that vinyl ethers have the edge over epoxides and acrylates on the grounds of safer handling properties but their hydrolytic instability gives rise for concern. The free radical vinyl ether-maleate system is highly attractive on the grounds of cost and range of materials including photoinitiators but unfortunately the cure speed appear to be somewhat slower than the free radical cure of acrylates although its sensitivity to oxygen quenching is less. Needless to say the virtues of mixed systems e.g. vinyl ether-acrylate systems are also being extolled but this is an admission that an ideal alternative to acrylate chemistry has yet to be found.

Space saving can also be an important economic issue since the cost of purchase or renting floor space is often a major expense. In many cases changing to radiation curing frees up large areas of floor space previously occupied by drying ovens for storing printed material before binding.

(ii)   The Graphic Arts[9, 123]

For the UK this is an area of strength and covers printing processes such as screen, litho, letterpress, gravure, intaglio and jet print processes. The inks that are required for these process differ enormously in their properties e.g. silk screen use paste inks (buttery consistency) and lays down a thick layer (20-80µm), litho inks must be reasonably hydrophobic and relatively thin films, letterpress uses ink pastes and lays down a relatively thick film, gravure and roller coating inks have a relatively low viscosity and intaglio uses paste tube inks. The amount of pigment in the formulations varies enormously and consequently the conditions required for cure are very different for the various systems.

(iii)   The Wood Coating Industry[10, 272]

More than 20,000 tonnes of radcure products are used in Europe by this industry. There are two main types of formulation used: styrene unsaturated polyester systems and acrylate systems. To some extent the system of choice appears to be related to geographical preferences eg southern Europe uses predominantly the styrene polyester systems whereas in the UK mainly fully acrylated are preferred. Undoubtedly the styrene polyester system is far loss costly (40%) of the acrylated system but it does suffer from disadvantages such as having a low flash point, high odour, low speed and high weights are required. There are water-based acrylate systems available for wood coatings. For parquet flooring the formulations must produce a coating that exhibits good adhesion, abrasion and scratch resistant properties. This calls for the use of urethane acrylates e.g. a difunctional aromatic urethane acrylate.

(iv)   Production of Optical Fibres

Optical fibres are the bedrock of modern communications systems and are of course used to relay an optical signal from one point to another. If this is to be done efficiently there should be no loss in intensity of the signal during transmission. To help the optical signal travelling within the optical fibre (usually a doped silica glass) it is necessary for the fibre to be coated with a material possessing a lower refractive index than the fibre (Figure 230). In this way the fibre acts as a waveguide.

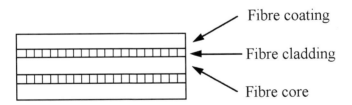

Figure 230: An ideal optical fibre

The production of optical fibres has to be subject to the strictest quality assurance since surface scratches in the fibre or occlusion of dust particles will reduce the working life of the fibre. To prevent damage to the fibre through bending etc. the fibre usually carries two protective coatings (Figure 231).

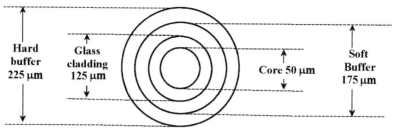

Figure 231: Two coat optical fibre

The soft buffer is a polymer having a low modulus and acts as a cushion between the optical fibre and the hard outer coating. The outer coating is designed to give protection to the inner parts from the harsh environmental conditions. These buffer coatings can be applied using u.v. curing. Figure 232 shows how a fibre is drawn and one coat applied.

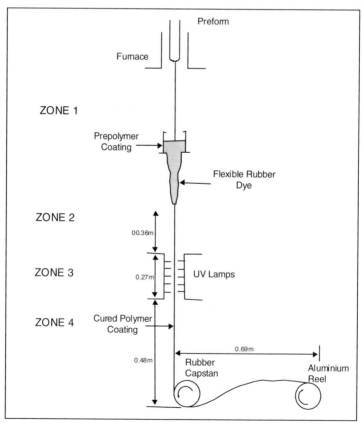

Figure 232: Production of radcure coated optical fibres

The currently favoured materials for these coatings are urethane acrylates and siloxanes.

(v) Digital Optical Recording and Laser Vision Video Discs[16, 273]

Probably the most familiar of these devices is the compact disc. Other devices include laser readable video information carriers and digital optical recording for storage associated with computer applications. U.v. curing can be used in the replication process and in producing a durable coating for the device. The replication process is shown in Figure 233.

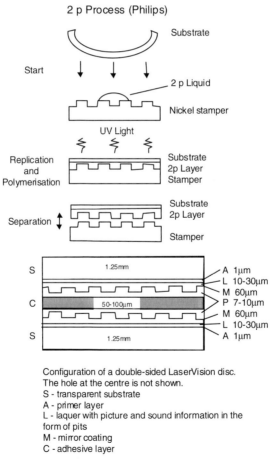

Configuration of a double-sided LaserVision disc.
The hole at the centre is not shown.
S - transparent substrate
A - primer layer
L - laquer with picture and sound information in the form of pits
M - mirror coating
C - adhesive layer

Figure 233: Schematic representation of the photoreplication process used to produce laser vision discs by the "2p process"

This process is sometimes referred to as the "2p process" (from photopolymerisation). In step a, u.v. curable formulation is applied to the mold. In step b the substrate is applied thereby creating a layer of photopolymerisable material. Irradiation through the substrate polymerises the resin. In step c, the substrate is lifted off the mold. This is then coated with a thin layer of metal followed by a u.v. curable layer which on irradiation generates the protective coating (step d). Whilst in principle the process seems simple, a large number of problems had to be overcome. It is known, for instance, that acrylates and methacrylates shrink upon polymerisation and shrinkage could have a disastrous effect upon the integrity of the replica. As a consequence of this, the structure of the oligomers used and the concentration of methacrylate groups had to be carefully controlled.

(vi)   Adhesives[274, 275]

Normally an adhesive is applied to a part in a liquid state and then the second part put in position. It is necessary for the adhesive to wet both parts thoroughly if a strong bond is realised. Usually liquid adhesives are a solution of a solid adhesive in an organic solvent or are a dispersion of an adhesive material in water. For adhesive bond to form the solvent (water or organic) has to evaporate. This process can be slow and in the case where organic solvents are used, unwanted VOCs are released into the atmosphere. Ways of overcoming these problems include: a) the use of hot melt adhesives; b) use a reactive adhesive system; or c) use a photopolymerisable adhesive system. Hot melt adhesives are applied in the molten state and solidify on cooling and thereby create the adhesive bond. Reactive adhesives usually consist of two components which upon mixing undergo a polymerisation reaction which often includes the formation of crosslinks. Such a system suffers certain disadvantages e.g. the polymerisation process is often slow and when the components are mixed the mixture must be used straightaway. A photopolymerisable adhesive has the advantage that it can be applied to the surfaces in liquid form and cure can be induced at will by exposing the system to a light source. However, for such a system to be of value at least one of the parts to be joined must be transparent to light. This clearly is a serious limitation but nevertheless glass and organic polymer laminates etc. can be produced in this way.[276] Applications include the production of liquid crystal display devices.

One way of overcoming the limitation that one of the parts must be transparent to light is to use a light activated slow curing system. The cationic cure of epoxides is known to be slow. Irradiation of an epoxide plus an onium salt generates acid.

Thus if such a formulation is applied to a part, irradiated and then the second part applied, the thermal acid catalysed polymerisation will proceed until all the epoxide groups are utilised and thereby an adhesive bond formed. Some light activatable anaerobic adhesives have been devised as alternatives. Such a system may contain an onium salt which is the source of acid. The acid in the presence of ferrocene is used to decompose a hydroperoxide which in turn is used to polymerise a monomer such as a methacrylate. The cure of the methacrylate is very slow in the presence of oxygen (oxygen inhibition Section V.i) but when oxygen is excluded cure occurs. When such a mixture is sandwiched between two substrates, diffusion into the polymerisable adhesive is greatly reduced and consequently polymerisation occurs and an adhesive bond is formed.

(vii)   Rapid Prototyping[277]

Rapid prototyping is a relatively new development and is a rapidly developing technology. It allows a three dimensional model on a CAD system to be translated directly into a 3D functional model. Applications in the engineering industry are legion e.g. production of mold castings, production of functional models such as an engine manifold. There is also an increasing awareness of the value of the methodology to medicine. From appropriate imaging data life size models of bone structures e.g. a skull, hand or foot can be made. Surgeons find that examining an exact replica of the damaged bone structure can be invaluable in helping them arrive at the most effective way of operating upon the patient to repair the damage.

Several rapid prototyping systems exist and two of these rely upon radiation curing. The most frequently encountered process is known as stereolithography. A diagrammatic version of the apparatus is shown in Figure 234.

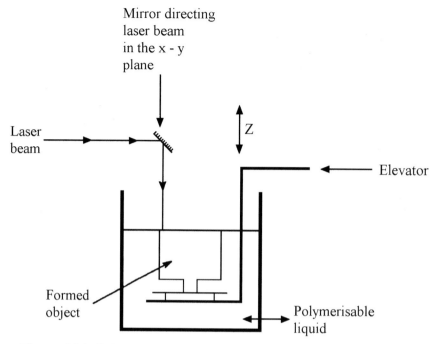

Figure 234: Schematic representation of the stereolithography apparatus

The model on the computer system is sliced (Figure 235).

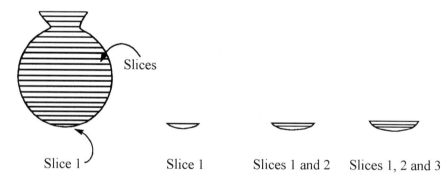

Figure 235: Building up a 3D model

Slice 1 is selected and the computer used to cause the laser to polymerise the resin so as to produce a solid replica of slice 1. The tray in the bath is lowered so that the height of the resin above slice 1 corresponds to the thickness of slice 2. Slice 2 is then produced via the laser beam tracing out (as directed by the computer) the required shape thereby layer down a second layer of polymerised material.

Until 1994 acrylates were mainly used as the polymerisable material in the resin tank. However, although the cationic cure of epoxides is slower than the polymerisation of acrylates, the use of cationic cure is gaining rapid acceptance. Models made from epoxides are usually much stronger than their acrylate counterparts. Needless to say the time required to build a part of an epoxide is longer than that required to make one from an acrylate. Models made from composites have also been produced in this way.

In an alternative process models are built from slices with each slice being produced by irradiation through a negative. The computer is used to produce a negative in a similar way to which an image is produced by electrophotography i.e. the opaque image is produced by deposition of a toner powder.

(viii)   The Dental Industry[278]

Man was born to die and according to the Bible we are lucky if our lifespan is greater than three score and ten.[279] The effects of growing old manifest themselves at an early age and this is well exemplified by the deterioration of our teeth over the passing years. The animal that loses its teeth dies of starvation but as humans we have the opportunity of allowing a dentist to ameliorate the situation. In the early 1970s photopolymerisable dental resins were introduced. These materials offered several advantages over amalgams and thermally cured materials. The advantages include: immediate readiness for use, absence of air bubbles, extended working time, longer shelf life, higher polymerisation rate and better colour stability. Several problems had to be overcome before the methodology could be adopted. It would not, for instance, be acceptable to use u.v. radiation below 330nm since this could cause damage to tissue surrounding the teeth and would of course require the dentist and patient to be shielded from the radiation. For these reasons curing systems employing initiators which absorb at >340nm (usually 450-500nm) were developed with the most successful one being camphorquinone (λ_{max} 468nm). This is usually used with ethyl 4-dimethylaminobenzoate or N,N-dimethylaminoethyl methacrylate as synergist. Care had to be taken in selecting the polymerisable species. Acrylates often cause skin irritation and consequently cannot be used near the sensitive tissue present in the mouth. Methacrylates, although slower curing than acrylates, were chosen because of their inherent lower irritancy. To give some mechanical strength to the cured resin (e.g. a resin used for filling cavities, building up a tooth) fillers such as silica are added. The correct selection of particle size is very important if the finished product is to be visually acceptable ie the filled area should like the tooth. Needless to say the cured resins must look like the tooth. To achieve this methacrylates were devised which showed a relatively small amount of shrinkage upon cure (2.5%) eg bisphenol A diglycidylether dimethacrylate. To gain good adhesion it is better to carry out the cure slowly rather than rapidly. Other properties which have to be taken into consideration include, thermal properties (similar coefficient of expansion to that of tooth enamel or dentine). The cured material should not contain leachable components and should not be eroded by saliva, beverage etc. The cured material should exhibit good mechanical properties, it should be polishable so as to give a smooth finish, and it should be opaque to x-rays so as to enable the detection of defects etc. A variety of formulations are now commercially available and many of them have been tailored to meet a specific need. Some of the applications of these materials include temporary cements, dental restorative materials, fissure sealants, cavity liners, denture base materials, crown and bridge veneers and impression materials.

(ix)   Composites

There is a constsnt demand for new materials which exhibit high strength combined with low weight. Such materials are of great value to the automotive, aircraft, space, electronic and shipbuilding industries. The use of metals replaced the use of natural materials such as wood but although metals exhibit strength, they are readily machined, shaped etc. but on the downside they exhibit corrosion and fatigue. Aluminium alloys which exhibit great strength, and fairly high stiffness at low weight in some ways set the benchmark for composites since for these materials to be of commercial value they had to equal or even better outperform these alloys. Current composites based on carbon and glass fibres having excellent strength, machinability and of a weight equal to 20 to 25% of aluminium alloys.

Composite technology relies on the stiffness and strength of fibres by dispersing them in a matrix (organic polymer, metal or ceramic) which acts as a binder and transfers forces from one fibre to another. Composites are often stronger than the the fibres in bulk form although their strength is derived mainly from the fibres with the resin only making a small contribution. The performance properties of a composite are determined by such factors as the stiffness and strength of fibres, fibre diameter, fibre length, fibre uniformity, fibre volume, fibre orientation and the integrity of the fibre-matrix interface. The fibre-matrix interface is itself influenced by the presence of voids, the strength of the interfacial bonding and the properties of the matrix.

There is a variety of types of composites and these include particulate re-inforced (e.g. as in the radiation curing formulations used in dentistry), laminar, discontinuous fibre-reinforced (the reinforcement has its length much greater than its cross-sectional dimension with the properties of the composite being determined by the length of the fibres) and continuous fibre-reinforced (similar to discontinuous but called continuos because there is no change in elastic modulus if the length of the fibres is further increased).

The most commonly used glass fibres are E-glass (Electrical) and are a calcium aluminoborosilicate glass which possesses a good balance of mechanical, chemical and electrical properties and are available at moderate cost. Other glasses are available which offer more chemical resistance, higher tensile strength etc. Boron fibres are very much more expensive but have an elastic modulus nearly six times greater than glass fibres. Carbon fibres exhibit very high strength, have a low density, good creep and fatigue resistance and are chemically resistant (although not to strong oxidising agents). Unfortunately these fibres are brittle, exhibit low impact resistance and low elongation to break. Aramid fibres have a higher modulus, similar tensile strength and a lower density than E-glass fibres and are also commonly used.

The matrix is very important since it binds the fibres together, transfers the load to and between fibres and protects them from the environment and from the effects of handling. The properties of the matrix will determine the overall service temperature limitations and environmental resistance of the composite. Currently thermosetting and thermoplastic resins are commonly used with the great challenge being to find ways of employing radiation curing.

What advantages could radiation curing offer? If thermosetting polymers are used, a liquid resin is converted into a hard brittle solid by crosslinking. Although this curing process may take place at ambient temperatures it is more usual to heat in order to effect a faster cure and this may involve relatively long times. Typical materials include epoxy resins, polyesters and vinyl esters/acrylics. Thermoplastic resins in common use include polyamides, polypropylenes, polyetherimides etc. Use of radiation curing should lead to energy savings since cure is effected in a relatively short period of time. The speed of the radiation curing process also offers the possibility of increasing production rates. In the processing volatile materials are not generated thereby avoiding issues associated with emission of volatile organic compounds.

The radiation curing process is easier to control than a thermal process since it can be started or shut down at the throw of a switch. If the formulation has been optimised, cure will occur at the top, middle and bottom of the composite as soon as the light is switched on whereas with a thermal process it may take a long time before an even temperature distribution temperature is attained and hence even cure. In the case of thermosetting resins a curing agent (e.g. a crosslinking species such as a diamine) may have to be added to the formulation prior to application to the fibres which means that cure is occurring before the fibres are optimally covered and if the processing line has to be stopped temporarily, cure is occurring during the stoppage which may lead to processing problems (e.g. on start up the resin will be much more viscous and hence wetting of fibres may be adversely affected). A radiation curable formulation does not suffer from these disadvantages since it can be fully formulated for the user (i.e. it is a one pot formulation) and should the processing line be stopped, cure stops.

To use radiation curing for producing thick, fibre-filled composites poses a real challenge. Curing of thick films is not easy since one has to find a way of getting the light necessary for initiation through the film so that that the bottom of the film is cured. As noted in a previous section, use of initiators with high extinction coefficients at short wavelengths and low extinction coefficients at long wavelengths enables fast cure at the surface (due to absorption at the short wavelengths) and at the bottom of the film (due to absorption at the longer wavelengths). It has also been pointed out that the use of bleachable initiators such as acylphosphine oxides are valuable for curing thick sections since they allow the light to reach the bottom of the film following the destruction of initiator molecules nearer the surface. The curing of composites is in addition complicated by the absorption, reflective and refractive properties of the filler (glass fibre, carbon fibres etc.). The contribution that these properties have is determined by the physical form of the filler, e.g. is it particulate and if so what is the shape and size of the particles or is it filamentous in which case the dimensions of the fibres will be important.

An important factor in determining the efficiency of light penetration is the absorption properties of the resin mix. As the thickness of the section to be cured increases so the contribution from weak absorption's in the tail of the u.v. spectra become more important. Many resins containing aromatic components (e.g. as found in epoxy resins based on bis-phenol A) absorb out to 330nm. and in addition the presence of antioxidants such as 4-methoxyphenol which are present in acrylated resins can also make contributions leading to absorption out to 350nm. In many cases absorption of light below 330nm is going to be restricted to at and close to the surface of the section to be cured. Initiators will need to have absorption bands below 330nm. which possess high extinction coefficients if they are to compete successfully with the resin for the light and to bring about efficient surface cure in the face of oxygen inhibition.

Composites based on glass fibres (E-type, used in finely chopped form) and an acrylated polyester resin have been cured using conventional initiators such as benzoin ethyl ether[280]. The form of the fibres used did not yield a composite having the best properties but since but it meant that light scattering was exacerbated and therefore the system gave some idea as to the part played by this property in curing. Curing was relatively efficient and this could be further increased by incorporating a thermal initiator in the formulation. In the curing of thick sections a lot heat is evolved and this can be used to trigger a thermal initiator which can aid cure in those areas where light penetration may not have been optimal. It was found that with the system employed that temperatures of 130° C could be attained. Perhaps an even more surprising finding was that the initiator underwent bleaching upon irradiation and this no doubt played an important part in the curing process.

There have been a number of reports describing the curing of glass fibre composites in which the fibre is used in the form of a stitched woven fabric. If the mechanical properties are to be optimised it is necessary to have a glass fibre content of between 50 to 70% and the resin must be applied to the fibres so that the void (spaces) content is < 1%. Thick sections e.g 2 cm. have been successfully cured using a conventional u.v. curing unit with initiator systems such as camphorquinone- ethyl N,N-dimethylamino benzoate and also 2-benzyl-2-dimethylamino-1-(4-morpholinophenyl)butan-1-one. Further improvements were obtained when a conventional Type I initiator was used in combination with a bis acylphosphine oxide. If the radiation cured composites are to match the physical properties of equivalent systems produced thermal processes it is necessary to achieve maximum cure and for cure to occur at temperatures at or above the temperature attained in the thermal process. The maximum extent of cure attainable is determined by the concentration of polymerisable groups in the formulation, the degree to which highly functionalised resins have been employed and the temperature of cure. Vitrification is favoured by the use of highly functionalised compounds and if a high degree of cure is to be attained it is necessary for cure to occur above the Tg of the vitrfied resin. The dilemma for the formulator is that the use of highly functionalised materials speeds up the curing process but can lead to vitrefication before the properties of the cured resin are fully developed. To overcome these problems it may be necessary to use infra red heaters in conjunction with u.v. lamps.

The curing of composites containing polyimides and carbon fibres is a particularly difficult challenge. Encouraging results have been obtained using a cocktail of initiators such as a mixture of a classical Type I initiator (to enhance surface cure), a hexaarylbisimidazole in conjunction with a sensitiser and thiol synergyst, and a near i.r. absorbing dye having a fragmentable borate counterion.

Use of electron beam radiation to cure composites has the great advantage that the penetration by the electrons is little impeded by the filler and for thick samples there is no problem in getting the electrons to cure the face opposite the irradiated face cured. It has been shown that for glass fibre and carbon fibre filled samples that a substantial amount of heat is evolved during the process and the amount liberated decreases as the fibre content increases[281]. The heat evolution is of paramount importance to obtaining fully cured films having optimal physical properties.

The success of these u.v. and e.b. curing systems suggests that composites produced by radiation curing will soon be a commercial reality.

(X)   Outdoor Applications of Radiation Cured Coatings[282]

There are many potential applications for u.v. cured products in which they will be subjected to prolonged exposure to daylight, to rain and or high humidity, abrasive action etc. Perhaps the greatest commercial opportunity is for automobile finishes and it is ironic that the Ford Motor Company were one of the early entrants into radiation curing with this commercial objective in mind since they wished to do away with the hazardous and polluting process of painting cars by paint spraying followed by thermal drying. The understanding of radiation curable systems is such that this goal of the 1960's may soon be realised. Other applications include garden furniture outdoor building panels, double glazing etc.

Many radiation cured coatings exhibit poor durability when exposed outdoors. In the case of u.v. cured systems this may be due to the presence of unused photoinitiator and/or photoinitiator residues. However many such formulations from which the initiator system has been omitted and when cured using e.b. radiation exhibit a similar poor performance. Such a finding does not exclude the participation of initiators and their residues in the degradation of the coatings but it is clear that they are not wholly responsible. It is now known that the durability of clear coatings is closely linked to the resin and diluent structure. Polyethers exhibit very poor durability due to their ease of autoxidation and same is true to a more limited extent of aliphatic esters. Aromatic residues pose a problem since they undergo rearrangemant reactions (e.g. the photo Fries rearrangement) to give phenolic species which readily oxidise to give highly coloured species. Such processes exclude the use of curable novalak and resol resins. Aliphatic urethanes appear to be the champions with their only drawback being their cost.

When pigments are present in a coating they may exhibit some protection by acting as uv screens. Some pigments e.g. the anatase form of titanium dioxide can initiate radical formation and therefore act as prodegradants in the coating. Surface treatments which aid the dispersing of pigments may also lead to unwanted reactions e.g. polyamines autoxidise giving coloured products.

Other factors which can affect the durability include the extent of cure, moisture permeability of the film and the substrate, the homogeneity of the coating, the mechanical strength of the coating and the effectiveness of the adhesive bond between coating and substrate. To enhance durability it is essential to utilise as many of the polymerisable groups as possible since these may start participating in radical reactions leading to the production of peroxidic species which of themselves can act as thermal initiators of degradative reactions. Crosslink density is very important since as this increases moisture permeability decreases. If moisture reaches the adhesive bond between substrate and coating delamination is likely to occur. The presence of pinholes in the film can also lead to delamination via water ingress and also they increase oxygen access to the film and increase the surface area of the film thereby favouring ixdative degradation. The mechanical strength of the film is particularly important in situations where the coating may be subject to stresses and strain e.g. flexing or to abrasion from dust particles (particularly important for car finishes!). Many polymers which include radiation cured systems also undergo non oxidative (that is to say not involving molecular oxygen) degradation which leads to an increase in crosslink density which builds up stress in the coating and can ultimately lead to mechanical failure.

For u.v. cured films to exhibit durability akin to that exhibited by films produced thermally it is essential that the degradative processes are either eliminated or reduced to an absolute minimum. For this to be achieved it is necessary to add antioxidants and u.v. screens. Of the many antioxdants available, the hindered piperidines (HALS, e.g. 2,2,6,6-tetramethylpiperidine and its derivatives) are currently the most favoured. Such compounds are very effective in suppressing peroxide and peroxy radical mediated reactions and are available carrying a variety of substituents to aid formulation. The u.v. screen workhorse is based on 2-hydroxybenzophenone and compounds based on this material are widely available. More expensive and more effective materials have been developed which are now widely used. These are based on 2-hydroxyphenylbenzotriazole and 2-hydroxyphenyltriazines[283] (Figure 236).

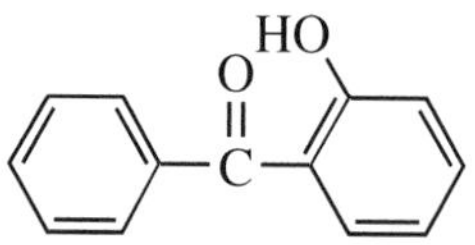

2-hydroxybenzophenone 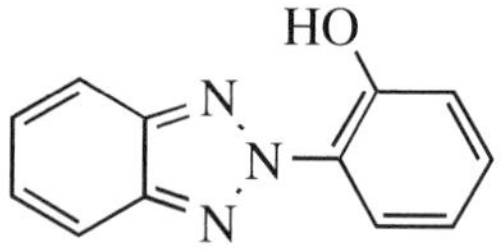   2-hydroxyphenylbenzotriazole

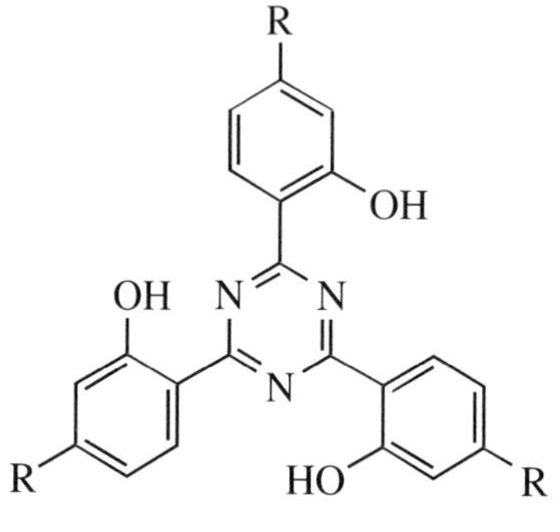

R = alkyl, alkoxy

2-hydroxphenyltriazine

Figure 236: Some u.v screens

It is usual practise to use a cocktail of u.v. screens in order to cover as wide a range of wavelengths as possible. Since u.v. screens are designed to absorb light below 400nm they often absorb those wavelengths that are required to activate the photoinitiator. Bleachable photoinitiators based on acylphosphine and bisacylphosphine oxides are most popular for this purpose. Durable u.v. cured coatings have been produced using such initiators in combination with u.v. screens, antioxidants and aliphatic urethane resins.

(xi)   Powder Coatings

Powder coating technology is well established holding a significant portion of the surface coatings market It is particularly useful for coating metal surfaces since highly durable coatings exhibiting good adhesion are obtained. In the themal process the polymer in powder form is applied to the surface and then melted. There are two stages to the melting process which are; (1) sintering of the polymer particles and (2) flow out of the resulting molten film[284](Figure 237).

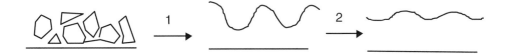

Figure 237: Diagram of melting process

This flow out has to produce an even film if a durable and aesthetically pleasing coating is to be produced. If thermosetting resins are used cure also has to take place in the molten coating. Examples of thermosetting resins used include acrylics (isocyanate-cured, epoxy-cured and acid-cured), epoxy (dicyandiamide-cured carboxy-terminated poly-ester cured), and polyester (hydroxy terminated plus isocyanate, triglycidyl isocyanate cured). Thermoplastic systems include polyolefins (polyethylene, polypropylene), vinyl polymers, polyamides, polyesters etc. It is obvious that these thermally curing systems are very versatile and in addition offer some real cost advantages. And advantages over liquid spray coatings. A particularly valuable facet is that material utilisation is as high as 90 to 98% provided the powder that does not adhere to the surface is recovered and re-utilised.

How can u.v. curing help to expand this coating technology even further? The melting and curing process can require temperatures of 180^0 and a period of 15 to 30 minutes. We know that u.v. curing is fast and therefore use of u.v. should reduce the time and also the heat required for cure. Application of u.v. also means that powders having a melting range e.g. around 100^0 much lower than the thermally cured materials can be used since these powders will not cure thermally and hence they will possess good shelf lives. A thermally cured powder having such a low melting range would be likely to undergo cure on storage under ambient conditions. Availability of a powder system melting a little above ambient and which can be cured under such conditions also offers the great advantage that the range of substrates that can be coated is substantially increased since thermally sensitive materials such as wood and wood composites may now be utilised. Powder coating also has some advantages over conventional application of liquid coatings. Usually to achieve a good working viscosity reactive diluents have to be added to a resin and some of these diluents do present toxicity and handling problems. In some cases the use of a diluent can reduce the effectiveness of the resin to the coating properties. With a powder coating there is no need to use any diluent thereby avoiding these problems. Furthermore the toxicity of a u.v. curable powder is likely to be lower than that of a u.v. curable liquid (e.g. less likely to be ingested via inhalation or skin contact).

The use of a low temperature curing powder is also not without its problems. When these powders are melted the liquid coating has a much higher viscosity than a conventional u.v. curable coating and this creates difficulties in obtaining even coverage the substrate as well as getting effective cure of the polymerisable groups. Despite these problems u.v. curable powder coatings are now emerging as a very valuable coating process having a great commercial potential.

How is u.v. curing used in powder coating? A simplified picture of the equipment used is shown in Figure 238.

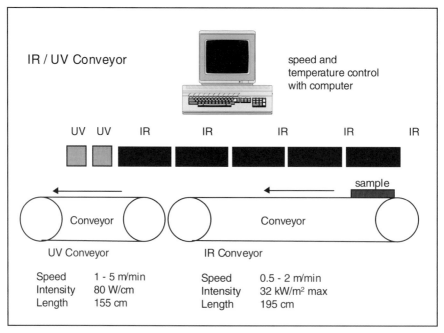

Figure 238 Diagram of u.v. powder coating apparatus

The powder which is applied at the beginning of the process has of course to be u.v. curable, to melt in the right temperature range and to flow out on the substrate to give a good coating. The powder may be based on a free radical (acrylates[285] and vinyl ether-maleate[286] ester systems) or cationic (epoxides)[287] curing processes and it must contain an appropriate photoinitiator. Application of the powder to the substrate is usually carried out electrostatically (e.g.tribocharging) although another method which is growing in popularity is to pass the part to be coated through a fluidised bed of powder. Following coating the parts are passed through a heating zone where the heat is supplied by i.r. and convection heaters. The time required to pass through this zone depends upon the melting characteristics and flow-out properties of the formulation. The coated article is passed under u.v. lamps to effect cure. In this way wood, MDF boards and metal substrates have been coated and with the appropriate choice of resin systems coatings exhibiting good outdoor durability can be obtained.

REFERENCES

1.) C E Hoyle in Radiation Curing of Polymeric Materials in Am Chem Soc Symp Ser, eds C E Hoyle and J F Kinstle, 1990, <u>417</u>, 1.
G E Senich and R E Florin, Rev Macromol Chem Phys, 1984, <u>C24</u> 239.

2.) Sources and Applications of UV Curing, R Phillips, Academic Press, London, 1983.

3.) J P Fouassier and J F Rabek (Eds), Lasers in Polymer Science & Technology (1990), CRC Press Boca Raton Florida USA.
C Decker and Elzaouk in Current Trends in Polymer Photochemistry, eds N S Allen, M Edge, I R Bellobono and E Selli, Ellis Harwood, Hemel Hempstead UK (1995), 130.

4.) Some useful texts which describe the primary photophysical and photochemical processes include:
P Suppan, Chemistry and Light, Royal Society of Chemistry, Cambridge UK , 1994.
A Gilbert and J Baggott, Essentials of Molecular Photochemistry, Blackwell London UK, 1991.
N J Turro, Modern Molecular Photochemistry, J Wiley & Sons Chichester UK, 1986.

5.) J F Kinstle, Radiation Curing of Polymeric Materials in Am Chem Soc Symp Ser, eds C E Hoyle and J F Kinstle, 1990, <u>417</u>, 17.

6.) R S Davidson in Radiation Curing in Polymer Science & Technology Vol III, (eds J P Fouassier and J F Rabek), Elsevier Applied Science London, 1993, 301.

7.) J Sutcliffe in Radiation Curing of Polymers, Vol II, Royal Society of Chemistry (Cambridge UK), Special Publication No 89, ed D R Randell, 1991, 22.

8.) H J Hageman, Progress in Organic Coatings, 1985, <u>13</u> 123.

9.) R Holman, UV and EB Curing Formulations for Printing Inks, Coatings and Paints, 1984, SITA Press London UK.

10.) R S Davidson and M S Salim in Formulations for Radiation Curable Coatings in Chemistry & Technology of UV & EB Formulations for Coatings, Inks and Paints, Vol 4, ed P K T Oldring, SITA Technology Ltd 1991, chap. 3, p217.

11.) R. E. Knight in Chemistry and Technology of UV and EB Formulation for Coatings, Inks and Paints Vol. I, ed. P. K. T. Oldring, SITA Technology Ltd. London, 1991, p159-274.

12.) A. Roth, RadTech Europe, (Lyon) 1997, 91-104.

13.) A. Roth and M. Honig, RadTech North America 1998, 112-116

14.) R. A. Burga, RadTech Europe, (Lyon) 1997, 425-433.

15.) J F Rabek in Radiation Curing in Polymer Science & Technology, vol 1, eds J P Fouassier and J F Rabek, Elsevier Applied Science London UK, 1993, 453.

264

16.)   S V Nablo in Radiation Curing in Polymer Science & Technology, vol 1, eds J P Fouassier and J F Rabek, Elsevier Applied Science London UK, 1993, 503. T J Menezes and S V Nablo, Radiation Curing, 1985, 12(2) 1.

17.)   G.G. Skelhorne in Chemistry and Technology of UV and EB Formulations for Coatings, Inks and Paints Vol.1 ed. P. K. T. Oldring, SITA Technology Ltd. London 1991, 101-157.

18.)   J. I. Davis and G. Wakalopulos, RadTech North America, 1996, 317-328.

19.)   A useful text on polymerisation processes- J M G Cowie, Chemistry and Physics of Modern Materials, 1991. Chapman & Hall, New York.

20.)   W. Wang and G. H. Hu, J. Appl. Polym. Sci., 1993,47, 1665-1672.

21.)   G Roffey, Photopolymerisation and Surface Coatings, J Wiley & Sons Chichester UK, 1982 and Photogeneration of Reactive Species for UV Curing, J. Wiley and Sons, Chichester UK, 1997.

22.)   For a discussion of the effects of oxygen upon radical initiated polymerisation reactions, R S Davidson in Polymer Science & Technology, Vol III, eds J P Fouassier and J F Rabek, Elsevier Applied Science London UK, 1993, 153.

23.)   J G Kloosterboer, Adv Polym Sci, 1987, 84, 1.

24.)   J G Kloosterboer and G F C M Lijten, Polymer 1990, 31 95.

25.)   J G Kloosterboer, G M M van de Hei, R G Gossink and G C M Dortant, Polymer Communication, 1994, 25, 322.

26.)   K S Anseth, C N Bowman and N A Peppas, J Polym Sci Part A, Polym Chem, 1994, 32, 139.

27.)   J G Kloosterboer and G F C M Lijten, Polymer Communications, 1987, 28 2.

28.)   G C Eastmond in Comprehensive Chemical Kinetics, eds C H Bamford and C F H Tipper, Elsevier Amsterdam, 1976, 14A, 65.

29.)   UV-Curing Science and Technology, Vol 1 ed S P Pappas, Technology Marketing Corp Stamford USA, 1985.

30.)   A F Jacobine in Polymer Science & Technology, Vol III, eds J P Fouassier and J F Rabek, Elsevier Applied Science London UK, 1993, 219.
    A F Jacobine, D M Glaser, P J Grabek, D Mancini, M Masterson, S T Nakos and J G Woods, J Appl Polym Sci, 1992, 45, 471.

31.)   C R Morgan, F Magnotta and A D Ketley, J Polym Sci Polym Chem Ed, 1977, 15, 627.

32.)   European Patent Application 0322 808 AZ, 1988 to PPG Industries Inc.
    E P Zahora, S C Lapin, G K Noren and E Wehman, Modern Paint and Coatings, 1994 (Oct), 120.

33.)   S Jönsson, W Schaeffer, P-E Sundell, M Shimose, J Owens and C E Hoyle; Radtech

'94 North America Conference, Proceedings 194.

H Andersson, U W Gedde and A Hult, Macromolecules, 1996, <u>29</u>, 1649.

34.) P. Kohli, A. B. Scranton, and G. J. Blanchard, Macromolecules 1998,31,5681-5689

35.) C. E. Hoyle S. Jonsson, M. Shimose J. Owens and P-E Sundell, ACS Symposium Series 673, 1997, 133-149.

36.) S. Jonsson, C. Hasselgren, J. S. Ericsson, M. Johansson, S. Clark, C. Miller and C. E. Hoyle, RadTech North America 1998, 189-206

37.) S.C. Clark, C. E. Hoyle, S. Jonsson, F. Morel and C. Decker RadTech North America 1998, 177-181.

38.) C. W. Miller, S. Jonsson, C. E. Hoyle, C. Hasselgren, T. Haraldsson and L. Shao, RadTech North America 1998, 182-188.

39.) S P Pappas in Photopolymerisation and Photoimaging Science and Technology, ed N S Allen, Elsevier Applied Science Barking Essex UK, 1989, 55.

40.) F Lohse and H Zweifel, Adv in Polym Sci, 1986, <u>78</u>, 62.

R F Eaton, B D Hanrahan and J F Beaddock, Proc Radtech North America Chicago, 1990, 384.

41.) J V Crivello and J H W Lam, Macromolecules, 1977, <u>10</u>, 1307.

J V Crivello and J H W Lam, J Polym Sci Polym Chem, 1979 <u>17</u> 977.

42.) J. V. Crivello and U. Varlemann, J. Polym. Sci. Part A Polym. Chem. 1995, <u>33</u>, 2473-2486.

43.) J A Dougherty, E A Jurczak, F J Vara and W J Burlant, Polymers Paint Colour Journal, 1994, <u>184</u>, 478.

44.) J. V. Crivello and S. S. Liu, J. Polym. Sci. Part A Polym. Chem. 1998, **36**, 1179-1187.

45.) I. R. Bellobono, RadTech Europe 1989, 243.

46.) A. D. Ketley and J-H. Toao, J. Radiation Curing April 1979, 22 and W. C. Perkins, J. Radiation Curing, January, 1981,16.

47.) F. J. Vara and J. A. Dougherty, RadTech Europe 1989, 523

48.) C Decker, D Decker, TNT Vit., H.L. Xuan, Macrmole. synp. 1996 Volume II, 63-71.

49.) E. V. Sitzmann, R. F. Anderson, J. G. Cruz, S. A. Bratslavsky and R. L. Haynes, RadTech North America 1998, 53.

50.) T Nishikubo, E Takehara and A Kameyama, J Polym Sci Part A Polym Chem, 1995, <u>31</u>, 3013.

51.) S Kutal, S K Weit, S A MacDonald and C G Wilson, J Coatings Technology, 1990, <u>62</u>, 63.

52.) V. Hall-Goulle and S. C. Turner PCT Int. Appl. WO 98 32,756.

53.) Y. Toba, Jpn. Kokai Tokkyo Koho JP 10 152,548.

54.) G E Green, B P Stark and S A Zahir, J Macro Sci Rev Macro Chem, 1981, <u>C21</u>, 187.

55.) A Reiser, Photoreactive Polymers: The Science and Technology of Resists, J Wiley & Sons, New York USA, 1989.

56.) LM Minsk, J G Smith, W P Van Deusen and J F Wright, J Appl Polym Sci, 1959, 2, 302.
H Tanaka, M Tsuda and H Nakanishi, J Polym Sci, 1972, Part A-1, 10, 1729.

57.) A A Lin, C-F Chu, W-Y Huang and A Reiser, Pure and Applied Chemistry, 1992, 64, 1299.

58.) R S Davidson and C Lowe, Eur Polym J, 1989, 25, 173.

59.) K Ichimura and S Watanabe, J Polym Sci A : Polym Chem Ed, 1980, 18, 891.

60.) E S Cockburn, R S Davidson, S Wilkinson and J Hamilton, Eur Polym J, 1988, 24, 1015.

61.) N S Allen, I C Barker, M Edge, D A R Williams, J A Sperry and R J Batten; J Photochem Photobiol A, Chem, 1992, 68 227.

62.) J Finter, Z Hanictis, F-Lohse, K Meier and H Zweifel, Angew Makromol Chem, 1985, 133, 147.

63.) H J Hageman in Photopolymerisation and Photoimaging Science and Technology, ed N S Allen, Elsevier Applied Science Barking UK, 1989, 1.

64.) K Dietliker in Chemistry and Technology of UV and EB Formulation for Coatings, Inks and Paints Vol 3, ed P K T Oldring, SITA Technology, London UK, 1991, 189.

65.) J-P Fouassier, Photoinitiator, Photopolymerisation and Photocuring, Hanser Publishers, Munich Germany, 1995, Chaps 3 and 4.

66.) J-P Fouassier, Progress in Organic Coatings, 1990, 18, 229.

67.) R Bowser and R S Davidson, J Photochem Photobiol A: Chem 1994, 77, 269.

68.) H-J Timpe, U Miller and P Möckel, Angew Makromol Chemie, 1991, 189, 219.

69.) J Eichler, C-P Herz, I Naito and W Schnabel, J Photochem, 1980, 12, 225.

70.) R S Davidson in Molecular Association Vol 1 ed R Foster, Academic Press, London UK, 1975, 215.

71.) R S Davidson and S P Orton, J Chem Soc Chem Commun, 1974, 209.
R S Davidson and P R Steiner, J Chem Soc, 1971, 1682. J Chem Soc Perkin Trans 2, 1972, 1357.

72.) D R G Brimage, R S Davidson and P R Steiner, J Chem Soc Perkin I, 1973, 526.

73.) R S Davidson, S Korkut and P R Steiner, J C S Chem Commun, 1971, 1052.

74.) A Borer, R Kirchmayr and G Rist, Helv Chim Acta, 1978, 61, 305.

75.) H Fischer, R Baer, R Hany I Verhoolen and M Walbiner, J Chem Soc Perkin Trans 2, 1990, 787.

76.) J E Baxter, R S Davidson, H J Hageman, G T M Hakvoort and T Overeem, Polymer, 1988, 29, 1575.

77.) H J Hageman, F P B van der Maeden and P C G M Janssen, Makromol Chem, 1979, 180, 2351.

78.) H G Heine, Tetrahedron Letters, 1972, 4755.

F D Lewis, R T Lauterbauch, H G Heine, W Hartmann and H Rudolph, J Amer Chem Soc, 1975, 97 1519.

79.) W U Palm, H Dreeskamp, H Bouas-Laurent and A Castellan, Ber der Bunsen Phys Chem, 1992, 96, 50.

80.) V. Narayanan, K. K. Baikerikar and A. B. Scranton, RadTech North America 1998, 31-37.

81.) H A Gaur, C J Groenenboom, H J Hageman, G T M Hakvoort, P Osterhoff, T Overeem, R J Polman and S van de Werf, Makromol Chem, 1984, 185, 1795.

82.) H J Hageman and L G J Jansen, Makromol Chem, 1988, 189, 2781.

83.) G Berner, G Rist, W Rutsch and R Kirchmayr, Radcure Basel (1985), Technical Paper FC85-446 SME Dearborn Michigan USA.

84.) P Bosch, F del Monte, J L Mateo and R S Davidson, J Photochem Photobiol A: Chem, 1994, 78, 79.

85.) M R Sandner and C L Osborn, Tetrahedron Letters, 1974, 415.

C L Osborn, J Radiat Curing, 1976, 3 (3), 2.

86.) K Meier, M Rembold, W Rutsch and F Sitek in Radiation Curing of Polymers, Vol.1 ed D R Randell, Royal Society of Chemistry, London 1987, 196.

87.) G Rist, A Borer, K Dietliker, V Desobry, J-P Fouassier and D Ruhlmann, Macromolecules, 1992, 25, 4182.

88.) R S Davidson, J Photochem Photobiol A: Chem, 1993, 73, 81.

89.) J Martens and K Praefcke, Chem Ber, 1974, 107, 2319.

C Bak, K Praefcke, K A Muszkat and M Weinstein, Naturforsch, 1977, 326, 674.

90.) T Sumiyoshi, W Schnabel, A Henne and P Lechtken, Polymer, 1985, 26, 141.

T Sumiyoshi and W Schnabel, Makromol Chem, 1985, 186 1811.

T Sumiyoshi, W Schnabel and A Henne, J Photochem, 1985, 30, 63.

W Schnabel, J Radiat Curing, 1986, 26.

91.) J E Baxter, R S Davidson, H J Hageman, K A McLauchlan and D G Stevens, J Chem Soc Chem Commun, 1987, 73.

J E Baxter, R S Davidson, H J Hageman and T Overeem, Makromol Chem Rapid Commun, 1987, 8, 311.

92.) S. Newman and T. Godfrey, PCT Int. Appl. WO97/35232.

93.) D Leppard, K Dietliker, G Hug, R Kaeser, M Koehler, U Kolczak, L Misez and W Rutsch RadTech North America, 1994, Vol 2, 693.

U Kolczak, G Rist, K Dietliker and J Wirz, J Amer Chem Soc 1996, 118, 6477.

W Rutsch, K Dietliker and R G Hall, European Patent 413567-A (1989).

K Ellrich and C Herzig, European Patent 304782-A (1984).

94.) K Dietliker in Radiation Curing in Polymer Science & Technology, Vol II, eds J P Fouassier and J F Rabek, Elsevier Applied Science London UK, 1993, 155.

95.) D. A. Simoff, M. A. Paczkowski, R. Ragan and A. Palmer, RadTech North America 1998, 42.

96.) N Arsu, R S Davidson and R Holman, J Photochem Photobiol A: Chem, 1995, 87, 169.

97.) C. Decker and K. Moussa, J. Polym. Sci. Polym. Lett., 1989, 27, 347-54

98.) D Ruhlmann and J-P Fouassier, Eur Polym J, 1991, 27, 991.

99.) D G Anderson, R S Davidson and J Elvery, Surface Coatings International, 1995, 11, 482.

100.) A W Green, A W Timms and P N Green, Proc Conf Radtech Europe, Edinburgh, 1991, 636.

101.) B E Hulme and J J Marron, Paint Resin, 1984, 54, 31.

V D McGinnis, Photograph Sci Eng, 1979, 23k, 124.

102.) N S Allen, J P Hurley, G Pullen, A Rahman M Edge, G W Follows,

F Catalina and I Weddel in Current Trends in Polymer Photochemistry, eds N S Allen, M Edge, I R Bellobono and E Selli, Ellis Harwood, Hemel Hempstead UK 1995, 58.

103.) M V Encinas, J Garrido and E A Lissi, J Polym Sci Polym Chem Ed 1989, 27, 139.

104.) WG McGimpsey and J C Scaiano, J Amer Chem Soc, 1987, 109, 2179.

105.) S. Hu R. Popielarz and D. C. Neckers Macromolecules, 1998, 31, 4107-4113.

106.) W D Cook, Polymer, 1992, 33, 600.

107.) D G Anderson, R S Davidson and J J Elvery, Polymer, 1996, 37, 2477

108.) J L R Williams, D P Specht and S Farid, Polym Eng Sci, 1983, 23, 1022.

S Wu, J Zhang, J-P Fouassier and D Burr, Ganguang Kexue Yu Kuang Juaxue (2), 1989 47, Chem Abstr 1989, 113, 61293w.

109.) N Arsu, R Bowser, R S Davidson, N Khan, P M Moran and C J Rhodes in Photochemistry and Polymeric Systems, eds. J M Kelly, C B McArdle and M J de F Maunder, Royal Society of Chemistry, Cambridge UK, 1993, 15.

110.) G Berner, J Puglisi, R Kirchmayr and G Rist, J Radiat Curing, 1979, 6, 2.

G A Delzenne, U Laridon and H Peeters, Eur Polym J, 1970, 6, 933.

S L Hong, T Kurasaki and M Okawara, J Polym Sci Polym Chem Ed 1974, 12, 2553.

111.) X Z Qin, A Liu, A D Trifunac and V V Krongauz, J Phys Chem, 1991, 95, 5822.

A Liu, A D Trifunac and V V Krongauz, J Phys Chem, 1992, 96, 207.

Q Q Zhu, M Fink, F Seitz, S Schneider and W Schnabel, J Photochem Photobiol A: Chem, 1991, 59, 255.

112.)   G B Bradley and R S Davidson, Rec Trav Chem, 1995, <u>114</u>, 528.

113.)   D Baum and C P Henry, US US Pat 3,652,275.

114.)   J D Coyle, European Patent 0271,195 (1987).

G Pawloski, F Erdman and H Lutz, European Patent 332 042.

S Shimizu, S Fumya and T Urano, Japan Kokai Tokkyo Koho JP 6 344,651.

115.)   G B Schuster, Pure and Appl Chem, 1990, <u>62</u>, 1565.

X Yang, A Zaitsev, B Sauerwein, S Murphy and G B Schuster, J Amer Chem Soc, 1992, <u>114</u>, 793.

S Chatterjee, P D Davis, P Gottschalk, M E Kurz, B Sauerwein, X Yang and G B Schuster, J Amer Chem Soc, 1990, <u>112</u>, 6329.

116.)   S.Sugita, H. Kamata Jpn Kokai Tokkyo Koho JP 08 188 632, S. Sugita H. Kamata S. Myazaki Jpn Kokai Tokkyo Koho JP 08 100 012 08 100 011, N. Tanigchi M. Yokoshima Jpn Kokai Tokkyo Koho JP 08 188 609).

117.)   K. Feng, H. Zang and D. C. Neckers RadTech North America 1998, 215.

118.)   S. Hassoon, A. Sarker, D. C. Neckers and M. A. J. Rodgers J. Amer. Chem. Soc., 1995, <u>117</u>, 11369.

119.)   C. J. Groenenboom, H. J. Hageman, P. Oosterhoff, T. Overeem and J. Verbek J. Photochem. Photobiol. A.: Chem. 1997,<u>107</u>, 253.

120.)   B. Strehmel, A M. Sarker J. H. Malpert and D. C. Neckers, Polymer Preprints, 1998, <u>39(2)</u>725-726.

121.)   A. M. Sarker, A. Y. Polykarpov, A. M. de Raaff, and D. C. Neckers J. Polym. Science Part A Polymer Chem. 1996, <u>34</u>, 2817.

122.)   A. Cunningham and M. Kunz, RadTech North America 1998, 38.

123.)   A M Horton in Radiation Curing in Polymer Science and Technology, Vol IV, eds J-P Fouassier and J F Rabek, Elsevier Applied Science, Barking UK, 1993, 133.

124.)   B Klingert, A Roloff, B Urwyler and J Wirz, Helv Chim Acta 1988, <u>71</u>, 1858.

J Finter, M Reidiker, O Rohde and B Rotzinger, Makromol Chemie, Macromol Symp, 1989, <u>24</u>, 177.

125.)   N S Allen, S J Hardy, A F Jacobine, D M Glaser and F Catalina, Eur Polym J, 1990, <u>25</u>, 1219.

N S Allen, S J Hardy, A F Jacobine, D M Glaser, B Yang and D Wolf, Eur Polym J, 1990, <u>26</u>, 1041.

N S Allen, S J Hardy, A F Jacobine, D M Glaser, D Wolf, F Catalina and S Navaratnam and B J Parsons, J Appl Polym Sci, 1991, <u>42</u>, 1169.

126.)   R. Sato, T. Kurhara and M. Takeishi, Polymer International, 1998,47,159-164.

127.)   J V Crivello in Radiation Curing in Polymer Science and Technology, Vol 2, es J-P Fouassier and J F Rabek, Elsevier Applied Science, Barking UK, 1993, 435.

128.) N P Hacker in Radiation Curing in Polymer Science and Technology, Vol II, eds J-P Fouassier and J F Rabek, Elsevier Applied Science, Barking UK, 1993, 473.

129.) M R V Shayun, R J De Voe and P M Olofson in Radiation Curing in Polymer Science and Technology, Vol IV, eds J-P Fouassier and J F Rabek, Elsevier Applied Science, Barking UK, 1993, 505.

130.) W Schnabel in Current Trends in Polymer Photochemistry, eds N S Allen, M Edge, R R Bellobono and E Selli, Ellis Harwood, Hemel Hempstead UK, 1995, 81.

131.) J L Dektar and N P Hacker, J Chem Soc Chem Commun, 1987, 1591.
J L Dektar and N P Hacker, J Amer Chem Soc, 1990, 112, 6004.
J L Dektar and N P Hacker, J Org Chem, 1990, 55, 639.
J L Dektar and N P Hacker in Radiation Curing of Polymeric Materials, eds C E Hoyle and J F Kinstle, ACS Symposium Series 417, American Chemical Society Washington DC USA, 1990, 82.

132.) N P Hacker, D V Leff and J L Dektar, Mol Cryst Liq Cryst, 1990, 183, 505.

133.) R S Davidson, K S Tranter and S A Wilkinson in Radiation Curing of Polymers, Vol II, ed. D R Randell, Royal Society of Chemistry, Cambridge UK, 1991, 400.

134.) K W Allen, E S Cockburn, R S Davidson, K S Tranter and H S Zhang, Pure and Applied Chem, 1992, 64, 1225.

135.) J-M Francis and C. Priou RadTech North America 1998, 476-485.

136.) A Ledwith, S A Kass and A Hulme Lowe, "Cationic Polymerisation and Related Processes", ed E J Goethals Academic Press London, 1984, 275.

137.) Y Yagci and W Schnabel, Makromol Chem, Macromol Symp, 1988, 13/14, 161.

138.) N. Taniguchi, T. Ozaki and M. Yokoshima, Jp. Kokai Tokkyo Koho JP 10 279,616

139.) A Ledwith, Makromol Chem, Suppl, 1979, 3, 348.
H Baumann and H J Timpe, J Prakt Chem, 1984, 326, 529.

140.) X-H Ma, Y Yamamoto and K Hayashi, Macromolecules, 1987, 20, 2703.

141.) R J Batten, R S Davidson and S A Wilkinson, J Photochem Photobiol A: Chem, 1991, 58, 123.

142.) R J Batten, R S Davidson and S A Wilkinson, J Photochem Photobiol, 1991, 58, 115.

143.) K Meier and H Zweifel, J Radiation Curing, 1986 (Oct), 26.
K Meier and H Zweifel, Eur Pat Appl 109,851 and 126, 712 (1984), 152,377 (1985).
K Meier and H Zweifel, Radiation Curing Conf Basel, 1985, Society of Manufacturers and Engineers, Dearborn USA, Paper FC85-417.

144.) A Ledwith in Reprints Amer Chem Soc Meeting Las Vegas, Division of Polymer Chemistry, 1982, 23 (1), 323.
J-H Tsao US Pat 4,139, 655 (1979).

A D Ketley and J-H Tsao, J Radiation Curing, 1979 (April) 22.

145.) R S Davidson and S A Wilkinson, UK Pat Appl 2235199A.

146.) G Berner, R Kirchmayr and G Rist, J Oil and Col Chem Assoc, 1978, 61, 105.

147.) P Bosch, F del Monte, J L Mateo and R S Davidson, J Photochem Photobiol A: Chem, 1993, 73, 197.

148.) S Hayase, Y Onishi, S Suzuki and M Wada, Macromolecules, 1985, 18, 1799, 1986, 19, 968.
S Hayase, Y Onishi, S Suzuki, M Wada and A Kurita, J Polym Sci Part A: Polym Chem, 1987, 25, 763.

149.) W Mayer, H Rudolf and E De Cleur, Angew Makromol Chem, 1981, 93, 83.

150.) J F Cameron and J M J Frechet, J Org Chem, 1990, 55, 5919.
J M J Frechet, Pure and Appl Chem, 1991, 64, 1239.
J F Cameron and J M J Frechet, J. Amer Chem. Soc. 1991, 113, 4303.
J E Beecher, J F Cameron and J M J Frechet, Polym Mater Soc Eng, 1991, 64, 71.

151.) V. Hall-Goulle, S. C. Turner and A. F. Cunningham PCT Int. Appl. WO 98 38,195.

152.) D B Yang and C Kutal in Radiation Curing Science and Technology, ed S P Pappas, Plenum Press New York USA, 1992, 21.

153.) W A Green and A W Timms in Radiation Curing in Polymer Science and Technology, Vol II, es J-P Fouassier and J F Rabek, Elsevier Applied Science, Barking UK, 1993, 375.

154.) K. W. Allen, R.S.Davidson and H. S. Zhang RadTech Europe '91 Edinburgh, 787-797.

155.) D. G. Anderson, N. R. Cullum and R. S. Davidson RadTech '98 North America, 457-467.

156.) J-P Fouassier, D Burr and F Wieder, J Polym Sci Part A, Polym Chem, 1991, 29, 1319.

157.) R S Davidson, J Photochem Photobiol A: Chem, 1993, 69, 263.

158.) D. R. Illsley, A. A. Dias R. S. Davidson and R. E. Burrows PCT International Application WO 97/17378.

159.) R. S. Davidson, H. J. Hageman and S. P. Lewis, J. Photochem. Photobiol. A: Chem, 1998,116,257-263.

160.) H J Hageman, R S Davidson and S P Lewis, Proceedings Radtech Europe Edinburgh, Radtech Europe Fribourg Switzerland, 1991, 691.

161.) E.C. Directives 85/572/EEC, 89/109/EEC, 90/128/EEC

162.) T Doi and G Smets, Macromolecules, 1989, 22, 25.

163.) M A Abd-Alla, Makromol Chem, 1991, 192, 277.
(This is not the first citing of this compound - H Oppenheimer, Ber, 1886, 19, 1814.)

164.) R Huesler, R Kirchmayr, W Rutsch and M Rembold, Eur Pat EPO 0.304886 (1989).

165.) J-P Fouassier, D J Lougnot, G Li Bassi and C Nicora, Polymer Communications 1989, 30, 245.

166.) A Ledwith, Pure and Appl Chem, 1977, 49, 431.
A Ledwith, J A Bosley and M J Purbick, J Oil Col Chem Assoc, 1978, 61, 95.

167.) C Carlini, F Ciardelli, C Donati and F Gurzani, Polymer, 1983, 24, 299.
C Carlini, L Toniolo, P A Rollo, F Barigellitti, P Bartolus and L Flamigni, New Polym Mater, 1987, 1, 63.
C Carlini, Br Polym J, 1986, 18, 236.

168.) M Yamamoto, Y Mishijima, K Tsubakiyama, M Kuzuba and K Yoshimuta, Polym J, 1991, 23, 6781.
J L Mateo, J A Manzarbeita, R Sastre and R Martinez Utrilla, J Photochem Photobiol A: Chem, 1987, 40, 169.
J L Mateo, P Bosch, E Vazquez and R Sastre, Makromol Chem, 1988, 189, 1219.
J L Mateo, P Bosch, F Catalina and R Sastre, J Polym Sci A, Polym Chem, 1990, 28, 1445.

169.) R S Davidson, A A Dias and D R Illsley, J Photochem Photobiol A: Chem, 1995, 91, 153.

170.) J V Crivello and J L Lee, US Pat 4780511 (1988), Polym Bull, 1986, 16, 243.

171.) JV Crivello and J L Lee, J Polym Sci Polym Chem Ed, 1987, 25, 3293.

172.) J V Crivello and J H W Lam, J Polym Sci Polym Chem Ed, 1979, 17, 3845.

173.) J V Crivello and J L Lee, US Pat 4,804977 (1987).

174.) W Y Chiang and S C Chan, Angew Makromol Chem, 1990, 179, 57.

175.) D. G. Anderson R. S. Davidson N. R. Cullum E. Sands PCT Int. Appl. WO 96 33,156 PCT Int. Appl. WO 96 33,157.

176.) W Baeumer, M Koehler, J Ohngemach, Radcure '86, Baltimore USA, SME, Dearborn Michigan USA, 1986.

177.) K D Ahn, C J Ihnn and J Kwon, J Macromol Sci Chem A, 1986, 23, 355.
K D Ahn and J Kwon, J Photopolym Sci Technol, 1990, 3, 137.

178.) R Klos, H Gruber and G Greber, J Macromol Sci Chem A, 1991, 28, 925.

179.) P Green and A Green, Speciality Chemicals, 1991, 11, 411.

180.) D Braun, W Neumann and J Faust, Makromol Chem, 1965, 85, 143.

181.) N S Allen, F Catalina, C Pienado, R Sastre, J L Mateo and P N Green, Eur Polym J, 1987, 23, 985.
N S Allen, C Pienado, E Lam, J L Kotecha, F Catalina, S Nauaratnam and B J Parson, Polymer J, 26, 1237.

182.) M. Ohwa, H. Yamoto, J-L Birbaum, H. Nakashima, A. Matsumoto and H. Oka, UK

Pat. Appln. GB 2 320 027.

183.) W.D.Davies, I. Hutchinson and G. Walton, RadTech'98 Chicago, 20-270.

184.) K R Kase and W R Nelson, Concepts of Radiation Chemistry, Pergamon New York USA, 1978.

185.) C Lowe in Chemistry and Technology of UV and EB Formulations for Coatings, Inks and Paints (Vol 4) ed P K T Oldring, SITA Press London (1991), chap 1.

C Lowe and P K T Oldring in Chemistry and Technology of UV and EB Formulations for Coatings, Inks and Paints (Vol 4) ed P K T Oldring, SITA Press London (1991), chap 2.

186.) O Schafer, M Allan, E Haselbach and R S Davidson, Photochem and Photobiol, 1989, 50, 717.

187.) L D Snow, J T Wang and Ff Williams, Chem Phys Lett, 1983, 100, 193.

X Z Qin, L D Snow and Ff Williams, J Amer Chem Soc, 1985, 107, 3366.

T Bally, S Nitsche and E Haselbach, Helv Chim Acta, 1984, 67, 86.

188.) P K Sengupta and S K Modak, Makromol Chem, 1985, 186, 1593.

189.) J E Baxter, R S Davidson, H J Hageman and T Overeem, Makromol Chem, 1988, 189, 2769.

190.) R F Bartholomew and R S Davidson, J Chem Soc C, 1971, 2342.

191.) J G Kloosterboer, G M M Van der Hei and H M Boots, Polym Commun, 1984, 25, 354.

192.) H M J Boots in Integration of Fundamental Polymer Science and Technology, ed L J Kleintjens and P J Lemstra, Elsevier Applied Science London, 1986, 204.

193.) R S Davidson, R Ellis, S Wilkinson and C Summersgill, Eur Polym J, 1987, 23, 105.

194.) C Armstrong and S Herlihy in Aspects of Photoinitiators, Paint Research Association Conference Egham UK, 1993, 1.

195.) R S Davidson and J W Goodin, Eur Polym J, 1982, 18, 589.

196.) N S Allen and M Edge in Radiation Curing in Polymer Science and Technology, Vol I, ed J-P Fouassier and J F Rabek, Elsevier Applied Science, Barking UK, 1993, 225.

197.) J. Jansen and H. Hartwig, RadTech '98 North America, 207-214.

198.) B. Guyot, B. Ameduri, B. Boutevin M. Melas, M. Viguier and A. Collet, Macromol. Chem. Phys. 1998,199, 1879-1885.

199.) K Lawson and C Robinson in Radiation Curing in Polymer Science and Technology, Vol IV, eds J-P Fouassier and J F Rabek, Elsevier Applied Science, Barking UK, 1993, 467.

200.) M Uminski and L M Saija, Surface Coatings International, 1995, 78 (6), 244.

201.) M. Bernard, RadTech Europe 1997, 134-143.

202.) J. A. Dougherty, F. J. Vara and P. F. Wolf, RadTech'96 North America, 80-85.

203.) R Dowbenko, C Friedlander, G Gruber, P Prucnal and M Wismer, Prog Org Coatings, 1983, <u>11</u>, 71.

204.) X Coquevet, A A Hajaeij, A Lablache-Combier, G Loucheuz, R Mercier, L Pouliquen and L Randrianarisoa-Ramnatsoa, Pure and Applied Chem, 1990, <u>62</u>, 1603.

205.) J. Wendrinsky, RadTech Europe, 1989, 453-463.

206.) R. H. Hall, A. A. M de Krom and J. B. J. van der Sanden, RadTech Europe 1991, 239-253.

207.) W. Davies, I. Hutchinson and G. Walton, RadTech North America, 1998, 20-27.

208.) J. J. Gummerson, ACS Symposium Series 417, 1990, 176-193.

209.) B. Ranby and W. Shi, PCT Int. Pat. Appln. WO 96/07688, W. Shi and B. Ranby, J. Appl. Polymer Sci., 1996,59,1937-1944, 1945-1950 and 1951-1956.

210.) M. Johansson, E. Malmstrom and A. Hult, J. Polym. Sci. Part A Polm. Chem, 1993, <u>31</u>, 619 and A. Hult, E. Malmstrom, M. Johannson and K. Sorensen, Swedish Patent SE 468,771 B (1993).

211.) I. Ihre, A. Hult and E. Soderlind, J. Amer. Chem. Soc., 1996, <u>118</u>, 6388.

212.) A. Hult, E. Malmstrom, P. Busson and H. Ihre, Proceedings of the 37th International Symposium on Macromolecules Australia 1998, 753.

213.) R. Moors and F. Vogtle, Advances in Dendritic Materials 1995, **2**, 41-71, JAI Press Inc.

214.) J G Kloosterboer and G F C M Litjen, Polymer, 1987, <u>28</u>, 1149.
A T Doornkamp and Y Y Tan, Polymer Commun, 1990, <u>31</u>, 3.
D J Broer, G N Mol and G Challa, Polymer, 1991, <u>32</u>, 690.
J G Kloosterboer and G F C M Litjen in Biological and Synthetic Networks, Elsevier Applied Science London, 1987.

215.) H Rauch-Puntigam and T Völker in Acryl and Methacrylverbindungen, Springer, Berlin, 1967, 205.

216.) P J Moles, Proceedings of Radtech 1991, Edinburgh, Paint Research Association Teddington UK, 1991, 374.

217.) K Horie, I Mita and H Kambe, J Polym Sci Part A.1, 1968, <u>6</u>, 2663.

218.) P G Garratt in Radiation Curing of Polymers II, ed D R Randell, Royal Society of Chemistry 1991, Cambridge UK, 1991, 103.

219.) K Dorfner in Radiation Curing of Polymers II, ed D R Randell, Royal Society of Chemistry 1991, Cambridge UK, 1991, 216.

220.) Titanium dioxide pigmented films have been cured: see A Carroy in Aspects of Photoinitiation Egham, Paint Research Association Teddington, 1993, 65.
A Carroy, Radtech Europe '95, Maastricht Holland, Radtech Europe Fribourg Switzerland, 1995, 523.

221.) J V Crivello in UV Curing: Science and Technology, ed S P Pappas, Technology Marketing Corporation, Norwalk Co USA, 1978, 73.

222.) J. V. Crivello and R. Narayan, Chem. Mater., 1992, 4, 692, S. Chakrapani and J. V. Crivello, J. Macromol. Sci., Pure and Applied Chem. 1998, A35, 1-20, 691-710.

223.) A. M. Miller, V. Narayanan and A. B. Scranton, RadTech North America, 1998, 486 – 493.

224.) M J M Abadie and Z Seghier, Eur Coatings J, 1994, 5, 264.

225.) C. Decker and T. H. Ngoc, ACS Symposium Series, 1998, 704, (Functional Polymers), 286-302, A. Mathur, V. Narayanan and A. B. Scranton, RadTech North America 1998, p486-493.

226.) H. Kubota, K. Ueki and M. Yamamoto, Jpn. Kokai Tokkyo JP 10 130 367.

227.) E-J Gerard and J Schneider, RadTech Europe 1997, 175-180.

228.) A F Jacobine and S T Nakos in Radiation Curing Science and Technology, ed S P Pappas, Plenum Press New York USA, 1992, 181.

229.) J V Crivello, D A Conlon, D R Olson and K K Webb, J Radiat Curing, 1986, 13, 3.

230.) I. Igarashi and H. Sasaki, U.S. US Patent 5,674,922(1997), A. Yu, F. Yamashita, Y. Takaya and O. Isozaki, UK Pat. Appln. GB 2310211 (1997).

231.) A. S. Pell and G. Pilcher, Trans. Faraday Soc., 1965, 61, 71, O. Nuyken, R. Bohner and C. Erdmann, Macromol. Symp., 1966, 107, 125-138.

232.) R. Schaefer, D. Heindl, O. Nuyken, R. Bohner and C. Erdmann, U.S. US Patent 5,750,590 (1998), T. Volkel, S. Stein and V. Rheinberger, European Patent EP 0 867 443 A2.

233.) H. Saski, A. Kuriyama, FR Demande FR 2758557.

234.) S C Lapin in Radiation Curing Science and Technology, ed S P Pappas, Plenum Press New York USA, 1992, 241.

235.) C Lowe and A E Wade in Radiation Curing of Polymers II, ed D R Randell, Royal Society of Chemistry 1991, Cambridge UK, 1991, 326.

236.) S R Sauerbrum and D C Ambruster, Radtech '90 Conf Proc, Vol 1, RadTech International Northbrook Ill USA, 1990, 303.

237.) W Reppe, US Pat 1,959,927.

238.) W H Watanabe and L E Conlon, J Amer Chem Soc, 1957, 79, 2828.
M A Smith and K B Wagener, Polym Prepr, 1987, 28, 264.

239.) S C Lapin and S A Munk, US Pat 4,749,807 (1988).

240.) J V Crivello and R P Eckberg, US Pat 4,617,238 (1986).

241.) J F Rabek in Radiation Curing in Polymer Science and Technology, Vol 1, RadTech International Northbrook Ill. USA, 1990, 303.

242.) C Lowe, Test Methods for UV and EB Curable Systems, SITA Technology London,

1994.

243.) A K Davies in Radiation Curing of Polymers II, ed D R Randell, Royal Society of Chemistry 1991, Cambridge UK, 1991, 379.

244.) C. Lowe Surface Coatings Technology Vol. VI, Test Methods for UV and EB Curable Systems SITA Technology Ltd.London UK 1996.

245.) A G Bell, Philosophical Mag, 1881, 11 (Ser 5), 510.
R S Davidson, K S Tranter and S A Wilkinson in Radiation Curing of Polymers II, ed. D R Randell, Royal Society of Chemistry 1991, Cambridge UK, 1991, 400.

246.) J E Baxter, R S Davidson, M A U De Boer, H J Hageman and P C M Van Woerkom, Eur Polym J, 1988, 24, 819.

247.) W. Nelson, A. B. Scranton. J. Polym. Sci. Polym. Chem. 1996, 34, 403 and E. W. Nelson and A. B. Scranton, J. Raman Spectroscopy, 1996, 27, 137.

248.) W. Schrof, L. Haussling, R. Schwalm, W. Reich, K. Menzel, R. Koniger and E. Beck, RadTech Europe 1997, 538.

249.) W. Schrof, E. Beck, R. Koniger, U. Meisenburg K. Menzel W. Reich and R. Schwalm RadTech North America 1998, 363-374.

250.) W. D. Davies and I. Hutchinson, in Waterborne Coatings and Additives, eds. D. R. Karsa and W. D. Davies Royal Society of Chemistry, Cambridge UK, 1995, Special Publication No. 165, 81-104.

251.) R S Davidson, L Merritt and G Bradley, Aspects of Analysis, Paint Research Association Teddington UK, 1994, Paper 3.

252.) C Decker, J Polym Sci Chem Ed, 1992, 30, 913.

253.) O Valdes-Aguilera, C P Pathak and D C Neckers, Macromolecules, 1990, 23, 689.

254.) W Rettig, Angew Chem Int Edn, 1986, 25, 971.

255.) J C Song and D C Neckers, ACS, Div PMSE, Papers, 1994, 71, 71.
Z J Wang J C Song R bao and D C Neckers J. Polym. Sci. Part B Polym. Phys. 1996, 34, 325.

256.) K. G. Specht, R. Popielarz, S. Hu and D. C. Neckers RadTech North America 1998 348.

257.) G Bradley, R. S. Davidson, G. J. Howgate, C. G. J. Mouillat and P. J. Turner, J. Photochem. Photobiol. A: Chem. 1996, 100, 109-118.

258.) A. A. Dias, H. Hartwig and J. F. G. A. Jansen RadTech North America, 1998, 356-362.

259.) C E Hoyle in Radiation Curing Science and Technology, ed S P Pappas, Plenum Press New York USA, 1992, 57.

260.) R S Davidson, A A Dias and D Illsley, J Photochem Photobiol A: Chem, 1995, 89, 75.

261.) A A Dias, PhD Thesis, University of Kent, 1994.

262.) J.-P. Fouassier, Photoinitiation, Photopolymerisation and Photocuring, Hanser Publishers, Munich, Germany, 1995.

263.) R G W Norrish and G Porter, Nature, 1949, 164, 658.

264.) L Patterson and G Porter, Chem in Britain, 1970, 6, 246.

265.) M Jabbin, K Heihoff, S E Braslavsky and K Schaffner, Photochem and Photobiol, 1984, 40, 361.

266.) R S Davidson in Advances in Physical Organic Chemistry (Vol 19), eds V Gold and D Bethell, Academic Press, 1983, 1.

267.) E G Janzen, Acc Chem Res, 1971, 4, 1.
C A Evans, Aldrichimica Acta, 1979, 12, 23.

268.) S Göthe, Dissertation Royal Inst Technol, Stockholm Sweden, 1982.

269.) J G Kloosterboer, G F C M Litjen and F J A M Greidanus, Polym Commun, 1896, 27, 268.
M E Best and P H Kasai, Macromolecules, 1989 22, 2622.

270.) C. J. Groenboom, H. J. Hageman, T. Overeem and A. J. M. Weber, Makromol. Chem. 1982, 183, 281, H. J. Hageman, P. Oosterhoff, T. Overeem, R. J. Polman and S. van der Werf, Makromol. Chem. 1985, 186, 2483

271.) Radcure Letter, 1995, No 1, 1.

272.) M S Salim in Radiation Curing of Polymers II, ed D R Randell, Royal Society of Chemistry 1991, Cambridge UK, 1991, 1.

273.) A Ledwith in Photochemistry and Polymeric Systems, eds J M Kelly, C McArdle and M J Maunder, Royal Society of Cambridge UK, 1991, 1.

274.) S M Ellerstein, S A Lee and T K Palit in Radiation Curing in Polymer Science and Technology, Vol IV, ed J-P Fouassier and J F Rabek, Elsevier Applied Science UK, 1993, 73.

275.) H F Huber in Radiation Curing in Polymer Science and Technology, Vol IV, ed. J-P Fouassier and J F Rabek, Elsevier Applied Science UK, 1993, 51.
H F Huber, Radtech '91 Edinburgh, Paint Research Association Teddington UK, 1991, 291.

276.) J G Woods in Radiation Curing Science and Technology, ed S P Pappas, Plenum Press New York USA, 1992, chap 9.

277.) P Bernhard, M Hofmann, M Hunziker, B Klingert, A Schulthess and B Steinmann in Radiation Curing in Polymer Science and Technology, Vol IV, eds. J-P Fouassier and J F Rabek, Elsevier Applied Science UK, 1993, 195.

278.) L-A Linden in Radiation Curing in Polymer Science and Technology, Vol IV, eds. J-P Fouassier and J F Rabek, Elsevier Applied Science UK, 1993, 387.

279.) The Bible, Psalm 90, v 10.

280.) L. S. Coons, B. Rangarajan, D. Godshall and A. B. Scranton in ACS Symposium Series 673, 203.

281.) T Glauser, M. Johansson and A Hult, World Polymer Congress, 37th International Symposium on Macromolecules Australia, 1998, 555.

282.) A. Valet and D. Wostratzky, RadTech North America, 1998, 396-410.

283.) A. Valet and D. Wostratzky, RadTech Report, 1996, November, 18-22.
       A. Valet, T. Jung and M. Kohler, RadCure Letter 1997, No. 5, 96-101.

284.) S. G. Yeates, T. Annable, B. J. Denton, G. Ellis, R. Nazir and D.W. Cornwell, Surface Coatings International, 1995, 78,422-425.

285.) D. Maetens Proceedings RadTech'98 North America, 1998, 170.

286.) S. Udding-Louwrier, E, Sjoerd de Jong and R. A. Baijards, Proceedings RadTech'98 North America, 1998, 106.

287.) J. Finter, I Frischinger, Th. Haug and R. Marton, Proceedings RadTech' Europe 97, 1997, 489.

INDEX

Symbols

A

D

E

F

P

T